Air Transport Economics
in the Supersonic Era

Air Transport Economics in the Supersonic Era

ALAN H. STRATFORD, B.Sc. (Eng.), F.R.Ae.S., F.R.S.A.
Air Transport Consultant

SECOND EDITION
Revised and Extended

MACMILLAN
ST. MARTIN'S PRESS

First edition 1967
Second edition 1973

Published by
THE MACMILLAN PRESS LTD
London and Basingstoke
Associated companies in New York Toronto
Dublin Melbourne Johannesburg and Madras

Library of Congress catalog card no. 72–84866

SBN 333 05463 6

Printed in Great Britain by
WESTERN PRINTING SERVICES LTD
Bristol

Contents

List of Plates

between pages 50 and 51

List of Plates

Preface

In the five years since this book was originally prepared there have been remarkable developments in Air Transport, some of which have certainly exceeded the expectations of the author. But few have created a need for major changes in the text, except for the deletion of material on defunct projects, and reference to the inevitable upward sweep of costs. The Widebody Jets and Inclusive Tour Holiday transport are now fully discussed, and there are new chapters on Jet Transport developments and on Airports and Noise problems. I hope the new version, which has been thoroughly revised, will be of enhanced value. I certainly believe myself that, like the transport aircraft itself, a book on transport can only become really effective when it has been put into service and stretched as a result of the lessons that have been learned from the first edition.

I set out in the book to show how a positive approach can solve some of the key problems of the economy of civil air carrier operations and in the evolution of marketable transport aircraft to meet the needs of the future. It is impossible to attempt in a book of this length to record the development of ideas covering the whole field of air transport.

I begin with some account of the historical development of the commercial aeroplane since the 1920s. It is thought to be of importance to bear in mind the road along which the aeronautical industry has come, even though we are so deeply involved in the air transport problems of tomorrow.

A prime object of this book is to stimulate interest in the solution of the commercial air transport problems in those fields not entirely within the range of aircraft design, economics and/or cost accountancy. It is the development of the transport aircraft, in its changing forms in relation to the world markets that must be found for it, and in relation to the operational systems within which it must find an economic use, which is the principal object of our study.

The operator, the manufacturer and the departments of government which are each concerned with the healthy development of civil aviation and with the new projects upon which its future depends, have each been considered. I have tried to provide data which will be of value to European, American, Japanese and British Commonwealth readers.

Aeronautics is now one of the greatest fields of international enterprise. We are learning more and more to speak one common language and it is hoped that the ideas developed and reported in this book will have a reference and application in many parts of the world.

Spring 1972   A. H. STRATFORD

Acknowledgements

I would like to acknowledge with thanks the permission given by the British European Airways Corporation and by Hawker Siddeley Aviation Limited to quote from studies which I originally prepared on their behalf. William Heinemann Ltd, the publishers of *Supersonic Engineering*, were also kind enough to allow me to develop material which I originally contributed to my chapter in that book.

Finally, I am indebted to the editors and publishers who have kindly allowed quotation and reference to works by authorities in the various fields of aviation. I have tried to ensure that none has been omitted from the text or from the Bibliography.

A. H. S.

Abbreviations

ACV	Air cushion vehicle(s)
ADAP	Airport Development Aid Program (USA)
AGC	Affinity group charter
AIAA	American Institute of Aeronautics and Astronautics
ALPA	Airline Pilots Association (USA)
APT	Advanced passenger train (British Rail)
ARB	Air Registration Board (UK)
ATLAS	A technical co-operation scheme (Chap. 1)
ATLB	Air Transport Licensing Board (UK)
ATA	Air Traffic Association of America
ATC	Air traffic control
ASA	Alan Stratford Associates (Report References)
BAA	British Airports Authority
BAB	British Airways Board
BALPA	British Airline Pilots Association
C of A	Certificate of Airworthiness
CAA	Civil Aviation Authority (UK)
CAB	Civil Aeronautics Board (USA)
CG	Centre of gravity
CNR	Composite noise rating (USA)
CTM	Capacity-Ton-miles
CTK	Capacity-Ton-kilometres
CTOL	Conventional take-off and landing
DCF	Discounted cash flow. System, in costing long-term projects of discounting the value of current expenditure.
DME	Distance measuring equipment (Air Nav. Aid)
DOC	Direct operating costs
DOT	Department of Transport (USA)
DTI	Department of Trade and Industry (UK)

ECAC	European Civil Aviation Conference
EARB	European Airlines Research Bureau
EAS	Equivalent air speed
EDP	Electronic data processing
EPNdB	Effective perceived noise level, decibels
FAA	Federal Aviation Agency (USA)
FAAP	Federal Aid Airport Program (USA)
GCA	Ground control approach
GETOL	Ground effect take-off and landing
GIT	Group inclusive tour
GNP	Gross national product
HMSO	Her Majesty's Stationery Office (UK Government publishing house)
IAS	Institute of Aeronautical Sciences (now AIAA)
IATA	International Air Transport Association
ICAO	International Civil Aviation Authority
ICE	Institution of Civil Engineers (UK)
ICN	Index of community noise
IFR	Instrument Flight Rules
IMC	Instrument meteorological conditions
ISA	International standard atmosphere
ILS	Instrument landing system (Airfield Approach Aid)
IOC	Indirect operating costs
ITA	Institut du Transport Aérien
ITC	Inclusive tour charters
ITX	Inclusive tours on scheduled air services
IUOTO	International Union of Official Travel Organisations
KSSU	A technical cooperation scheme (Chap. 1)
LCN	Loading classification number (for runways)
M	Mach number (Airspeed relative to speed of sound)
MIT	Massachusetts Institute of Technology
NASA	National Aeronautics & Space Agency (USA)
NASP	National Airport System Plan (USA)
NEF	Noise Exposure Forecast. (US index)
NNI	Noise and Number Index (UK)
NOAA	National Oceanographic and Atmospheric Administration (USA)

NPL	National Physical Laboratory (UK)
PNdB	Perceived noise level in decibels
PNYA	Port of New York Authority
R.Ae.S.	Royal Aeronautical Society
RTOL	Reduced take-off and landing
RVR	Runway visual range
RAE	Royal Aircraft Establishment
SFC	Specific fuel consumption
R&D	Research & development
SARC	Systems Analysis & Research Corpn (USA)
SBAC	Society of British Aircraft Constructors
SBR	Standard busy rate (of airport movements)
SD	Standard deviation
STOL	Short take-off and landing
TBO	Time between overhauls
SST	Supersonic transport
TARC	Transport Aircraft Requirements Committee
TMA	Terminal area controlled air space
TO	Take-off
VMC	Visual meteorological conditions
V/STOL	Vertical or short take-off and landing
VTOL	Vertical take-off and landing
VHF	Very high frequency (radio communications)
VOR	VHF omnidirectional range
WAT	Weight, altitude and temperature restriction (in transport aircraft flight manual)

UNITS EMPLOYED

Short tons (1 ton = 2000 lb = 907·2 kg)

Statute miles (1 mile = 1760 yd = 1·609 km) (unless UK nautical miles specified: 1 nm = 6080 ft = 1·853 km)

Knots (1 kt = 1 nm per hour)

British new pence (p) and US dollars and cents (100 p = £1 = $2·40) unless old pence (d) are quoted (240d = 20 shillings = £1)

1 Early Days and the Pattern of Growth

There is little difficulty in recognising the importance of transport in the development of modern industrial society and much has been written of the key role played by it in the economic growth of communities. In the undeveloped countries, the lack of well organised and co-ordinated transport is a seriously retarding factor, and it is in the development of roads and railways that the first heavy capital investment in progressive new countries is being made. In the Government of India's Third 5-year plan, for instance, the allocation of funds to transport and communications reached 20 per cent of the total in the public sector.

With the Industrial Revolution in Britain came the first opportunities for the use of power beyond the direct capabilities of men and horses and much of the newly released energy was expended on the construction of new and more effective transport systems. This awaited the development of a successful engine, in the first place the steam engine, just as one hundred years later the Wright Brothers achieved successful flight (Kitty Hawk, Carolina, 1903) only after they had designed and built a successful lightweight internal combustion engine. But aviation began before Kitty Hawk, just as the railway age preceded the age of steam when horse-drawn and cable-drawn trains provided extensive services on prepared tracks.

Lack of a means of efficient, i.e. speedy and economic, transport hampered many activities of life in earlier societies. In Europe, for example, it restricted for centuries trade and social intercourse between nations and delayed the development of strong Government. On the other hand, the poor communications available in early times and in some inaccessible areas even today, have contributed much to the independence and character of some of the world's most individual national groups.

The remarkable surge of railway building which continued in England through the first half of the nineteenth century and in Europe, America and Asia well into the twentieth century, required little prompting from Government; it was a golden age for the private investor. The stories of the railway age make fascinating reading in the annals of many countries, and the historic race to the Pacific Coast between rival railway companies who in their independent and often ruthless fashion were creating a national service of inestimable value in opening up the great mid-western territories of the United States and Canada will remain one of the great stories of modern history. The laying of the cables, especially the first lines linking Europe and Australia in the 1830s, is a similar story of immense significance to our theme, for the communication of human thought by word alone is a form of transport which has many common features with the passenger and cargo transport which are generally considered to be the limits of the subject. Cable and satellite relay for the transmission of messages and vision are new aspects of the field of transport which can be profitably considered by the student of the subject because of the interesting analogies which arise. The technologies may differ very greatly, but the economic principles can be usefully compared.

The part played by transport in the creation of wealth has become of great concern to modern governments, and most studies of industrial growth and productivity have paid careful attention to its contribution. Comparative studies are being used increasingly to help in the assessment of that mode of transport or combination of modes which will most effectively achieve some chosen objective. The objective may not, of course, be reached by the most economic means. A railway, a road or an airway may be required to provide prestige or some other national objective of a political nature.

In general both goods and people are more desirable or useful in certain locations than in others. This is the origin of the need for transport although the value may not always be definable in strictly economic terms. A potential difference in position will generally have no relation at all to the cost of transport between two places, nor does the speed of communication necessarily have a bearing upon either. It is our concern here however to provide answers to questions concerning the

2

speed- and time-relationships which arise through the possibilities of high-speed transport. Other needs can be met of course which will not on their own increase value or create wealth. For example, much passenger air transport, and especially the holiday and tourist trade, depends for its appeal upon the pleasure of the journey itself, and climatic conditions at the destination and the limitations upon the time available to the traveller.

The case for air transport of goods may often lie in economic factors relating to wider considerations than the value of the goods at one time and place. Some reduction of the total cost of production and distribution may be achieved by the employment of higher speeds of transport. Wider markets in time and space, and hence greater profitability, may arise through a particular combination of transport modes. We shall attempt to establish methods for determining criteria for these modes of transport at a later stage in this text.

J. Mercier in an address in October 1964 to a Conference of European Ministers of Transport, entitled *L'homme et le transport*, drew attention to the many ways in which man is 'conditioned' by the transport media and the dependence of these upon man. Research was proposed within a framework defined by the three aspects of Sociology, Transport and Tourism, which, it was believed, would assist the better understanding of the basis of the need for one form of transportation or another.

Employment statistics show that in certain countries about 6 per cent of the population registered for labour are employed directly in the provision of transport services of one kind or another. Many groups not directly employed in transport are not included in this figure. Mr Mercier has shown (1964) that in heavily industrialised countries between one-seventh and one-fifth of the working population is directly or indirectly concerned with transport. The number employed in air transport is a minute proportion of these total numbers, but the significance of the air is far greater than the relative employment figures would indicate. The predominant mode of transport on the major international and national routes, except where the short distance involved makes a private car journey competitively attractive and of course progressively cheaper with an increasing number in the party, is now the scheduled airline aircraft. Thus air transport, especially on the international scene, has become a political, social and economic factor of the greatest significance.

Air transport has now developed into five major groups:

1. Business
2. Private
3. Tourist
4. Cargo
5. Government

Each of these requires separate consideration in relation to routes, acceptable fares, service standard and frequency, and on each sector of every route the significance of these primary groups will be found to be different and require individual study.

In the beginning the prime object was to achieve a moderate level of operating cost at a standard of safety acceptable to the initiated few; the air transport industry has, however, now reached a stage where the product has become highly differentiated. The air vehicle of vastly improved performance, safety and capability is now deployed so as to meet the complex demands of timing, price, service standard and opportunity for travel which now exceed the range and scope offered by long-established surface carriers. Transport cannot be produced and held as inventory. The matching of the supply and the demand sets the classic problem for the transport operator. There are many approaches to its solution; but let us first step back four decades and consider how the pioneers encountered it.

The first two decades

Air transport did not begin as a serious commercial venture until after the First World War, when the first enterprises with converted wartime aircraft were put into service on selected stages in many parts of the world. From the records the most noteworthy early operations were:

1. Blackpool–Southport on 10 August 1910. Air mail experiments by Holt Thomas and Grahame White with Farman aircraft. Within a year a Humber biplane was carrying mail between Allahabad and Nairi in India.

2. St Petersburg–Tampa (Florida, USA, 23 miles) from 1 January 1914. The first passenger air service with the

Benoist Flying Boat. This lasted four months and 1200 passengers were carried.

3. Hendon–Buc (near Paris) from January 1919 to December 1919. Passenger and mail service operated by the RAF for the Peace Conference with Airco DH 4 and DH 4 A aircraft, Martinsyde F.4s and Handley Page 0/400s.

4. Berlin–Leipzig–Weimar from February 1919 to August 1919. The first sustained regular daily passenger service operated by Deutsche Luft Reederei with LVG., Rumpler, AEG., and Sablatnig aircraft. 1574 passengers were carried.

5. Paris–Brussels operated by Lignes Aériennes Farman from March 1919 with Farman 'Goliath' aircraft. The first international passenger air service. The flight schedule 2 hours 50 min. The fare 365 French francs.

6. Manchester–Southport–Blackpool from May to September 1919. Operated with Avro 504 aircraft by A. V. Roe & Co. Ltd. The first UK domestic air service. 194 flights completed. The fare 4 guineas.

7. Aircraft Transport & Travel Limited operated the first sustained and unsubsidised daily international passenger service with Airco DH 4A, DH 16 and DH 18 aircraft from August 1919. This was between Hounslow and Le Bourget. Other routes followed. At one period in 1920 no less than three British and three French companies were operating services across the English Channel.

8. Western Australia. Geraldton–Derby route. Operated by Norman Brearley in 1921. The first scheduled air service in the Southern Hemisphere.

The post-World War I transport aircraft were single- and twin-engined biplanes of wooden construction. The principal types in use in 1919 are noted in the previous summary of the outstanding early services. These are more fully described in Mr Peter Brooks's book *The Modern Airliner* (1961) which gives a very full and interesting account of development in the early days.

The French Farman 'Goliath', for example, was a 12-passenger aircraft with two Salmson Z9 engines of 260 h.p. each. From the basic civil type 0/400 developed by Handley Page (7 seats) was evolved the W/8 and W/8B series which could carry 12 passengers with two of the more powerful Napier Lion and Rolls Royce Eagle IX engines. These aircraft were probably the first to achieve specific total operating costs of one shilling per seat-mile (at contemporary prices).

Aircraft Transport & Travel used single-engined de Havilland designs, the DH 4 A converted from the military DH 4 and the DH 16 type developed from the DH 9 A, which allowed the passenger capacity to be increased to 4. One Rolls-Royce Eagle VII engine of 325 h.p. was installed. Mr Peter Brooks has made careful comparative studies of these early types of transport aircraft and established the total operating costs of the DH 16 at the contemporary money value to have been 21–23 pence per seat-mile.

Using standard formulae, and methods discussed in Chapter 2, it is instructive to compare the costs of the various aircraft under development at that time both in the contemporary setting and against the levels achieved by later technological development. Because the value of money has fallen to a level which is approximately one-fourth of what it was in 1919, it may be seen that in terms of current (1965) monetary values the first single-engine (DH 4 A type) civil aircraft in operation in Europe operated at a level of approximately 12s od per seat-mile, while the larger twin-engine (HP 0/7 and 0/10 types) offering 6 seats at rather lower cruising speeds, cost approximately 8s od per seat-mile.

Looking at the economic development of the transport aeroplane from the United States, Dr E. P. Warner computed the contemporary costs of the early aircraft as follows (1938).

Type	Passenger seats	First flight	Direct costs (Per ton-mile)	Total operating costs
DH 4 A	2	1919	88·1 cents	161·0
B 40	4	1926	33·7	72·7
Lockheed Vega	4	1927	22·4	56·5
Boeing 247	10	1933	15·1	37·2
C 3	21	1935	10·7	27·4

The downward trend in the level of cost is strikingly shown in these figures. The influence of increased seating capacity on the specific operating costs (or costs per unit of capacity) of the later aircraft is also apparent. Fig. 1.1 shows the effect of size on the operating cost of these first generations of transport aircraft.

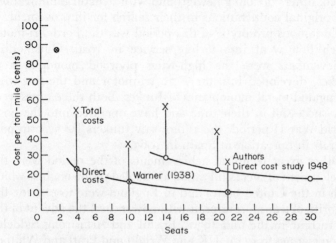

FIG. 1.1. Specific Operating Costs in Relation to Seat Capacity

The poor economic showing of the early air operations will be recognised at once, but even at that time the next objectives were being set by imaginative men who, at each stage, were isolating the crucial factors to ensure economic advance. Foremost among these men was Holt Thomas who was the outstanding protagonist for commercial air services in the UK in the post-World War I period. His classic paper (1918), which was read before the Royal Aeronautical Society, estimated that the total operating cost of a single-engine 12-passenger transport aircraft on a hypothetical operation between London and Paris could be covered at a 75 per cent load factor with a £5 single fare. He clearly recognised how much depended in the final count on the design of aircraft, as well as the utilisation which could be achieved in actual operation. His later experience was to show that aircraft of the capacity and operating cost which he envisaged were not to be available until about fifteen years later.

The decade from 1920 to 1930 was to be noted for the many

7

apparently unrelated attempts which were made to engineer acceptable transport aeroplanes. Single- and multi-engined types, some developed from successful war-tested designs such as De Havilland, Handley Page, Fokker and Avro had produced, others breaking new ground with structural innovations and original contributions in their search for improvement. A world-famous prototype of this period was the Ford Tri-motor which first went into airline service in 1926. Outstanding achievements were the high-wing plywood monoplanes of Fokker, developed into the F 10 tri-motor and the low-wing corrugated metal monoplanes of Junker. Both these types were very successful in their time and have operated into the post-World War II period: the author saw Junkers JU 52 transport aircraft in operation in Spain in 1963.

Other great technical achievements of the period were the development of successful radial air-cooled piston engines which both in the United States and in England were to provide the majority of transport aircraft with power until the advent of the gas turbine in the mid 1950s. Bristol and Armstrong Siddeley piston engines from the UK and Wright and Pratt and Whitney engines in the USA are still today in worldwide operation. Other technical achievements in the late 1920s and early 1930s were the trailing-edge wing flap, and the engine cowling of aerodynamic shape to provide not only minimum power plant drag, but also more effective cylinder cooling for engines which were required to provide the maximum available power for take-off and at low airspeeds in the initial stage of the climb.

Perhaps the most historic of the transport types was developed by Boeing as Model 247-D, and first certificated in 1934–5. It was of a low-wing, twin-engined design and incorporated adjustable metal propellers and a retractable undercarriage. The type has been on charter operations in very recent years. This classic design was the forerunner of the long line of all-metal internally braced low-wing monoplanes which through the close co-operation of the US aircraft manufacturing industry and the air carriers, aided by the gradual availability of larger power plants, was to provide the greater proportion of the air transport capacity through World War II and the following decade.

William Littlewood, a former President of the IAS, who for

so long directed the Engineering Department of American Airlines, has reminded us that many of the major advances in air transport technology have been accomplished by the use of moving surfaces, or as it is commonly called today, variable geometry. He cites the Wright Brothers, whose aircraft, besides its movable rudder, was controlled in pitch and roll by surface warping. The elevator, aileron, wing flap, Handley Page slat, variable-pitch propeller and engine cowling ducts, and even the retractable undercarriage may be so termed. The greatest step of all in this direction may yet be taken with the use of variable-geometry designs of wing dihedral and wing plan form. The variable-sweep wing already in flight in the General Dynamics F 111 (TFX) for military applications is now being proposed by the Boeing Company as their design solution with the greatest high- and low-speed cost effectiveness for a Mach 2·7 supersonic airliner (Chapter 9). Together with variable geometry, the greatly increased output and propulsive efficiency of engines, and the increasing size of vehicles, have been the dominant factors in that part of increased economy which has stemmed from the aircraft itself.

The development of air transport was carried through the 1930s by the vision and unbounded energy and enthusiasm of pioneers such as Sir Alan Cobham, Sir Francis Chichester, Sir Charles Kingsford Smith, Emilia Earhart and Charles Lindbergh, whose flights opened up most of the principal air routes of the world and who were the first to develop the traditional methods of Dead Reckoning (DR) and Astro navigation for safe non-stop flight on the long distances between the land masses. They were backed by the keen support of aircraft manufacturers such as Sir Geoffrey de Havilland, Sir Frederick Handley Page, Louis Breguet, Donald Douglas and Glenn Martin, as well as Government and Service Chiefs such as Lord Thomson, Sir Philip Sassoon, Commander Byrd, General Balbo and Captain Costes. Nor should the contribution of the engine builder be forgotten, for without the immense growth in power, in power-weight ratio and improvement in fuel economy, often only hesitatingly sought and with meagre funds from European governments, the increase in performance and capability would have been marginal and might have been inadequate to support the onward progress of aviation in those years.

The civil transport air service was not long in following on the routes explored by the first pilots, and the imperial responsibilities which England still bore throughout the Middle East, in India and beyond, gave her a special incentive to open up the routes to the East with landplanes and flying boats. Italian and German ambitions of a different kind drove these countries into long-range airship and flying-boat operations into unexploited regions as far apart as South America and the North Pole. The subsequent development of aeronautics has shown that some of these enterprises were of less direct significance to civil aviation although it was not evident at the time. It was in the USA, however, that the steady and fruitful development of the twin-engine cantilever low-wing transport plane of the type pioneered by Boeing with the 247, proceeded unhindered by the political unbalance which was influencing European civil aviation.

While the German airline Deutsche Lufthansa, heavily subsidised by the Third Reich, was gaining intensive operational experience with the JU 52, JU 86 and the Heinkel 111 in spite of uneconomic load factors, and Imperial Airways were experimenting with the first all-in 'Empire Air Mail Scheme', the US carriers were introducing the DC 3, the first civil aircraft to allow air transportation to operate a truly commercial air service. This US experience was later to be developed even farther by the gruelling tests which the war years provided. This was the background to a development which has faltered little in the past 25 years. From the mastery of the North Atlantic with flying boats in 1938 (jointly achieved by Pan American and Imperial Airways) to the present era, the US achievements in the technological exploitation of the transport aeroplane has been remarkable.

Seen from the European aviation industry in the late 1930s, the picture was dominated by:

1. The British and German efforts to master the design and control of commercial airships with hydrogen and helium gas: this ended in disastrous failure.

2. The German perseverance with the low-wing cantilever monoplane culminating in the JU 52, which was the mainstay of Luftwaffe transport in the Second World War.

3. The opening up of long-distance world routes and finally

the North Atlantic by a series of large landplanes and flying boats (the latter having comparatively little influence on subsequent civil aircraft design) which laid the foundations of the modern intercontinental air transport system.

The economics of the operation of the Imperial Airways route system in the last pre-war years are not easy to interpret. Less openly non-commercial than the domestic operations of Deutsche Lufthansa, they were nevertheless supported by a subsidy which, in 1937, represented 24 per cent of total revenue. At that date DLH received 42 per cent and Air France 66 per cent of their revenue in the form of direct Government subsidy. The Cadman Committee was set up in 1938 by the British Government to satisfy trenchant criticisms of the competitive anomalies arising from the subsidising of the two airlines, Imperial Airways and British Airways. From this emerged the new organisation of British Overseas Airways Corporation, created by Act of Parliament on 4th August 1939.

Following the tough experience of long-distance air services built up through the war – during which the North Atlantic was finally mastered, facilitating the transport of VIPs, key service personnel and convoy patrol – the prospect of a much expanded opportunity for civil aviation was apparent to many. Thus the need to prepare for the post-war demand for new types of economic transport aircraft was recognised in the United Kingdom, and a committee under the chairmanship of Lord Brabazon was set up to prepare outline specifications of the several aircraft types that would be needed. They were also asked to suggest the firms suitable for tendering designs, and to consider with them the existing war-time types which could best be converted for peace-time use. They reported also on the best uses to be made of spare design and productive capacity. The Brabazon Committee and the second committee which followed it, recommended the design of seven aircraft types ranging from a small 8-seat twin-engine landplane to a 130-ton landplane for North Atlantic services powered by eight propeller-turbine engines. Here lie the origins of the Dove, the Viscount and the Brabazon aircraft itself.

Sir Richard Fairey in his Wilbur Wright lecture in 1950 showed that up to 1948 over 256 thousand million dollars had been spent on aviation development since the Wright Brothers made their great contribution towards the achievement of flight. A very high proportion of this was, of course, expended in the course of the Second World War. The upsurges of activity in the two World Wars were each followed by dramatic reductions in output. However, the insistent development of the aeroplane for military and commercial purposes has inevitably led to a gradual increase in research and development, production and operation. Indeed, the IATA carriers have already reached an annual turnover exceeding two thousand, five hundred million pounds (7200 million dollars) with a rate of growth which is at present close to 12 per cent per annum. In production the US industry alone exceeds 50 million pounds of air-frame weight per annum, and world production (some 50 per cent in excess of that figure) is growing at the rate of 10 per cent every five years.

An important contribution was made by Oliver Lissitzyn to the discussion on the political aspects of air transport management in his book *Air Transport and National Policy* published by the Council on Foreign Relations in New York in 1942. He strongly argued that civil aviation, being primarily an instrument of national policy, should be supported by far-sighted governments by means of mail payments or direct subsidies so as to encourage its active development not for profit in financial terms, but for political, military and prestige purposes. At the time at which he wrote, the return to the investor was minimal and other reasons needed to be sought to justify the immense development costs incurred. His views had been quite naturally accepted in Europe in the decade before, but needed to be stated clearly at that time in the USA.

However, the improving economy of the transport aircraft which occurred through the 1950s not only permitted the trunk carriers in the USA to dispense with subsidy, but allowed international operations to move within measurable distance of independent subsidy-free existence, certainly in the more favourable periods of international business. Civil aviation, although still too often the subject of political interference and, especially outside the USA, in need of public support, rapidly became able to operate over a wide field as a commercial business in the world of competitive enterprise.

Air transport development up to the 1970s

It may be of interest to illustrate the more recent history of the transport aeroplane by choosing some of the outstanding transport aircraft in the periods from 1945 to 1970. Tables 1.1 and 1.2 indicate the size, price and first flight date of significant aircraft produced in the US and in Europe. This remarkable continuity of development illustrates the success of the transport aeroplane in stimulating an increasing demand in the two decades subsequent to the Second World War.

TABLE 1.1. *Summary of the Principal US Civil Aircraft 1945–70*

Type	Passenger seats*	Max. TO weight in lb (kg)		First flight date
Douglas DC 6 B	80	107,000	(48,300)	10. 2.46
Boeing Strato-cruiser 377	100	145,800	(65,700)	8. 7.47
Martin 404	52	44,900	(20,250)	27. 7.51
Convair 340	44	45,000	(20,300)	5.10.51
Lockheed Constella-tion 1049 G	99	137,500	(61,900)	7.12.54
Lockheed Electra	85	116,000	(52,660)	6.12.57
Douglas DC 7C	105	143,000	(64,500)	20.12.55
Convair 880 (22M)	110	193,000	(87,540)	3.10.62
Boeing 707-320C	189	332,000	(150,590)	31. 1.62
Boeing 727-200	180	175,000	(79,380)	27. 7.67
Douglas DC 9-30	115	98,000	(44,450)	1. 8.66
Douglas DC 8-63	259	350,000	(158,760)	10. 4.67
Boeing 737-200	125	114,500	(51,925)	27. 7.67
Boeing 747 B	490	775,000	(351,540)	9. 2.69
Douglas DC 10-10	345	410,000	(185,970)	29. 8.70
Lockheed 1011 Tristar	330	409,000	(185,550)	16.11.70

* Maximum Economy Seating

The series of Douglas civil types, beginning with the DC 1 certificated in 1933, and leading to the DC 3, DC 4, DC 6 and DC 7 (the last being certificated in 1953), had gross weights increasing from 17,500 to 122,000 lb. The well-known Convair

240, 340 and 440 types, the Martin types 202 and 303, and the post-war British and European types up till the Comet I (which introduced new features determined by the pure jet engine) were of a similar general layout. The nose-wheel undercarriage was introduced with the Douglas DC 4, cabin pressurisation on the DC 6, turbo superchargers in the piston engines on the Lockheed Constellation L 1049, and propeller turbine engines on the Viscount and Britannia. The same design formula with regard to fuselage, powerplant and wing and tail configuration was held substantially unchanged in the types (Brooks, 1961).

In Chapter 4 the more recent developments in jet transport aircraft are explored in the context of economic airline opera-

TABLE 1.2. *Summary of the Principal European Civil Aircraft 1955-70*

Type	Passenger seats*	Max. TO weight in lb (kg)		First flight date
BAC Viscount 810 series	65	72,500	(32,886)	14. 2.58
BAC Vanguard	132	146,500	(66,448)	20. 1.59
HS Comet 4C	102	162,000	(73,500)	31.10.59
BAC Britannia 320	118	165,000	(74,842)	31.12.56
Fokker VFW Friendship 200	52	43,500	(19,730)	24.11.55
Aerospatiale Caravelle 6 R	87	110,230	(50,000)	6. 2.61
HS Argosy 200	—	90,000	(40,840)	11. 3.64
HS 748 srs 2	58	44,495	(20,182)	6.11.61
BAC Super VC 10	169	335,000	(151,950)	7. 5.64
HS Trident 2E	149	143,500	(65,090)	27. 7.67
BAC 1-11 srs 500	119	99,650	(45,200)	7. 2.68
Fokker-VFW F 28 Mk 1000	65	63,000	(28,580)	9. 5.67
BAC-Aerospatiale Concorde	144	385,000	(175,000)	2. 3.69
Fokker-VFW 614	44	41,000	(18,600)	71
Dassault Mercure	155	114,640	(52,000)	28. 5.71
Airbus A 300 B	259	291,000	(132,000)	72

* Maximum Economy Seating.

tion. Table 4.1 lists the current wide fuselage jets and SSTs which are on the new plateau of aircraft development. Between 1965 and 1969 few significant new marks of transport aircraft appeared in airline service. Notable examples however were developed versions of the Boeing 727, Douglas DC 9, Trident 2 and BAC 111-400.

Figures 1.2–1.4 show three aspects of the development of the transport aircraft through the last two decades. Speed, gross weight and selected service amenities have been chosen as factors representative of the increasing commercial importance of the aircraft in this period.

The steadily improving operational economy of the aircraft, through better detail design, more predictable reliability, greater flexibility of operation in range and operating altitude (made possible by pressurisation) was of greatest significance

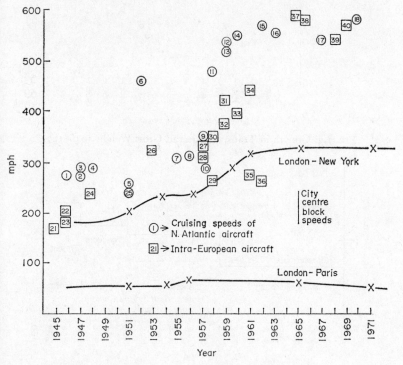

FIG. 1.2. Post-War Cruising and City Centre Speeds

and, above all, the increasing payload capacity which the growth in air traffic made it justifiable for the air carriers to provide in the post-World War II period on the principal international traffic routes.

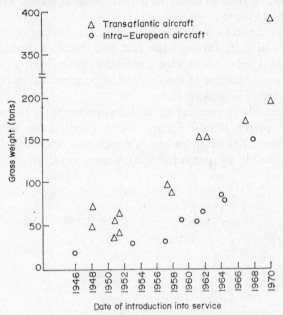

FIG. 1.3. Growth in Transport Aircraft Gross Weight 1946–1970

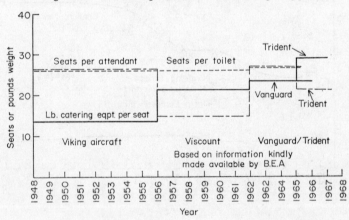

FIG. 1.4. Standards of Airliner Comfort and Catering

16

The Douglas range of transports

The history of the Douglas Commercial Transport Aircraft is of particular interest since the story runs more continuously than that of any other aircraft manufacturer under an unchanging name, and begins as early as July 1933 with the first flight of the DC 1. This was the forerunner, but was in fact developed almost immediately into the DC 2 which first flew in May 1934. Thirty-one aircraft of this type were originally ordered by TWA and the price was about $65,000. A total of more than 150 of these aircraft was built up to the outbreak of the Second World War and deliveries were made to airlines all over the world. The DC 3 was first flown in December 1935 and the first aircraft were sold to American Airlines for $115,000 each. By the outbreak of the war the DC 3 was the predominant aircraft on all US air routes and was already in service with over 30 foreign airlines. Over 800 civil aircraft of the type were built, but during the war years 10,123 Dakotas and C 47s of similar typess but incorporating various type of Pratt & Whitney and Wright engines were built for military transport purposes. It is the converted military transports that have been the mainstay of so many air services in the post-war period. In 1944, the last year of production of the DC 3, 32 were built and sold for approximately $100,000 each. Even in 1965 a large number of DC 3s or variants of the types are still in operation. In Donald Douglas's Wilbur Wright Memorial Lecture to the Royal Aeronautical Society in 1935, he was drawing attention to the airworthiness requirements for multi-engined aircraft after engine failure. But Douglas' efforts to develop a four-engined version of the DC 3 were not successful in 1937 (DC 4 E) and the first effective four-engined type went into production as the C 54 which flew in March 1942. A total of 1163 (C 54 and R 5 D–US Navy) transports were built and 74 civil transports known as the DC 4. At mid-1965 approximately 250 DC 4 transports were still in worldwide commercial use. The initial price was probably about $400,000. The DC 5 was the only high-wing transport in the DC range to date. Production ceased after only 11 were built, of which 6 were in the commercial form. The first flight was in 1939. The DC 6 was a pressurised and enlarged development of the DC 4. The first commercial plane first flew in March 1947. The DC 6 B first flew in a civil airline with United Airlines in 1951 and the DC 6 A (freighter) in May 1953 with American Airlines. About 540 aircraft of the various DC 6 types are thought to have been built.

The DC 7 was in the event the final development of the four piston-engine transport aircraft in the Douglas range. The aircraft first flew in May 1953 and went into service with American Airlines in November of that year. At the peak 15 aircraft per month were produced. A total of about 260 of the general DC 7 type were produced. The DC 7 B and 7 C has by 1955 reached a price of approximately $2,500,000. In the 1960s a large number of DC 7s were converted to the DC 7 F form for use as freighters. This was largely because the introduction of the large subsonic jet aircraft had reduced the real value of the aircraft to something well below airline book value and it was deemed desirable to use an aircraft of proved record which required no special engineering or crew training for the air cargo development then in train rather than sell on a weak market and introduce new and advanced types of cargo plane.

The DC 8 was the Douglas answer to the strong challenge from Boeing with the new-generation 4-jet passenger transport. Unlike Boeing, Douglas were obliged to develop the DC 8 from the outset as a commercial transport. It first flew in May 1958. A number of versions are currently available which range from the DC 8–30, to the DC 8 F long-range freighter. The second generation of long-haul jets was introduced by provision of turbo-fan engines of the Pratt & Whitney JT 3 D 1 type. The DC 8–60 has a gross weight of 335,000 lb and offers a maximum payload of 49,000 lb (189 passengers) for a still-air range of about 6000 statute miles. The current price of the standard long-range DC 8–60 is $12 million (£5 million). The further development of the DC 8 to carry up to 259 passengers was put in train. This is the DC 8 type 63. The DC 9, built in various marks, is a smaller aircraft carrying 115 economy-class passengers on medium-short stages. Reports of the ITA (Paris) provided much of the above data.

It has been said that aircraft designers like artists are tempted to build the aircraft they enjoy building rather than the aircraft that the world needs. There was a time when the chief designer, probably one of the original directors of the company, could of his own accord decide with very little outside restraint, apart from the limitation of resources, just what his next project might be. Those days should have passed with the Second World War, but more than a vestige of the technical director's hunch still remains an important factor in the European plants engaged in the manufacturing of civil aircraft. The US industry have probably proceeded farther along the road to the fully rationalised decision based on the state of the art, the requirements of production, the sources of finance and on detailed market research with its scientific study of the product in its manifold relations to the pattern of worldwide demand. It is certain that there has been more hard thinking than intuition behind their long record of success in meeting the rapidly changing criteria in an era of technical revolution.

Glenn Martin, the well-known American designer, said in 1954, 'My files have been bulging for years with proposals for new aircraft, the fruit of engineering imagination and ambition. These are the fundamental ingredients of our capacity for progress, but such beautiful and arresting sketches are not progress until a customer says: I want that.' To gain some insight into the rationalisation behind this demand seems to be the greatest of all needs in the industrial field today.

The British aircraft industry

This industry, including the engine, equipment, instrument and component manufacturers, steadily increased its output and export production in the post-war era up to the year 1959 when £158 million was exported. Of this total approximately 51 per cent was destined for civil use. In the subsequent years the totals fell, largely due to the completion of the Viscount and Vanguard orders. More recent sales have not been comparable to the export success of the US industry with the DC 8, Boeing 707 in its various marks, Lockheed Electra or Boeing 727. French aviation exports average about three-quarters those of the United Kingdom, which have reached a new peak in 1971 of £328,105,000.

In evidence to the Estimates Committee (1963–4) concerning UK expenditure on transport aircraft (HMSO, 1963–4), the Society of British Aircraft Constructors pointed out that the US Export-Import Bank financed recent sales of US aircraft at more attractive terms than could have been offered by British manufacturers for comparable aircraft. The Export Credit Guarantee Department of the Board of Trade, which offers a credit insurance scheme, cannot however be directly compared to the Export-Import Bank which itself advances the funds which are sought in approved cases. By the early 1970s however the terms offered by the US and the UK industries are thought to be more evenly matched.

The British Aircraft Industry reached a peak employment in 1961 of 298,000. Subsequently it has declined and by 1970, after the industrial re-organisation and merging which took place in the previous decade, it had contracted to 228,000.

The need to export in order to maintain the UK balance of payments encouraged successive governments to support an industry which offered such a high potential. Though judged by some critics as not justifying the public investment in Research and Development which had been spent in the past, the aircraft industry has nevertheless commanded immense respect as a breeding ground for talent and ideas with a 'fall-out' of high significance to all branches of science and engineering. Sir Arnold Hall said in a lecture to the Institute of the Aeronautical Sciences (1957) that 'aviation research has been responsible for advances in the properties of materials to an extent far greater than any other industry, and these improvements have benefited engineering at large'. It is, however, true to say that without extensive government support on both sides of the Atlantic, in fields which are not only related directly to aviation, but which was provided primarily with the objective of extending military preparedness, the commercial aviation industry would never have been able to develop at the rapid rate achieved in the 1950s and 1960s.

Glenn Martin in his paper on the 'First Half Century of Flight in America' (1954) said that there is 'a proper role for the Government in aviation progress. As a customer it must establish clearly and precisely the goals that we will be required to meet. It must, moreover, assume the financial cost of the research and development work required in the perfection of that goal.' The achievement of a military goal in aviation has repeatedly offered a handsome 'fall-out' to the air transport industry after a necessary period of technical and commercial development of some 10–15 years. It is important for the industry to take the fullest possible advantage of these facts without necessarily being diverted from areas of development where the interests of the defence authorities are less apparent.

The task of directing Research and Development (R & D) towards civil aviation projects has become formidable indeed. A more general basis for its promotion is usually required unless a defence application can be identified. Already the scale of investment in commercial aviation is immense; in spite of the difficult years (1960–70) the incentives and the margins of profit are increasing in each five year period, and the forces at work in international collaboration are becoming progressively ambitious. If the SST has not as yet found military application, the hypersonic transport with a range half-way round the world may obtain great assistance from the space shuttle. If the civil aero engine is developing along lines essentially different from the military requirement, nevertheless the quiet civil engine is a project likely to receive, in increasing magnitude, the backing and resources of socially conscious governments with engine industries of their own.

The organisation of air transport

Chicago and Bermuda

The scientist, technician and airline operator having inspired the necessary confidence that air transport could support itself economically in a short period of years, if allowed the necessary freedom to operate and to expand naturally, it was clear that the principal task that would lie ahead in the immediate post-World War II period was to remove the political barriers to progress, many of which would be of a kind which are quite unnatural to transport by air.

An International Conference at Chicago was therefore convened in 1944 to consider the form which post-war International Civil Aviation Traffic policy should take. It must be remembered

that at that time the USA and the UK were the predominant partners in the Grand Alliance of the West, excepting
the USSR and were in a strong position in relation to other
powers who had taken a less active part in the war effort. The
USA was in a specially strong bargaining position since she was
providing a very large proportion of Allied air transport at that
time, and had indeed a virtual monopoly of transport aircraft
production due to agreements reached between Winston
Churchill and Franklin Roosevelt early in the war, that the
United Kingdom would concentrate her besieged resources on
military aircraft of all kinds. The Anson and Oxford training
aircraft were indeed the largest aircraft of civil type produced
in the British Isles during the war years.

At the Chicago Conference the USA favoured a policy of the
open and unrestricted market, but the United Kingdom strongly
opposed this view and received much support for the argument
that a freely competitive situation dominated by one or a very
small number of states would lead to the demand for extensive
subsidies, much political friction and, despite the theoretical
advantage of competition, would incur much wasted effort in
the new aviation industries which they were at that time at
great pains to encourage. The Australian delegation sought
support for a plan to set up a world organisation for the
operation of international Air Transport. This found little
favour. The outcome of this crucial conference was an agreement to disagree on the broad policy of international air traffic
regulation. A satisfactory *modus volandi* was not discovered, but
the Convention signed at Chicago set up the essential machinery
for the post-war regulation of International Aviation and in
particular established in a provisional form the highly successful
organiastion of ICAO.

In 1946, however, at Bermuda a further conference was held
between the Governments of the United Kingdom and the
USA at which a bilateral agreement was reached which has
proved to be of lasting and special significance to the development of international air traffic agreements during the last
twenty years. The very large majority of international air
traffic rights have been negotiated by agreements based on the
formula which was first established between the two Governments at Bermuda.

It was the hope and expectation at Bermuda that the principal agreements reached between the US and UK Governments would form a pattern for other bilateral agreements embodying a progressive policy of air transport expansion wherever social, economic or humane benefits could arise. The hopes of finally reaching an international multilateral agreement based on the Bermuda principles were not realised and a Conference called at Geneva by ICAO in 1947 ended in deadlock. Since that date the highly competitive mood of the international air operators has encouraged a more restrictive attitude to traffic agreements especially in cases where an imbalance in the traffic-generating capability of the states concerned is in evidence. Even the attitude of the US Government in the face of increasing pressure from European carriers on the North Atlantic (who by 1969 had acquired nearly 60 per cent of the total load ton-miles) is now becoming more restrictive as are the policies of new countries keenly determined to build up the image of active emergent societies with efficient air transport systems.

Mr Stephen Wheatcroft in his book *Air Transport Policy* (1964) summarises the essences of the Bermuda philosophy in five points:

1. The routes to be operated by the airlines of both countries are agreed in negotiations and specified in an annex to the agreement.

2. On route sectors directly connecting the territories of the two countries there are no restrictions upon the frequency of service which the designated airlines may operate and no other limitations upon capacity provided.

3. It is recognised that the economical operations of long-haul services necessitated carriers having rights to carry traffic on intermediate sectors, and this so-called fifth-freedom traffic is allowed to them providing that total capacity operated is reasonably related to the end-to-end potential of the route.

4. As a safeguard against the possibility that the airlines of either country may operate excessive capacity, the Bermuda system provides for an *ex-post-facto* review of capacity, if one party feels that its interests are being unduly affected by the capacity by the airline(s) of the other.

5. Fares and rates are regulated by governments by means of the approval which they must give to tariff agreements

reached in the first instance, by the airlines through the International Air Transport Association.

However, the 'fair and equal opportunity' to win the traffic on the principal routes between the major capital cities of the world can lead to many differences of interpretation and means of achievement in such a significant competitive business as Air Transport has now become.

The Five Freedoms

In the negotiation of International Traffic rights at the Chicago Conference it became apparent early on that some clarification of the degrees of freedom on the various flight sectors was essential, and they became identified as shown in the following diagrams. Some elaboration has been added as a result of later discussion, but an illustration of the basic concepts is shown below.

The first freedom
This allows the operator to fly over foreign territory without landing.

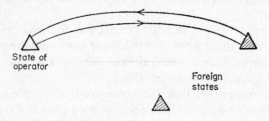

The second freedom
This allows the operator to land in a foreign state for purely technical (i.e. non-traffic) purposes.

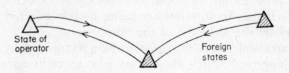

The third and fourth freedoms

These freedoms allow the air carrier to operate for traffic purposes between his own and a foreign state. The third freedom concerns outgoing traffic and the fourth freedom concerns the right to carry traffic from the foreign to the home territory.

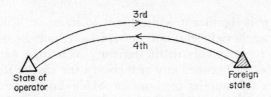

The fifth freedom

The fifth freedom introduces the rather more complex concept of traffic rights between two states foreign to the operator's home state. These are generally accepted as a supplementary freedom in association with third or fourth freedoms such as would arise on BOAC flights from London to New York *via* Shannon or Gander.

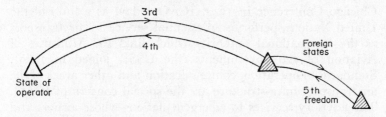

The geographical position of a state in relation to other states with whom it needs to develop air transport service will naturally influence very much its need to acquire fifth-freedom rights, and the nature of the variants on the simple fifth freedom which may arise. Inter-line agreements have made it possible for many benefits in through-flight connections to be provided for the passenger by airlines claiming commercial rights without full justification in law.

The sixth freedom

This freedom is a combination of third and fourth freedoms whereby an intermediately positioned state may seek rights to carry passengers between two states and make a landing en route within its own territory. Though similar to the fifth freedom, in recent years a distinction has been emphasised in the course of negotiations involving the potential value of traffic rights.

Cabotage is significant with regard to states with important overseas territorial rights and possessions. It may be defined as traffic between points in the territory of a state and its dependencies, or between any of them. In the case of the British territories this applies to those for which Britain has responsibility in foreign affairs. London–Bermuda, and Bermuda–Bahamas are cabotage routes.

International organisations

Mention has been made of the International Civil Aviation Organisation whose provisional organisation was set up at the Chicago Conference in 1944. ICAO today, as a limb of the United Nations, performs an essential service to air transport as the international authority which links the Ministries of Aviation of 120 governments (the USSR joined in 1969). Standards of operation, communication and other areas of the air transport infra-structure are the special concern of ICAO. The advisory services to emergent nations whose airport and navigational facilities are essential to safe and efficient international air transport are a most valuable feature of the current activities of ICAO. International regional organisations are also essential to the well-ordered development of air transport. Space only allows reference to one of the most influential.

The European Air Research Bureau with headquarters in Brussels established its position in the early 1960s as an organisation well equipped to record and analyse the statistical results of its European airline members. Its comparative reports on the development of scheduled European traffic have been of the greatest value to members and other aviation organisations concerned in this field. At the present time sixteen airlines are full members of the EARB. These are:

Aer Lingus	BEA	KLM	Sabena
Air France	BOAC	Iberia	SAS
Alitalia	DLH	Icelandair	Swissair
Austrian Airlines	Finnair	Olympic	TAP

The International Air Transport Association

It was an essential part of the agreements reached at Bermuda in 1946 that the fares and cargo rates should first be agreed by the airlines at the Conferences of the International Air Transport Association, and would subsequently be subject to approval by the respective governments. This essential function of the Association has in fact given it a status and importance which has strengthened its position in all fields. The traffic, financial, technical, and annual general conferences of IATA have contributed notably to the steady advance of international air transport and have encouraged contributions from a world-wide membership and other responsible organisations. Collaboration has been accelerated by the operation of common transport aircraft and equipment from the manufacturers in the USA, UK and France, as well as by the rapid communications available at nominal cost to member airlines.

Membership of IATA is open to any operating company which has been licensed to provide scheduled air service by a government eligible for membership of ICAO. Full co-operation is maintained with world organisations such as the International Federations of Airline Pilots Associations, the International Telecommunications Union, the World Meteorological Organisation, the International Standards Organisation, the Universal Postal Union and the World Health Organisation. Each airline, regardless of its size or the scope of its operations, has one single vote in the councils of IATA. Like ICAO, the headquarters of IATA are in Montreal.

Membership of IATA is open to all scheduled air carriers who are authorised by states which are members of ICAO.

The work of IATA is largely known outside the air transport world by the published reports of the Traffic Conferences concerned with routes and fares. There is often an impression given that IATA is a monopoly which encourages the maintenance of fares at the highest possible level. There is, however, very little evidence for this and indeed the record has shown that while the cost of living in Europe and in the USA has risen, fares have fallen and the average world-wide revenue yield for IATA members fell from 28 US cents per available tonne kilometre in 1959 to 19 cents in 1969. In Europe an increase in yield occurred, but this was 10 per cent as compared to the increase in the European cost of living in that period of approximately 39 per cent.

Conflict in policy arises constantly with regard to changes in the fare structure on the critical routes such as the North Atlantic and this reflects the national airline priorities in relation to the required share of the route traffic, and the economic characteristics of the transport aircraft types at present being operated or on order. Powerful states, with important international air carriers who are active in IATA, exert pressure in the committees, and generally provide much of the commercial and technical expertise as well. However unanimity in IATA is a requirement, and states have rarely challenged the imprint of an IATA agreement. In recent years unanimity has frequently required more than one conference to be arranged.

Comparison of intra-european and world-wide IATA fares

The level of fares in Europe is recognisably higher than that in the USA and in many other world areas. These reflect the operating costs in the respective areas. Principal reasons are the smaller aircraft and the shorter average sectors operated in Europe as well as the less intensively operated route patterns with lower traffic per sector and higher terminal costs per movement.

The Civil Aeronautics Board

In the USA the Civil Aeronautics Act of 1938 established the basis of public control over civil aviation. Since 1940 the economic regulation of public air services has been placed in the control of the five-man Civil Aeronautics Board whose chairman in 1950 was given greater power and authority. The Board was required to pursue the encouragement and development of an air transportation system properly adapted to the present and future needs of the foreign and domestic commerce of the United States, as being in the public interest and in accordance with the public convenience and necessity (Caves, 1962). Safety, economy and efficiency was to be promoted at reasonable charges without unjust discriminations or unfair competitive practices. Competition was to be established to the extent necessary to assure the sound development of air transport. A certificate of public convenience and necessity is required before an operator can take part in inter-state commerce, and is issued as thought fit for particular routes, sectors and specified terminal and transit points.

In 1953 the US Mail Pay function was transferred from the Post Office to the CAB. Responsibility resided with the Board as to the respective levels of the subsidy and the Mail Pay. As Richard Caves says in his study of the public regulations of Air Transport in the United States, 'Air Mail compensation fills the gap between the cost incurred by honest, economical and efficient management, and the revenues supplied by just and reasonable rates' (1962).

The development of air transport in the United States has reached the stage where the trunk operators are independent of government subsidy. It may be argued, of course, that many of the services, or imputs, to the air carrier industry are provided at less than cost. Airways, navigational and meteorological services are commonly referred to in this context. Airports, as in other parts of the world, may or may not fully recoup the cost of the service provided. In 1969 a total of $35·98 million, however, was paid by the US Government as subsidy, or 'Federal Aid', to the local service carriers. This was 5·8 per cent of their total revenues in that year, a percentage which had steadily decreased from 43 per cent in 1954. This is, however, only a part of the cost to the US taxpayer for the provision of service to the smaller cities served by the feeder airlines. Apart from this objective of CAB policy the aims would appear to be to promote the development of transport aircraft as an extension of the United States Military and Defence aims, to assist the aircraft manufacturing industry and to maximise the contribution of air transport to the economic welfare of the country at an acceptable level of safety.

Fares policy of the CAB

In general, the CAB has not strictly controlled the fare levels of the US domestic air transport industry except in so far as its policy of seeking to maintain a healthy level of profit to the airlines so as to promote sound economic conditions for growth has indirectly influenced the yield. After early misgivings over the introduction of high-density coach operations by the trunk operators, for example, the Board later supported the development of these services because they became convinced of the economic soundness of this approach to traffic growth. Fare increases seem to have been agreed, on the other hand, in the 1958 recession when carriers filed demands for increments which were felt justified by the CAB at that time. In the mid 1960s, the strong views of the CAB Chairman, Alan Boyd, were heard on the subject of the transatlantic fare levels which the majority of IATA members have sought to increase or at least to maintain in opposition to the two principal US carriers whose more intensive and lower-cost operations could undoubtedly benefit from a depression of the fares by some 5 per cent. Further conflict between the CAB and IATA is inevitable so long as the Board set first and foremost the interests of the healthy economic development of the US air transport industry, and IATA represents the wide-ranging views and operating standards of the 93* international airlines which are its members.

Recent Policy of the US Department of Transportation

The Department became a working agency of the Federal Government early in 1967. At that time the control of civil aviation policy in the USA became one element of the national transportation system. The object has been to co-ordinate the

* 1969.

various highway, marine and aviation programmes as part of the total transportation resources of the country in the broader perspective, to develop the required facilities and maintain the momentum of the economy. Under the first Secretary of the Department, Alan S. Boyd, the policy was initiated using convenience, cost and safety as the basis of decision-taking so as to provide the public with an adequate range of choice of transport modes.

The organisation of air transport development

It has been shown above that some regulation of both international and domestic air transport was recognised as necessary at an early stage in the development of the air transport industry. This arose initially, of course, from the need to give financial assistance to the early operators who were deemed to be providing a public service and whose promotion was important to the national interest.

At a later stage the air transport industry not only became an important element in the total transportation systems of the major industrial countries and a significant factor in their economic structure, but co-ordination between the different modes of transport was likely to be required and competition between the national air carriers acquired a political aspect which could not be left to chance. In more recent years the operation of a strong civil air fleet has become a matter of prestige with many governments and the retention of a suitable reserve of transport aircraft in time of peace for use in war became a defence factor. In some countries, also, the support of an aircraft manufacturing industry was considered as an asset of the highest value. In the 1950s a greater acceptance of national planning as a means of achieving industrial growth was noticeable in Europe, and even in the United States the Federal Aviation Act in 1958 declared again in clear terms the strict regulatory policy of the US Government. It has been the principal feature of governmental control of the air transport industries that competition, the entry of new operators on to established routes and the tariff structure should be closely controlled.

President Kennedy in March 1961 called for a statement of the US national aviation goals for the period up to 1970 so as to facilitate practicable long-range planning. This was carried out by a task force under Chairman Fred. M. Glass, who sought to define the technical, economic and military objectives of the Federal Government throughout the broad spectrum of aviation. Some of the most significant aims and policies suggested were in fact related to air transport development, although there were 'some areas where facile solutions, which might be popular, could not be properly offered'. It was the view of this committee that in the USA aeronautics was running 'a poor second to space technology in the time, talents, facilities and funds expended on it within NASA'.

At this same time the Transport Aircraft Requirements Committee, which had been set up by the UK Minister of Aviation in 1954, following an earlier Interdepartmental Committee on Aircraft Requirements, to co-ordinate and evaluate the requirements of the British Air Carriers, was under continuing criticism because of its ineffectiveness to meet the needs of the time. At the hearings of the Parliamentary Committee of Estimates 1963-4 (HMSO, 1963-4) it was clear that the principal objectives of TARC were not well defined and it was recommended that 'the terms of reference and working of the Transport Aircraft Requirements Committee should be reviewed, with the purpose of defining the Committee's functions with greater exactness, and of providing it with the necessary machinery with which to take a more active part in the early establishment of transport aircraft requirements and priorities at home and abroad'. A proposal made to the Estimates Committee that market research should be undertaken by TARC was vigorously opposed by the Ministry of Aviation. Unfortunately the impression was formed that very extensive market research was performed by the British Aircraft Industry. The Plowden Committee of Enquiry into the Industry reporting in December 1965 made it very clear that market research had been inadequate. In the recommendations it stated that 'The Government should in future . . . take a greater share of the responsibility for market studies and for formulating new requitements.'

It has been a notable feature of Independent Air Transport

development in the United Kingdom since World War II that the shipping companies have taken an active part. The decline in the share of the passenger traffic which has been retained by the shipping services between Western Europe and North America and between Europe and Australia and the Far East may be largely responsible for this. However, strong support for independent operators was forthcoming on all sides during the 1950s and early 1960s as a stimulant to competitive and more economic British transport services. The Labour administration of 1964, however, took action to counteract this trend following which the hearings of the Air Transport Licensing Board became for a time less concerned with the attempts of the Independent Air Transport Industry to seek a viable position in the scheduled air transport sector within and from the United Kingdom. As from the end of 1965, however, the policy of successive Ministers of Aviation has been to encourage again a limited competition between the Air Corporations and approved Independent Operators where traffic capacity is shown to be available.

The Air Transport Licensing Board set up by the Civil Aviation (Licensing) Act of 1960 was the instrument whereby the regulation of air transport in the United Kingdom was to be more vigorously enforced by means of new procedures as laid down in the Act, modifying some of the special privileges of the two air corporations. Standards of safety were to be enforced through a Director of Aviation Safety in the Ministry of Aviation and an air operator's certificate was to be issued subject to compliance with certain standards of operation, maintenance and overhaul, training and reasonable financial stability. This legislation was widely thought to be overdue. It now became possible for an airline to make formal application to the Board for a licence for a new route or for licence changes when operations have already been approved, and in a public hearing with full legal discussion, even though the air corporations might have long-established rights and investments in such routes and services. This has naturally caused the corporations, and especially BEA, considerable concern and every opportunity, such as the appearance of the new Government in 1964, was taken to challenge such new licences as have been approved and to appeal to the Minister through the procedure approved by the Act.

The Air Transport Licensing Board, incorporated since April 1972 within the Civil Aviation Authority is very broadly required to exercise its authority 'to further the development of British Civil Aviation' and the specific guide lines that were provided were far from inclusive, it has been a matter of wide interest to follow the pattern of the decisions which have been taken in the past few years. It is not possible to discuss this subject in further detail, but it may be said that a licence to operate a route has in general been considered to be in the public interest, unless another carrier already operating the route is able to establish that a material diversion of existing traffic from his services would be likely to occur. It was of special significance that in the early hearings a heavily promoted growth of traffic, with major commitments for the purchase of aircraft to meet such traffic expansion, was held to be no argument for the maintenance of a monopoly on UK routes. This Board's view would not at present be upheld by the Minister of Aviation in all circumstances if in conflict with the interests of the State Air Corporations. There has been much criticism of the lack of concern shown by the ATLB for the interests of the surface carriers when these have conflicted with those of the air operators. The responsibility of the Board to British Aviation and to the air-travelling public has apparently been a dominant consideration. In the case of an International route, it is of course necessary for the operation to be approved also by the foreign government whose views, like those of the British Government, will be determined by the terms of the bilateral agreements in force at that time (Wheatcroft, 1964).

In the author's view, one great weakness of the present regulatory establishment is that the permanent secretariat of the ATLB is extremely small and unable to provide the backroom service that is available, for example, to the CAB in the USA. There is every hope that under the new organisation the Licensing Board will adopt a more positive stance in UK Air Transport Development. To take one example, there is a strong case for the ATLB exerting their right to insist on the regular publication of operational and financial results when authorising new air services. Such action on their part would be invaluable for their own economic analyses, would help to develop a consistent and well-understood air-transport case law, and would greatly assist all forms of project planning in the aviation industry.

The Edwards Committee

This was set up in 1968 and reported in April 1969. The terms of reference were to inquire into the economic and financial situation and prospects of the British Civil Air Transport Industry and into the methods of regulating competition and of licensing. It was required to propose, with due attention to other forms of transport, what changes might be desirable to allow British Civil Aviation to make its full contribution to the development of the national economy and to the service and safety of the travelling public. This wide requirement was met very fully by the Committee, and the British Labour Government in office at that time and the subsequent Conservative Government has striven to implement its major recommendations.

The principal recommendations were that BEA and BOAC should retain their individual identities while engaging in scheduled, inclusive tour and charter operations, but under the control of a National Air Holdings Board with financial and policy control. It was envisaged that British air transport should develop with public, private and mixed public/private sectors, some emphasis being given to short-term action to implement this plan. The British Air Services Group was selected as the key example of a mixed operating Company and a new strongly based merger of BUA and Caledonian Airways was picked out as a solution to the weakness of so many airlines in the purely private sector. In the words of the report 'the private sector should be encouraged to create a "second force" airline which should be licensed to operate a viable network, covering scheduled and inclusive tour/charter traffic, both long-haul and short-haul'.

Of no less significance was the recommendation that a new statutory Civil Aviation Authority (CAA) should be set up. This would be responsible for the economic and safety regulatory functions (previously operated by the ATLB, the Board of Trade, and the ARB) and for the civil side of the Joint

National Air Traffic Control Services, for long-term planning and for traffic rights negotiations.

It was clear from the reports that the financial and managerial standards of the smaller UK airlines were thought to be inadequate. These areas were to be very thoroughly probed by the CAA on the grounds among other things of stability and safety. The Committee envisaged a small number of private UK airlines in the 1970s.

The author had the opportunity of giving evidence on air transport matters before the Committee on behalf of the Royal Aeronautical Society. The Committee was clearly very concerned to develop ideas and policies which would encourage the healthy growth of the industry on the basis of a mixed economy. However, experience has shown that much of the vitality of the UK air transport industry has stemmed from the enterprise and energy of individuals who brought little in the way of financial acumen and management skill to the task but acquired it as they went along. The advantages and the weaknesses of this approach to air transport enterprise are now apparent to all observers.

The British Civil Aviation Bill, 1971

The purpose of this legislation was to establish two new public bodies – a Civil Aviation Authority (CAA) whose task is to regulate the British Civil Aviation Industry as a whole, and a British Airways Board (BAB) concerned with the management of the two Air Corporations, BOAC and BEA, referred to in the act as the 'Public Sector Airlines'. These provisions follow closely the recommendations of the Edwards Committee.

The Authority was also required to take over functions previously exercised by the UK Air Transport Licensing Board (ATLB), and the Air Registration Board (ARB), along with other civil aviation functions of the Secretary of State. Foremost of the licensing functions is that of UK controlled air transport services. Functions include the regulation of the safety of civil operations and the airworthiness of the aircraft employed.

The aerodromes previously operated by the Board of Trade have been handed over to the new authority as has the joint operation (with the Ministry of Defence) of the National Air Traffic Control Service. Considerably increased powers in the control of airport operations have been reserved for the CAA.

The Board (BAB) is intended to control both BOAC and BEA and their subsidiaries as a group so as to develop in the words of the Act 'The group's services, and use its resources to best advantage. The group will be subject to economic and safety regulation by the Authority (CAA) in the same way as any other airline group.'

A provision of the bill was that dissolution of the Air Corporations could be made effective in certain circumstances with the approval of Parliament. This is generally interpreted as a clause allowing for the merging of the Air Corporations as a final step to the achievement of higher joint operating economy, a question on which the Edwards Committee came to no clear-cut decision, and proffered no specific recommendation.

International collaboration

One striking aspect of international collaboration is the possible economies that may be achieved by close collaboration between airlines. It has already been noted that to an increasing extent the major products of the aircraft manufacturing industries are operated by a number of different carriers so that it is not surprising that the co-operation was often initiated on an engineering basis. In the USA and within Europe, quite apart from the efforts of IATA, a great deal has been done and new possibilities of co-operation for the mutual benefit are continually being explored.

The principal sources of economy lie in the following areas:

1. The regulation of available space to match the demands of traffic without the wasteful generation of excess capacity by various means including perhaps in due course the multilateral negotiation of traffic rights.

2. The reduction of maintenance costs by the maximum utilisation of airline engineering resources and by decrease in the number of types.

3. The reduction of operating costs by the generation of maximum aircraft utilisation throughout a multilateral system.

4. The reduction of overheads by restricting duplication (such as in project development, maintenance burden, advertising, booking and handling).

Since transport cannot be generated and stored as inventory, both production and demand must be closely matched in any efficient transport undertaking. It is in this process of matching that the collaboration of the transport organisations is so essential. Probably in Europe where the intensity of operations on the majority of routes is still not high, where the seasonal traffic variations are so great and where the size of the national airlines is so different, the need for collaboration is greater than in North America.

Many forms of international collaboration are now being sought by the manufacturing industries and the Concorde project is the most striking example of the potential competitive power of Europe when the incentive to work together is strong enough. Other outstanding examples of recent collaboration in the transport field are (1) the Transall military transport developed jointly by the Weser, Hamburger & Blume aircraft groups in West Germany and Nord Aviation who together set up a development group, the Transall (Transporter Allianz), to design and produce the aircraft. (2) The Fokker F 28 short-haul twin-jet transport which is being jointly developed by Fokker VFW and the West German HFB manufacturing groups. Short Brothers & Harland of Belfast are also participating in the production programme. The proportional contribution in man hours of these organisations to the production of the F 28 has recently been stated to be planned as follows:

Fokker: 57%   West Germany: 24%   Shorts: 19%

Plans have now been prepared for a number of other joint European projects. Clearly a strong incentive exists because of the high capital cost of launching a new civil project. The UK administration in the period 1964–6 supported this trend as did the Plowden Committee reporting in December 1965.

The Anglo-French Concorde Project

Following a basic assessment of the potential technical feasibility of supersonic long-haul transport in the late 1950s, the UK Government sponsored a committee of specialists from the RAE, Air Corporations and Aircraft industry who reported in 1959 in very favourable terms. This led to negotiations between the British and French governments for the development of a commercially viable supersonic transport programme. Parallel agreements were signed between the two governments and between the selected British and French airframe and engine manufacturers. The agreements provide for a reasonable division of the work between the two countries and a sharing of development and production costs as well as overall project responsibility. The manufacture, test and flight development of two prototypes (001 in France and 002 in the UK) was agreed, as well as the building of two pre-production aircraft with an extensive engine build and test programme. A fifth and sixth airframe were ordered for ground tests including fatigue and structural testing.

Construction of the prototypes began in 1965 at Filton and at Toulouse and flight trials were initiated four years later, 001 making its first flight in March 1969. The complete flight programme, including 1,500 hours of route proving on the first three production Concordes, is expected to require 4,300 hours. Sonic boom trials off the west coast of the UK were carried out early in the flight programme, and generally confirmed theoretical estimates of the pressure rise. Delivery positions were reserved by 16 airlines for 74 aircraft by the early part of 1971. At this time it was announced that the US Congress had voted against the prosecution of the Boeing 2707–300 Supersonic project. This lack of resolution may yet be used by those of like mind in Europe to undermine the Concorde programme, which technically has reached all primary objectives.

A fuller treatment of SST technology and economics of operation is reserved for Chapter 9.

Concorde Contractors:

Airframe	British Aircraft Corporation Ltd
	Aerospatiale (SNIAS)
Power Plant	Rolls Royce Ltd
	Société Nationale d'Etude et de Construction
	de Moteurs d'Aviation (SNECMA)

The Soviet SST

It is at present anticipated that the TU 144 supersonic transport will go into regular production in 1973 and begin airline service in the USSR in 1974. The likelihood of operation by International airlines apart from those operated by states closely aligned to the Soviet Union is small. Undoubtedly extensive operations throughout the USSR and on certain international routes probably including the North Atlantic will be planned through the mid 1970s. Noise levels in the airport environment are believed to be a major impediment to international acceptance as also are airworthiness standards which will categorise the TU 144 outside the FAA and British CAA (ARB) codes in the foreseeable future. With the Soviet Union a member of ICAO, and Aeroflot a member of IATA, it seems quite certain that the time will come when transport aircraft built in the USSR will be designed to internationally accepted airworthiness codes and will then compete very seriously in the world markets.

The European Air Bus

The concept of a European international project to meet the needs of the European air carriers from the mid-1970s stemmed naturally from the Anglo-French SST collaboration. Initial studies in the UK in the early 1960s were prompted by the Lighthill Committee set up to consider Short-Range Minimum Cost Transport and BEA drew up a specification in 1963 for an Ultra-Short-Haul Low Cost Airliner seating between 100 and 150 passengers to be in service by 1970. European studies indicated a larger capacity and an Anglo-French outline specification for an Airbus suggested 200–225 seats for 800 nm (920 miles), with seat-mile costs 30 per cent below existing aircraft on short stages. Breguet and Nord Aviation worked together with Hawker Siddeley on the evaluation of the designs which had already been carried out in France and Britain.

In 1966 the German Government joined in talks with the

British and French Governments with regard to joint collaboration on such a project and work proceeded with the object of achieving a specification of direct application and economic value to the airlines of their respective countries. In 1969 it was decided by the UK Government that no contribution would be available from public funds, and Hawker Siddeley Aviation, who had already contributed considerably to the design concepts and were well advanced in studies of the wing system remained as the sole UK stake-holders in the project.

In 1971 international participation is understood to be arranged as follows:

Production %	*Airbus Industrie – A 300B Programme* Company participation	Production %	Finance %
France	Aerospatiale	36·5	43·0
Germany and	Deutsche Airbus	36·5	43·0
Holland	Fokker-VFW	7·0	7·0
Great Britain	Hawker Siddeley	20·0	7·0
(private participation)			

The European Civil Aviation Conference

An important aspect of government co-operation in the development of air transport was the establishment in 1954, following a recommendation by the Consultative Assembly of the Council of Europe, of the European Civil Aviation Conference. The Conference was composed of the states invited to be members of the 1954 Strasbourg Conference on the Co-ordination of Air Transport in Europe, together with other invited states. The object of the Conference was to review the development of Intra-European Air Transport with the object of 'promoting the co-ordination, better utilisation and the orderly development of such air transport' and to consider any other 'special problem arising in this field'.

Airline technical pooling

A number of technical pooling arrangements have been made by the international airlines which have been less widely noted than the commercial agreements concerning the sharing of operations and revenue and the interchange of flight equipment. It has not always been possible to obtain details of these arrangements, but the principles behind some of the most significant ones can be established.

In general, the arrangement is for two or more airlines operating common equipment to agree that a supply of spares and tools and also engineering service is made available by one of the airlines at each of an agreed list of airports. Typical of such an agreement is the one known as Beneswiss, originated in 1948 for the more economic servicing of the Convairliner by Sabena, Swissair and KLM, but the spares arrangements were extended to cover DC 3s, DC 4s and DC 6s at a later date. It has been estimated that the stock of spares was reduced by 30 per cent due to this pooling plan. Later a much extended scheme was participated in by 43 airlines. While the Lockheed L 1049 was in operation with Air France and KLM, a spares-pooling agreement was initiated which was later joined by DLH, Air India and Avianca. These arrangements extended from the Far East, through Europe to North and South America.

The 1958 agreement between Swissair and SAS is probably the most significant of all those made up to date, since it covers a wider field than those already referred to. The Caravelle 210, Convair 990 and DC 8 aircraft purchased by these airlines were identical in all respects except for the outside paint scheme. Identical flight decks led to co-operative crew training (shared use of simulators) and greater utilisation of crews and aircraft. Identical systems and equipment permitted minimum spares holding and maximum opportunities for interchange of components. Identical specifications for a given type greatly assisted in-line maintenance at overseas stations. Early decisions on the operation of the DC 8 over the North Atlantic routes might not have been possible if the operational and technical support for these large-capacity aircraft had had to be provided by the airlines individually. Similar equipment agreements have been approved by the CAB and are viewed very favourably by the European Civil Aviation Conference. A pool initiated by TWA involved Boeing 707 spares at 34 airports in the USA.

Other major pooling schemes for jet transports have been

established for some years. In 1959 an international Boeing 707 spares pool was initiated and by 1962, 16 airlines were participating. In 1960 a Comet IV pool was set up. The most recent stage of this development is the consolidated spares and equipment pool which has a membership of 43 IATA member airlines. This covers spares for 5 types of jet aircraft, 3 types of engine, radio and electronic equipment, ground equipment and tools. Over three years (1959–62) it has been estimated that BOAC have saved £806,000 by use of the shared pool and facilities available. A pool for Boeing 727 spares had been set up in the USA. The aircraft manufacturing industry naturally welcomes this major initiative by the operating industry to co-ordinate their activity and any move towards the overall economy of air transport means a further stimulation in the business of provisioning the advance of air transport.

KSSU

In May 1968 the airlines Swissair, SAS and KLM formed a consortium to standardise the layout, equipment and facility requirements of the Boeing 747 aircraft. This was later extended to cover technical collaboration with KLM handling airframe and SAS engine overhauls for this aircraft. Crew training became a joint exercise based on a simulator operated by KLM at Schiphol. In June 1969 the French airline UTA joined the consortium, following which the fleet of McDonnell-Douglas DC 10s was incorporated in the agreement. Of particular significance was the inter-governmental agreement of June 1969 which covered the work involved in the supervision of the airworthiness standards required for operation of the Boeing 747 B

These arrangements are generally known as the KSSU agreement.

Atlas

Air France, Alitalia, Luftansa and Sabena were also in search of economies in the technical field especially in relation to the Boeing 747. This led to the ATLAS co-operation agreement of 1969 whereby Air France took care of the airframe overhaul on the combined fleet while Luftansa overhauled the Pratt and Whitney JT 9 D engines. Alitalia and Sabena provided for the overhaul of components. The basis of such an accord was the agreement on identical technical specifications. Such standardisation is today a prerequisite for all such co-operation in maintenance, operations and training.

IATA Production Planning and Control Sub-Committee

The valuable work of this sub-committee did much to prepare the way for such arrangements as have been developed in Europe (KSSU and ATLAS). Twenty-five airlines participated in a Data Measurement exchange of production performance. During this work aircraft costs were broken down into Airframe Maintenance, Modifications, Engine Work and Component Work. The IATA PPC Handbook gives further information on this activity.

The Report of the Roskill Commission

The work of the Commission under Lord Roskill whose task was to advise the British Government on the site for a Third Major Airport in the London area will be fully considered in chapter 10 which concerns Airports. Its significance at this point in the record of air transport development is that it has required the efforts of a seven-man commission, backed by a large specialist research team working for two years with the combined efforts of many advisory boards, consultants, interested authorities and private groups to bring together a final report and a massive documentation which after five public enquiries and debates in both houses of Parliament did not receive universal acceptance in the United Kingdom.

Following an earlier Government plan to site a major new airport at Stansted, north east of London, which was turned down following public enquiry and extensive public resistance, the reaction of press, public and Parliament to the recommendation of a new site at Cublington, north west of London, has set the pattern of the seventies for the conflict between preservationists and progressives on the airport issue in the environment of our great cities. Concentrating principally upon noise in the airport region, but touching also the operation of supersonic aircraft, the conflict may hold in question the potential for air transport development in the seventies. Contributions to the solution of the problems are many and varied. They include improvements in the design noise levels of aircraft and engines in the take-off and landing regimes and in cruise (where the supersonic boom still needs to be controlled); the stricter control of noise abatement procedures in the climb-out and approach zones of major airports; the more disciplined use of land for noise-sensitive activity in the zones susceptible to aircraft noise; and greater investment in research to combat the critical technical and social problems. London is not alone in needing to face these difficulties. The social impact of the large transport aircraft is today manifest in all the technologically advanced countries of the world. The methods of science can be used as much to combat these problems as to create the products and the services the demand for which has initiated them.

US Airport and Airway Development Act, 1970

This Act created the revenue and resources required to overhaul and expand the US national airport and airways system. Federal sums are provided to assist cities, countries, states, and territories in the development of those facilities identified in the National Airport System Plan. (NASP.)

These include airline airports, and airfields in use primarily for general aviation. This wider ranging legislation expands the Federal Aid Airport Plan of earlier years and allows an Airport Development Aid Programme (ADAP) to meet major requirements (principally in land, runways, taxiways and aprons) subject to public enquiry and a detailed consideration of environmental factors. An Advisory Aviation Commission was set up.

The revenue part of the Act provides for increased financial support from the users of aviation facilities. This requires a passenger tax of 8 per cent, a new tax on international passengers leaving the US, a new 5 per cent freight waybill tax, and tax changes on fuel (which includes the abolition of the fuel tax on air carriers), and a 7 per cent tax on gasoline and jet fuel in non-commercial aircraft. A registration fee on all aircraft is levied by means of a system of charges differentiating general aviation, piston and turbine transport aircraft.

The needs of the Civil Aviation Industry in the next decade

The report of the Task Force on the aviation goals of the United States has already been referred to in this chapter. The pattern of these recommendations and the wise recognition by President Kennedy of the need for some such planning document have been widely noted in Europe where aviation policy has followed a far more uneven advance than has been the case in the United States. Nevertheless, the broad range of possible aims which lie open to the US Government has probably made their task of defining objectives a more essential one. Of major concern, especially in the United Kingdom, has been the random method of choosing objectives, and the apparent abandon with which long-argued and deeply studied projects and products, some already officially approved, have been discarded without economic, technical or defence studies justifying revision. Many specialists in the transport field have for some time felt that the planning of air transport should be more closely related to other modes of transport. The author was one of a group of consultants who studied the prospects for developing civil aviation in the north-eastern counties of England in 1964. We recommended research into the location of regional airports and limited national investment in their development rather than the encouragement of small local airfield projects. The need for an airport plan for Britain has recently been the subject of some public discussion since it is often found to be in conflict with local judgment based on more restricted objectives. We noted that 'a permanent National

Transport Research Group is widely recommended as a means of advising the Government on the optimum planning and investment in this great industry whose balanced growth is so essential to our regional and national life'. Mr Wheatcroft in his book (1964) subsequently supported the idea of a Transport Planning Council for Great Britain 'to maintain a continuous review of the appropriate parts to be played by each form of transport in meeting national needs'.

Trends in Air Traffic Development

In the early 1970s the air transport industry can claim an immense achievement since the pre-war years when the commercial feasibility of air services was by no means certain. But today its rate of growth despite world-wide inflation, its sensitivity to a market now becoming dominated by tourist demands, and its dependence upon outside finance to support the purchase of ever more costly vehicles, are the factors which challenge it.

The industry has always had problems to face, be they political, technical or economic and the means to combat these have been found in the merging of resources, in the research of governments and institutions and in the vitality of the manufacturing industries.

But the need to increase capacity and to re-equip with the wide-body jets, to become competitive with SSTs and to explore the new horizons with STOL and VTOL projects is pressing continually upon the airlines. And technology may seem to have no immediate solutions to the improvement of operating economy. Indeed the early years on the new plateau of productivity offered by the high capacity air bus types have shown that they do not meet the promises of cost reduction which were made in the late 1960s. This situation in a period of declining revenue yield is a major cause of anxiety in the airline industry.

The air transport industry comprises three distinct parts: the carriers themselves, the manufacturers who provide the advancing technology and the governments who control the entire complex. These three parts of the system must function together in full co-ordination. Productivity, growth and economic health must be the aim of all concerned with the healthy evolution of commercial aviation.

Here we are reaching very near to the task which lies ahead of us in our journey to the new frontiers of commercial aviation. We should already see the need to identify our objectives in the light of what has gone before (with the successes and the failures of the first sixty years of air transport to guide us) and in the light of our growing knowledge of what modern societies need from the providers of transport. The purely technical problems arising in the provision of an economic vehicle will be with us for a long time yet, and by the success of engineers and scientists in pushing forward the technical frontiers we shall be measuring our advance for many decades to come, but there should be some strategy behind our advance and since our resources are limited we may be well advised to consider the cost incurred and define our choice with all the means available to us in our time.

BIBLIOGRAPHY

G. J. Martin, 'The First Half Century of Flight in America', *Jnl. Aeronaut. Sci.*, 1954

J. P. Van Zandt, *The Geography of World Air Transport*, Brookings Institute, 1944

E. P. Warner, *The Early History of Air Transportation.* Cabot Professorship Lecture, Norwich, USA, 1937

E. P. Warner, *Technical Development and its Effect on Air Transportation*, Cabot Professorship Lecture, Norwich, USA, 1938

E. P. Warner, 'Post War Transport Aircraft', *Jnl. Aeronaut. Sci.*, 1953

W. Littlewood, 'Technical Trends in Air Transport', *Jnl. Aeronaut. Sci.*, 1953

P. W. Brooks, *The Modern Airliner*, Putnam, 1961

J. Mercier, *L'homme et le transport*, Institut du Transport Aerien, 1964

T. P. Wright, 'Aviation's Place in Civilization', *Jnl. Roy. Aero. Soc.*, 1945

Sir Richard Fairey, 'Some Aspects of Expenditure on Aviation', *Jnl. Roy. Aero. Soc.*, 1950

Sir Henry Self, 'The Status of Civil Aviation in 1946', *Jnl. Roy. Aero. Soc.*, 1946

Sir George Cribbett, 'Some International Aspects of Air Transport', *Jnl. Roy. Aero. Soc.*, 1950

S. Wheatcroft, *Air Transport Policy*, Michael Joseph, 1964

Key Problems in Aeronautics, A Symposium on Military and Civil Air Transport in 1973, The Cranfield Society, 1963

T. Holt, 'Commercial Aeronautics', *Jnl. Roy. Aero. Soc.*, 1918

K. Sealy, *The Geography of Air Transport*, Hutchinson, 1957

R. E. G. Davies, *History of World Air Transport*, Oxford University Press, 1964

Project Horizon. Report of the Task Force on Federal Aviation Goals, FAA, 1961

Sir Myles Wyatt, 'British Independent Aviation – Past and Future', *Jnl. Inst. Trans.*, 1963

Parliamentary Committee of Estimates. Transport Aircraft 1963–4, HMSO

R. E. Caves, *Air Transport and its Regulators*, Harvard University Press, 1962

Sir Arnold Hall, 'Some Comments on Current Aviation Topics', *Jnl. Inst. Aaeronaut. Sci.*, Mar. 1957

F. Roth, 'Economic Factors in Aviation', *Jnl. Roy. Aero. Soc.*, 13–14 May 1970

The State of the Air Transport Industry, IATA, Annual Report, Oct. 1970

British Air Transport in the 70s, Edwards Committee Report, HMSO, 1969, Cmnd. 4018

C. Layton, *European Advanced Technology*, Allen & Unwin, 1969

2 Criteria for Transport Aircraft

It is necessary now to establish the lines along which the commercial value of the transport aeroplane may be defined. To do this, we should be clear as to the boundary conditions which determine the engineering feasibility of the vehicle in its operating environment. Our criteria will be necessary in the preliminary stages of design as well as in the planning of production in relation to markets, both those existing and those expected to open up in the future (Chapter 3). They will also be required in order to aid the airline planners, development engineers and economists in the selection of the most suitable project for an expansion programme or for replacement of part of an existing fleet. Of equal importance is the fact that economic and operating criteria are needful for the full exploitation of the type in day-to-day service on the routes.

A considerable number of criteria have already been proposed for the assessment of the economic value of an aircraft, but the great majority of these oversimplify the issue and can be used only as figures of merit for one or a few particular items of performance.

The most valuable criteria may be listed as follows:

1. Individual items of performance: Cruising speed; Balanced field length, etc.; Fleet utilisation hours per year; Maintenance man-hours per flying hour, etc.

2. Payload/All-up weight (or other Weight index).

3. Block air miles per gallon (Specific range).

4. Ton-miles per gallon (Tons of payload).

5. Maximum ton-miles per trip (when Payload = Consumable fuel load).

6. Ton-miles per year (Transport productivity).

7. Payload × Block speed/All-up weight or Cruise power.

8. Specific direct costs (pence per seat-mile or ton-mile).

PLATE 1 (a) BAC-Aerospatiale Concorde 002 takes off for its first flight: Filton, 9 April 1969

PLATE 1 (b) Concorde at take-off

PLATE 2 (a) McDonnell Douglas DC 8-63 carries 250 passengers

PLATE 2 (b) Boeing 747 aircraft of KLM

PLATE 3 (a) BAC One-Eleven 500 aircraft of Court Line

PLATE 3 (b) VC 10 on long-haul BOAC routes

PLATE 4 (a) Modern loading method

PLATE 4 (b) Loading container into Pan Am 747

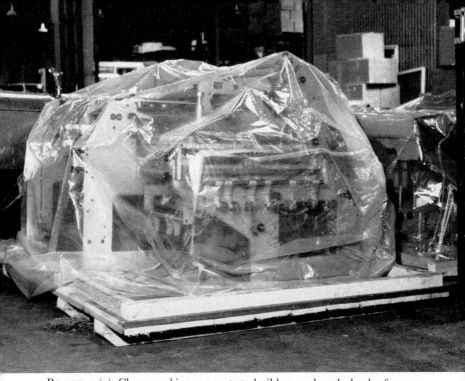

PLATE 5 (a) Cheap packing: no crate to build up and pack: load safe
when seen!

PLATE 5 (b) Easy load transfer: Rolamat Strip used on aircraft and
road truck

PLATE 6 DC 8s grouped around the Los Angeles terminal of United Airlines

PLATE 7 Gatwick Airport, Surrey, the second London airport. Road and rail links are a key feature

PLATE 8 (a) Breguet 941 in early STOL trials in Paris

PLATE 8 (b) VTOL project and scheme for city-centre airport

9. On-cost margin. Potential revenue less direct costs per aircraft per year.

Items (2) to (7) above are essentially simple functions of the six operational parameters, Cruise Speed and Power, Fuel Consumption, Payload, All-Up Weight and Fleet Utilisation. No attempt is made there to estimate the costs of operation or the potential revenue-earning capacity of the aircraft. The effect of block distance on the result is introduced by the use of the actual payload available and the block speed. Items (8) and (9) are in a different category and do enable a more complete assessment to be made.

The early criteria

Simplified parameters or figures of merit for the comparison of aircraft have been in use since the earliest days. In an early book (published in 1918) it is stated to be a necessary characteristic of a good aeroplane that it is capable of rising from ploughed land. It is there recommended that for high efficiency in that respect the relevant parameter is Horse Power ÷ Weight, while for good all-round capability a figure of merit of greater value is based on Horse Power ÷ Weight × Speed. It would seem that between 1918 and 1938 very little progress was made in the detailed appreciation of the factors determining the economic merit of a transport aircraft, even though the broad significance of the performance characteristics was apparent to designers. At a time when the aeroplane was still reaching in all directions towards the limits of performance, it was natural that specialisation in one direction at a time was an adequate objective in design. The economic value of speed and of the product of load and speed was recognised by many designers and writers such as Major F. M. Green, the Chief Designer of the Armstrong Whitworth Company (1934), and Louis Breguet (1935). Their work was developed by Edward Warner (1943), R. M. Clarkson (1946) and Peter Masefield (1951), whose papers are essential reading in the history of the economic development of the commercial aeroplane. Other references are given at the end of this chapter. The Proceedings of the Royal Aeronautical Society and of the former American

Institute of Aeronautical Sciences show very clearly how the thinking developed from the primitive idea of the simple performance rating to the more complex conceptions which guide air-transportation management in the modern era.

Modern parameters

Mentzer and Nourse (1940) published their classic paper which was based on their work in United Airlines on the rationalisation of the items of operating cost as experienced on the DC 3. Since then the assessment of the direct operating cost of transport aircraft by means of a formula based on a broad but limited selection of aircraft design and price data (notably gross weight, engine power, aircraft prime cost, fuel cost and crew pay) has become a conventional part of transport aircraft type assessment. On this original work the Air Transport Association of America (ATA) has based its direct operating cost formula for many years. At the present time, the Issue dated 1967 for turbine aircraft is in current use. Subsequently, the Society of British Aerospace Companies (SBAC) issued a method of estimating direct operating costs which more exactly suits the conditions of operations in Europe and the British Commonwealth. A study of these documents would be of particular value while considering the later sections of this chapter.

More recently the limitations of the cost formulae have become apparent and it is now recognised that a more complex assessment of the group behaviour of transport aircraft in a more precisely defined operational environment is essential to the better understanding of the interplay between many technical and commercial factors. In recent studies of jet and turbo-prop transport operations, and even in current supersonic aircraft investigations, few new principles seem to have been involved. A major shortcoming has been the lack of accurate estimates of the development, engineering and maintenance costs of radically new and different aircraft types. In Hawker-Siddeley, during studies of the comparative economic value of designs for freighter projects, it was recognised that new factors might enter into evaluation, since aspects of trans-

portation beyond the air element itself would require consideration. Current analysis of VTO projects is making similar demands for a fresh approach to economic evaluation. It is in the
relation of air operating cost and performance to that of the
fixed ground and surface transport systems that new approaches
are required.

FAA short-haul aircraft assessment

It is of interest to note that the method of comparison used
by the FAA when judging the best contenders of the many
proposed DC 3 replacement projects in 1964, gave economic
merit only 350 points of the total 1000 points available. The
points were weighted as follows:

Economics	350
Technical Ability	250
Manufacturer Management	150
Maintenance Requirements	150
Operational Characteristics	100
Total Available Points:	1000

While it is clear that maintenance requirements and operational characteristics should be reflected in the economics of
operation, many parts of these are difficult to quantify in the
cost formulae and in the other economic parameters used in the
final allocation of marks by the FAA. In the particular competition referred to, only three manufacturers succeeded in
achieving more than two-thirds of the available marks.

Characteristics of transport aircraft

It is inevitable that the higher speeds of air transport exact
higher unit costs of operation, compared with surface transport
vehicles of similar size, when operating on similar routes and
under broadly comparable conditions. However, the aeroplane
has been able to create an increasing commercial demand both
from the passenger and the freight shipper for two principal
reasons. The first of these is that an increasing size of vehicle

and an improved technology supported by military demands for higher capability in uplift and performance, have provided the air operator with increasingly productive vehicles. The second reason is that the customer finds in the higher speeds and direct service provided in the air, both for personal transport and the movement of goods, an asset of first-class value. Although this asset cannot always be measured in economic terms, it is the prime commercial parameter in the marketing of air transport. The continually growing capability of the aeroplane has provided the air operator with a tool which has become increasingly competitive in cost with surface-transport vehicles which have developed very much less rapidly in the last few decades. This is illustrated in Fig. 2.1 which shows the increase in transport aircraft productivity during the last twenty years, as measured by the capacity ton-miles per hour of the principal aircraft which have gone into airline service in this period.

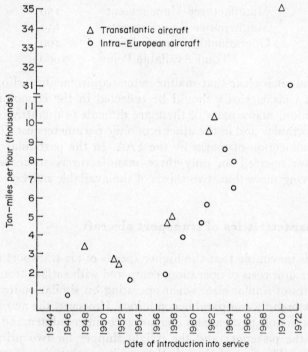

FIG. 2.1. Growth in Air Transport Productivity, 1946–72

We must never lose sight of the fact that the essential virtue of the aeroplane lies in its high speed and freedom from terrestrial barriers. Its speed arises through the low total resistance to motion offered by the air and its freedom stems from the technical development of engines and control systems of high output to weight ratios which give exceptional performance up to altitudes providing the necessary environment for economic flight. This was the revolution initiated by the Wright Brothers who were obliged to develop their own engine in order first to achieve and then to master a technique of controlled flight. Vertical flight, which may prove to be the last great revolution in aviation, also has had to await the development of engines. These are the high thrust/weight jet lift and deflected thrust engines which in the 1960s made vertical take-off and landing a practical achievement for high-performance aircraft. We have referred in Chapter 1 to some of the technical and political developments which came between these landmarks in the history of aviation. We should now turn to a consideration of the basic factors which determine the commercial value of the aircraft available to us today.

The scope and opportunity for aviation

There are a number of principal characteristics which determine the commercial performance of a transport aircraft. These may be summarised as follows:

1. The maximum available payload and the disposable volume for passenger and/or cargo use above and below the principal floor.

2. The range for which the maximum payload may be carried with specified fuel reserves and allowances.

3. The maximum economical cruising speed under specified conditions of aircraft weight, engine thrust and ambient air temperature.

4. The airfield requirements in length of runway for take-off and landing for a specified altitude above sea level and given meteorological conditions.

If we endeavour to set out the principal features of a transport aircraft design which promotes efficiency in earning profit,

55

we must clearly pay attention to the limits imposed by the present state of the art of aeronautical design. We shall also need to consider the costs of operation, especially the direct costs, which are notably effected by the size and capacity of the aircraft, but we must carefully weigh factors such as the frequency of service and its effect on load factor, and introduce aircraft utilisation, service regularity and some analysis of fuel reserves. In this way we may relate the problems of revenue earning to those of controlling the costs of operating the various types of civil aircraft.

The payload-range diagram

The payload-range characteristic is a unique feature of aircraft transportation since in no other vehicle is it necessary to replace payload by fuel as the length of journey is increased at the maximum operating weight. We should here exclude hovercraft and hydrofoil craft. This is due partly to the high fuel weight as a proportion of payload carried and partly to the required operational performance of an aircraft, especially on or near the ground, being closely related to the flying weight of the machine.

The diagram shown as Fig. 2.2 is the basis of the transport aircraft economy. It shows in a simple form for a hypothetical aircraft of 50,000 lb all-up weight that a payload of 8000 lb can be carried for a still-air distance of 500 miles. The still-air distance here drawn as the abscissa to the curve is theoretical only. It includes no allowance at all for fuel reserves or allowances and may need to be reduced by 200–400 miles if the scheduled route distance for the same payload is to be estimated. The payload shown by the line *AB* is limited by the difference between the take-off weight and the fully equipped weight of the aircraft (excluding only fuel and payload) so that a theoretical payload of 10,000 lb is possible for zero still-air range, and zero payload occurs at an ultimate range of 2000 miles. For a given equipped weight, therefore, the payload as shown by the line *AB* is dependent only upon the take-off weight of the aircraft. It is clear, therefore, that the total disposable load *OA*, 10,000 lb, may be divided between fuel and payload in a proportion depending on the still-air range that is required to be provided. No difference in principle arises whether the aircraft represented here is driven by propellors or by jet engines. The two payload range lines indicate, however, the difference in the miles flown per unit weight of fuel consumed in the two cases. The line $E^1 J^1$ represents payload for jet aircraft.

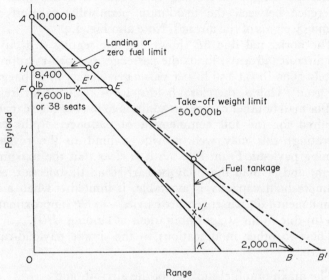

FIG. 2.2. Payload-range Characteristics of a Transport Aircraft

The simple relationship thus shown is modified in practice by a number of further considerations, the effect of which are also shown in Fig. 2.2. Here AB represents the same linear relationship of payload and range as it did before, but is replaced by the curve A^1B^1 which takes into account the variation of air miles per pound of fuel consumed as the length of flight increases and the average flying weight of the aircraft decreases also. This curvature is small on short stages and on still-air ranges up to 700–800 miles, but on larger stages, particularly on high cruising powers or with turbine engines, the effect may be considerable.

The horizontal line HG indicates the limit to payload that may be imposed on short range by the maximum allowable landing weight of the aircraft. This is frequently imposed by structural considerations and may well provide a ceiling to revenue payload when permissible take-off weights have been raised beyond the limits envisaged in the original structural design. Payload may equally well be restricted by the limited strength of undercarriage, fuselage or wing structure under landing conditions, but will only occur on block distances for which the weight of cruising fuel required is less than the difference between the maximum permissible take-off and landing weights of the aircraft. Note also Fig. 2.3.

The horizontal line *FE* shows that the seating capacity of this aircraft (38 seats) limits the passenger payload to approximately 7600 lb (at 156 lb per passenger plus 44 lb of baggage per head). Unless, therefore, hold space is available for freight and/or mail or other cargoes in addition to the baggage capacity required for the full complement of passengers (plus crew operating) this may well provide a limit to the revenue-earning payload. From Fig. 2.2 it is clear that the maximum freight and/or mail that may be carried on this aircraft, even if ample hold capacity is available, is limited – when a full complement (38) passengers are carried – to *HF* (approximately 800 lb) due to the weight limitations at landing (*HG*).

The two other modifications to the simple payload-range line are:

The maximum fuel tankage of the aircraft, and
The effect of engine operation.

There is quite obviously no justification for providing more fuel capacity than is required for the longest stage lengths likely to be undertaken – taking into account fuel reserves – nor perhaps in providing such a capacity that only an uneconomic payload can be carried the full distance although ferrying may be important. If fares per mile are no greater on long trips than on short (in practice they are slightly lower on longer trips in a given theatre of operations); and if aircraft operating costs per mile are sensibly constant whatever the trip length, then clearly a payload reduction is likely to lead to a marked deterioration in the economics of operation per passenger-mile flown. The cost per passenger or per seat-mile is the specific operating cost and has already been referred to as a key parameter in all transport economy studies. If, therefore, the payload at J is P_J lb and at G is P_G (maximum payload) the specific costs (at maximum range point J) will be approximately $P_G/P_J \times$ specific costs at G. In high-speed aircraft, employing high cruising powers, especially with turbine engines operating below their optimum altitude, the low air miles per gallon achieved may introduce in this way a serious limitation to medium and long-range operation. Clearly a payload at J less than half the payload at G, would be of little value for economic operations since, in any case, unnecessary fuselage accommodation, furnishings, etc., are being provided for the payload available and the direct specific operating costs, that is those relating to the aircraft and its operation only, are likely to be more than twice the minimum possible.

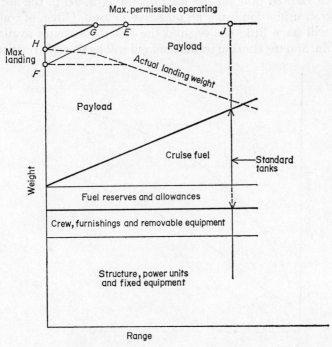

Fig. 2.3. The Weight Breakdown with respect to Range

The revenue rate structure is based on the passenger-mile or the freight load ton-mile unit, and it is for this reason that specific operating costs are reckoned on the same basis, but the direct cost of operation of a given aircraft is much more closely associated with the time of flight than with the load carried, or the miles flown. Moreover, the costs per hour of operation are generally reduced when the time in the air is in long stages, since many items of cost such as station and landing charges, the fuel costs on climb and descent as well as on the airport circuit are fairly constant factors which need to be considered once on each flight whatever its duration. Equally important, a higher aircraft annual utilisation rate is often possible when operating on longer stages so that the standing charges (i.e. aircraft and spares depreciation and insurance) per flying hour may be decreased. The wise airline operator is at pains to extract from his fleet the maximum ton-miles of transport in a given elapsed time for the least operating hours in the air, for aircraft utilisation is not an objective in itself. Often, of course, he will have little choice, and the system of routes available to him and the times of traffic demand will be severely restricted.

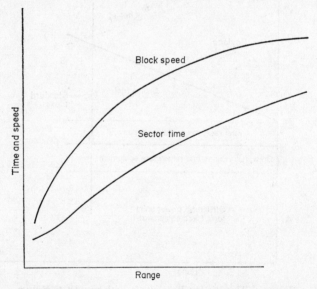

Fig. 2.4. Flight Time and Speed in relation to Range

Figure 2.4 shows a typical variation of flight time with block distance for a transport aircraft in which a basic time interval of 20 minutes is required for taxi, take-off, orbit and landing only. As block distance increases, some improvements in operating speeds due to increasing altitude and, on much longer flights, due to reduced weight, distort the linear form of the time curve. The variation of block speed is also shown in the same figure.

Effect of cruising speed on economy of operation

The influence of the block speed on the unit direct operating cost of a transport aircraft is direct and should not be under-estimated. It is the time at this speed which, together with the payload capacity, largely creates the productivity. While stimulating the public demand and providing the most sale-able element of the air transport product, speed is also the most active factor in the cost equation. Like the passenger or cargo capacity, however, the cruising speed is modified as an economic factor. The taxi, take-off, climb and descent phases of the flight and the lost mileage on the airway increases the block time. A block time (t_B) relationship with stage length (R) and cruising speed (V) may, for simplicity, be written as:

$$t_B = \frac{R}{V} + 25 \text{ min} \qquad (2.1)$$

On short-haul flights the maximum cruising speed is seldom useful since time in the air does not allow the attainment of the full cruising altitude. Moreover, the additional wing structural strength to allow high cruising speeds at lower altitudes may not be justified.

A combination of the block speed of Fig. 2.4 and the appro-priate payload-range (or flight weight) diagram enables the curve of Fig. 2.5 to be drawn. This shows the variation of available ton-miles per hour with the block distance flown. The maximum value, A, occurs at the maximum payload point of the payload range diagram. The form of this curve is very significant. It shows how rapidly the transport efficiency falls off on trips shorter than that giving the maximum payload point, in spite of the payload remaining constant on shorter sectors. It also shows that the gain in block speed on longer

61

flights can do little to correct the fall in economy due to the replacement of payload by cruising fuel. No account is here taken, however, of the effect of the length of flight on the overall operating economy, since in the criterion of Fig. 2.5 the sector flight time effects only the block speed. It ignores the transport production and the operating hours lost through aircraft standing idle on the ground. It also take no account of the terminal losses associated with each aircraft movement. With these considerations in mind, it will be of interest to define the optimum transport product per flight.

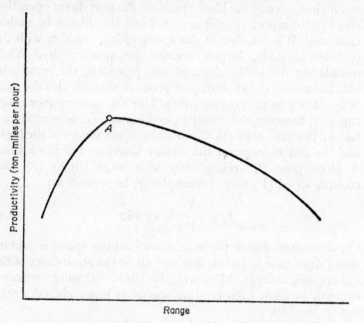

FIG. 2.5. Transport Productivity and its Variation with Range

In the ideal case of an aircraft with a linear Payload Range characteristic (such as is shown in Fig. 2.2) and with no limitation due to fuselage or fuel-tank capacity, the form of the Ton-mile v. Range curve is as shown by the full line in Fig. 2.6. It may be shown from first principles that since the curve is of regular parabolic form the maximum ton-mile point is at a block distance equal to half that at which the payload would theoretically be reduced to zero, i.e. at half the ultimate range with fuel reserves unconsumed. Referring to the diagram, we may say that if AB is the maximum ordinate, then $OA = AC$. One striking feature of the ton-mile curves is the fact that the optimum flight point occurs at a block distance which is quite independent of that indicated by the Payload-Range diagrams.

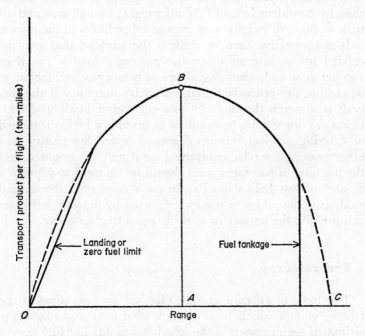

FIG. 2.6. The Transport Product with respect to Range

The passenger-freight distribution

The conventional Payload-Range diagram does to a great extent oversimplify the payload-carrying capacity of an aircraft. When a mixed load of passengers and freight are to be carried it must be remembered that the passenger seats are booked in advance by units for a particular service, and that mail and freight may either be booked for a particular service (through mail or newspaper contracts) or for the earliest possible delivery, which on a high-frequency sector may well permit deferred transport. Freight allotments may therefore, on particular flights, be related to the passenger bookings. The problem does not arise for aircraft on which freight is restricted by hold capacity (after the passenger baggage is stowed) rather than by considerations of take-off weight; though fore and aft trim or landing weight may impose other limits of their own.

It is instructive then to analyse the payload that may be carried by an aircraft when the passenger load is less than 100 per cent and, assuming a typical passenger load factor, to determine the potential freight capacity necessary if the aircraft is to reach the limits of take-off and/or landing weight. It may at other times be required to provide a higher standard of catering service, requiring greater space for pantry and other passenger service equipment, or it may be proposed that the pitching of passenger seats should be changed to provide a greater or less hold capacity. In such cases only the careful analysis of actual route results supported by detailed estimates can provide the answer in terms of operating economy.

Fuel reserves

The basis of all competently planned air operations is the reserve of fuel which must be onloaded over and above the estimated requirements of the scheduled flight. The fuel reserve is not essentially an emergency reserve. It is carried in order to cover the various contingencies which arise in the air and broadly increases the regularity with which a service can be maintained.

There are two general methods of arriving at a satisfactory fuel reserve for any route. (1) We may base our requirement on the past experience of the airline on a particular sector and season, and by means of a statistical survey relate a recorded schedule of flight consumption to the frequency of occasions on which the various levels had occurred. After an individual consideration of extreme cases and ensuring no repetition of the same chain of events, it is possible to arrive at an overall reserve which, under the same seasonal conditions will be unlikely ever to be required, but which will impose the minimum weight penalty. (2) We may base our estimate on calculated fuel requirements for a logically related chain of operational events which are known to be liable to occur. On new routes or where exact flight records have not previously been kept, the latter method is the only practicable one. It is based generally on an allowance for stacking (at an altitude directed by traffic control) near the airport of arrival, at an average cruising consumption for $\frac{3}{4}$ hour to $1\frac{1}{2}$ hours, depending on the particular airport and the time of year, as well as including an allowance for the fuel consumed if diverted to an alternate or supplementary aerodrome after arrival over the scheduled destination. The standard practice for the operations of European airlines is for the farthest supplementary aerodrome to be used as the diversion for fuel reserve calculation purposes, and this may vary from over 250 miles to under 100 miles.

Further allowances are, of course, made for the maximum fuel likely to be consumed during the engine run-up both on the tarmac and on the perimeter (piston engines only), for the taxi distance anticipated as well as for the take-off, orbit and landing at each airport. An additional calculation is made of the fuel requirements both for the cruise procedure and for the diversionary flight reserve. The basis for the estimation of equivalent wind components on an air route cannot here be discussed at length. It must suffice to state that estimations based on an average wind component along the track for the particular season offer in general an insufficient margin for high standards of safety if they are to be achieved with good punctuality and high payload capacity. Since winds that are more adverse than the average must be encountered on 50 per cent of occasions it stands to reason that arrivals would be late on this same percentage of occasions if excess thrust were not taken from the engines. This combination of excess wind and fuel consumptions above the scheduled level conspire to reduce the reserve of fuel remaining at arrival over the destination.

Bookable payloads (passengers, mail and freight) are based on long-term-forecast seasonal winds, and a margin is clearly required to prevent off-loading 'on the day' and/or serious curtailment of the effective fuel reserve. This margin is provided by the employment of a scheduled wind which is more adverse than the average, and is generally related to the standard deviation (Baumol, 1965) or the variance of the wind component about the mean value. Meteorological forecasts on which the actual flight plan is based (prepared immediately before take-off) may indicate an extra fuel requirement. This will, however, only require off-loading passengers in extreme conditions. Higher altitudes of operation will require greater variations in the fuel loads to cope with the higher adverse winds (greater average wind components and greater deviations from the average). However, supersonic flight altitudes will bring some alleviation from this factor (Chapter 9). The fuel to meet the possibility of a diversionary flight may need to include a further climb allowance if the aircraft is diverted after descent to the scheduled destination: a low-altitude cruise to the diversionary airport is seldom economic except on partial power.

The principal characteristic of the turbine engine is its efficiency at high output, hence an improved fuel economy at low airspeeds can be achieved when less than the full number of units are operated near their maximum continuous power or thrust. This means of fuel economy has, however, not been adopted by the airlines, largely because of the problem of restarting in flight, preparatory to the landing phase. Serious risks in icing conditions could arise.

An important item in the consumption of all turbine-driven aircraft – although not strictly a part of the fuel reserve, since it must be consumed on every flight – is the taxi and orbit allowance. These conditions of operation being necessarily on the ground or at low altitude, and with all engines running at low power, are extremely heavy on fuel. This is particularly true of jet aircraft for which it has even been suggested that, because of excessive consumption arising through the ever increasing delays at major airports before departure, taxi-ing should be completely obviated by ground towing by motor tractors. The practical method of the long-haul operator is the overloading of fuel above the take-off weight by the amount required for taxi-ing, although this will still limit the maximum range of the aircraft where fuel volume is critical. As in all considerations of aircraft fuel reserves, we are led to the conclusion that even with the newer types of low consumption fan-jet engine now being introduced into service, the essential need is for a fresh approach to the whole subject of traffic control on the ground as well as in the air. New solutions acceptable to all the interests concerned have, however, been hard to find.

The fuel reserve carried, but largely unconsumed on the average scheduled flight, directly displaces the bookable payload on all flights except where the seating or volumetric capacity of the aircraft is limited. Unlike the fuel consumed in climb and cruise, the fuel carried as a reserve may limit payload on short flights where landing weight is restrictive. The large fuel reserves carried today on many of the shorter European air services, especially in the winter season, provide an enormous economic burden. There is little doubt that the further systematic study of this single problem could still pay a rich dividend if managed by a competent operational research group working in association with airlines.

The effect of weight

The problem of weight is necessarily one that has been the concern of the aircraft designer, the operator and the National Aviation Authorities jointly. The problem has been modified to some extent by the introduction of jet and propeller-turbine aircraft. Disposable load in the form of fuel and payload, however, still is, to the designer, the best measure of his success in providing for the operator an effective tool for economic and competitive operations.

Some aspects of weight are largely outside the control of the aircraft designer. The weight of equipment, including the fixed items such as furnishings, seats, trim and soundproofing, etc., and radio equipment, as well as toilet accommodation, pantry equipment, food and catering weights, can all add up to a considerable total. The strict control of all these items of weight is an important part of the operating executive's task as moderator between the furnishing and catering specialists and the austere standards sought by the economic specialists on the other. The scope for original attitudes in the layout of aircraft interiors is enormous. In few other ways is it easier to throw away a first-rate design. Here the economics of weight arises clearly as an issue of the first magnitude, but fortunately for any aircraft operating over a specified route system, the loss of potential revenue-earning capacity may be usefully estimated and charged against the weight of the equipment under consideration.

Another aspect of weight is fundamental to the economic operation of the transport aircraft. In reducing seat pitch or increasing the number of seats per row and thereby lowering the volumetric space per passenger, an increased revenue-earning potential may be achieved although it is generally at a reduced standard of comfort. Clearly, limitations in disposable load would prevent large increases in this way unless the passenger baggage allowance was also decreased. Physical extension of the fuselage, with some weight penalty, can also make available some increased floor area for passenger seating. A detailed study of a number of such alternative solutions as well as the investigation of baggage and freight hold volumes in alternative fore and aft positions, giving due consideration to the catering amenities that are deemed to be necessary or profitable, will generally be found well worth while. This work is essentially within the province of the Operators' Technical or Project Branch. The virtue of flexibility in interior layout is one that will always be highly valued in the assessment of an economic transport aircraft, if only because the flight and schedule planning of the best-ordered airline in the period four of five years ahead (for which new aircraft are generally required) is more a matter of faith and hope than of scientific reasoning.

The value of weight saving on an aircraft can vary between very wide limits. It depends firstly on whether the aircraft is operating to its weight limits at take-off and landing. If operating on short routes with a bookable payload restricted by volumetric capacity alone then no immediate use can be made of weight saving except in the improvement of runway and flight performance because of the reduced flying weight. If increased bookable loads are obtainable it must be established that the extra capacity or some useful proportion of it can be sold and, if able to be sold, its revenue-earning value will depend both on the fare, or rate charged, and the revenue miles flown in a relevant period or in the life of the aircraft. In general, it may be said that payload capacity is usable in the long run, i.e. other essential weight increases will make it invaluable, at any rate on the longer sectors operated, and that revenue follows the capacity. It must be noted also that high-speed aircraft, especially modern transports of relatively high cost which will necessarily be required to operate over a long period of years, will repay the efforts made in weight saving because of their high revenue-earning capacity per pound of payload. A revealing fact is that a small unit of weight that is immeasurable on the scales required to weigh a large high-performance transport could earn more in a year, and relatively far more in the aircraft's full life, than the same weight saved in a small aircraft on which it may represent an appreciable proportion of the payload capacity.

Aircraft size and operational utilisation

We should not be correctly defining the limits of economy in design if we omitted to discuss broadly those which are imposed by traffic and revenue upon the size of aircraft required to meet the estimated route demand. It is enough here to indicate the factors which must be taken into account when the size of aircraft is decided.

The aircraft itself will generally be required to cover a number of different stages and routes making up the pattern or system. The North Atlantic and other critical long-haul routes present no exceptions to this since generally a marked flexibility of operation will be advantageous. The traffic on each stage or sector will vary to a different extent; it will need to be fed by other sectors of varying length; and superimposed on them all a seasonal or shorter-term fluctuation is likely to be frequently encountered. It is to be expected, therefore, that the traffic estimations which may suggest a large-size aircraft, e.g. 150-seater, under peak high-season conditions at a frequency of eight or ten services per day, must be carefully compared with off-season estimates so that neither the overall annual utilisation of the aircraft is drastically reduced due to curtailed off-season services, nor are the low-season operating costs out of all proportion to the revenue. The evening out of traffic demands in all the seasons of the year as well as throughout the operating day is a major problem for the air operator. Uneven demand increases the costs of operation since the aircraft fleets as well as the engineering potential must be matched to the peak of the demand unless business is to be turned away, and this may indeed be necessary in a final analysis!

The size of aircraft is, however, not governed only by design requirements or traffic demand since, with reduced frequencies of service, larger and larger aircraft could theoretically be operated to carry the same passenger load. In practice, however, an upper limit to size must often be set by the minimum frequency to provide a satisfactory passenger service as well as by the convenience of integration with other services. In addition to this, it must always be borne in mind that the smaller number of units of the larger aircraft can less easily be handled by the maintenance system of the airline, especially when operations are conducted on a small scale. To the manufacturer, on the other hand, size will be determined by overseas markets and by the need to maximise the demand for the type in relation to other manufacturers' products and projects. Larger aircraft will also meet a given total airline traffic demand in smaller quantity production. This generally will increase the unit loading of the costs of research and development, a factor which was of some importance in establishing the optimum design of the supersonic airliner projects in Europe and in the USA.

The economics of aircraft performance

The basis of the economic operation of transport aircraft is the power requirement for flight in the various conditions of climb, cruise, descent and standby. The power requirement governs not only the fuel consumption but also, in most cases, the uplift capability of the aircraft since fuel weight plus payload are normally limited by the maximum take-off weight of the machine. An appreciation of air operating economics requires that the principles governing the power required for flight and the estimation of performance under various operating conditions should be broadly understood. This will facilitate a more complete understanding of the primary design criteria which guide the comparison and selection of aircraft. This will further help in the study of the many types of power unit now available for transport aircraft since the power unit itself controls to a very large extent the domain of operation of the aircraft with regard to speed, altitude and range. This part of our subject overlooks an immense field and only the most significant aspects leading up to the effect of take-off performance and cruising speed on the economy of operation can be considered. Some readers may prefer to omit the next section of this chapter on a first reading.

The drag and power required for flight

We shall discuss first the drag of an aircraft at various speeds and altitudes, and the effect upon it of the geometrical form of the machine itself.

If V is the horizontal speed in m.p.h. at height, h, and relative density σ then it is possible to relate simply the total drag of a body in translation through the air at moderate speeds, and without lifting surfaces, by the equation

$$D_h = D_{100}\, \sigma \left(\frac{V}{100}\right)^2 \times \left(\frac{88}{60}\right)^2 \qquad (2.2)$$

Here D_{100} denotes the drag of the body at sea level at a speed of 100 f.p.s. It is common practice to express D_{100} in terms of the dimensions of the body and the wetted area (total skin area) or cross-sectional area (A) and a drag coefficient (C_D) may be used for this purpose

Hence $$D_{100} = C_D . A . 100^2 \qquad (2.3)$$

It can be shown, however (Glauert, 1947), that the drag of an aircraft in horizontal flight is increased by an additional factor associated with the wing lift and the deflection of the airflow after passing over the lifting surface. This extra drag is known as Induced Drag and at low speeds and/or high altitude

71

may become an important factor in the power requirement for flight.

If we write the lift force required to balance the weight of the aircraft in coefficient form, we obtain

$$L = W = C_L . S . \tfrac{1}{2} \rho_0 \sigma . V^2 \qquad (2.4)$$

where C_L is a lift coefficient

ρ_0 is the density of air under standard sea-level conditions

σ is the relative density at altitude

V is the air speed in m.p.h.

S is the wing area in sq. ft.

Now $\sigma . V^2$ may also be considered as V_i^2 where V_i is the equivalent speed that would be indicated on the pilot's airspeed indicator if all instrument position and speed errors were eliminated. Its significance lies in the fact that as a measured dynamic pressure, calibrated as speed, it indicates the air forces acting on the aircraft. The group $\tfrac{1}{2}\rho_0\sigma V^2$ in fact represents the dynamic pressure or head resulting from bringing the moving airstream to rest. If we denote this by q

Then
$$L = C_L . S . q \qquad (2.5)$$

S, the wing area, corresponds to the area A taken in Eqn. 2.3. In the UK it is usual to take the area on which the drag coefficient is based as the wing area S, denoting the drag coefficient (excluding induced drag) as C_0. In the US an equivalent parasite area is more usually employed. This is equal to the product $C_{d0} . S . C_{d0}$ will increase at high values of C_L and we may write then

$$C_{d0} = C_{d0 \text{ min}} + K C_L^2 \qquad (2.6)$$

A corresponding coefficient for induced drag may be used

$$C_{d_i} = \frac{C_L^2}{\pi A_R} (1 + \delta) \qquad (2.7)$$

where A_R = Aspect Ratio = $\dfrac{\text{span}^2}{S}$

and δ is a correction factor which allows for wing taper and the non-elliptic distribution of lift along the span.

Hence the total drag coefficient may be written as

$$C_d = Cd_{0\text{min}} + \frac{C_L{}^2}{\pi . A_R . e} \qquad (2.8)$$

where
$$e = \frac{1}{1 + \delta + K . \pi . A_R} \qquad (2.9)$$

δ was calculated by Glauert and approximate values may be used (1947). Considerable data from wind tunnel and flight tests are now available.

K is usually about 0·010. Drag at any true speed (V) and height (σ) may now be written down:

$$D = \left(Cd_{0\text{min}} + \frac{C_L{}^2}{\pi . A_R e .} \right) S\tfrac{1}{2}\rho_0 \sigma V^2 \qquad (2.10)$$

Two things here should be noted: (1) the effect of weight appears in the variable C_L which from Eqn. 2.5 may be directly calculated. (2) no allowance has been made at this stage for the effects of compressibility on the drag of the aircraft.

Fig. 2.7 shows the variation of Drag Coefficient with $C_L{}^2$. The drag parabola is generally closely approximated over the climbing and cruising C_L range of the aircraft. The full drag variation is also shown.

The characteristic swept-back wing was introduced in the latter stage of World War II to minimise the drag rise which sets in as airspeeds approach the speed of sound. With wings swept at 35° from the normal to the line of flight the wing drag rise can be retained to an economic level up to a speed of 85 per cent of the speed of sound $(M = 0·85)$. The drag of the aircraft is usually first estimated from an individual assessment of the component parts. A summation is finally made with allowance also for interference effects which may become a high proportion of the whole on a clean aircraft. Full correction for compressibility effects will be made at this stage.

It is important that data should be used which correspond to the appropriate values of two fundamental parameters in the field of aerodynamic force. These are the Reynolds Number R and the Mach Number M.

$$\text{Reynolds Number } R = \frac{VL}{v} \qquad (2.11)$$

where V = Aircraft speed

L = A linear dimension,* and

v = Kinematic viscosity of the air, $\dfrac{\text{viscosity}}{\text{density}}$

R determines the relation between the pressure (or dynamic forces), and v the viscous forces in the field of flow. At low forward speeds and with small bodies in heavy fluids the viscous forces predominate and the conditions of flow are of a different nature from those controlling the higher-speed flow encountered in aircraft flight.

Within the aircraft flight range (R = 1 to 10 million) a marked variation in the drag characteristics of aerofoils and other streamline shapes can be found. In this way arises one of the gains achieved by large high-speed aircraft. The Mach Number M will be of special significance in our later discussion of the supersonic airliner.

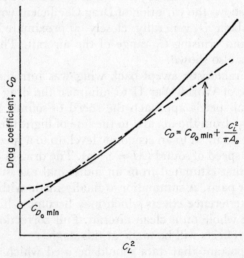

$$C_D = C_{D_0 \text{ min}} + \frac{C_L^2}{\pi A_e}$$

Drag coefficient, C_D

$C_{D_0 \text{ min}}$

C_L^2

FIG. 2.7. The Drag Characteristic of an Aircraft

* Wing chord is taken for aerofoil characteristics.

Reynolds himself, and Prandtl in Germany at a later date, carried out considerable research into the conditions of the flow of fluid through tubes and over rigid boundaries and they established that there are two conditions – Laminar Flow and Turbulent Flow, with transition from one to the other governed largely by the Reynolds Number. Because of the considerable drag rise when transition to the turbulent regime occurs it is important, so far as is possible, to delay this and while this is not possible behind rotating propellers or in the wake of obscrescences on the surface of an aircraft, it is promoted by the design of smooth wings with flush rivets and thick skins resisting wave formation under stress.

A considerable development in this direction has occurred during the last ten years, when the so-called laminar flow wing has been introduced which has as its object the delay of transition by means of a wing contour designed to provide a favourable pressure gradient postponing the breakaway of flow to a point farther back on the wing. These wings are characterised by their maximum thickness which occurs farther back than conventional aerofoils. To maintain precise wing contours a greater stiffness of skin is necessary and some weight penalty is necessarily incurred. The onset of turbulence can be even more powerfully deterred by sucking away or ejecting high-energy air into the boundary layer on the aircraft surfaces.

Values of $_v$, the kinematic viscosity, are given by Glauert (1947). For aerofoil data the wing chord is generally taken as the representative length. For bodies of revolution, fuselage models, etc., the diameter is the dimension most usually taken. The Royal Aeronautical Society data sheets as well as NASA and RAE reports give useful information of this subject and the effect of Reynolds Number on wing and fuselage drag can be readily seen from the charts provided. The other non-dimensional parameter, the Mach Number, governing the drag of aircraft has become of considerably more importance in recent years because of the greatly increased speed of jet aircraft. Pure-jet propulsion has provided thrusts of sufficient magnitude for the speed of sound to be closely approached with swept-wing designs of transport aircraft so that the drag rise associated with flight at high subsonic speeds has become a familiar problem. Currently planned supersonic transports are designed for the speed range of $M = 2 \cdot 2$ (BAC-Sud 'Concorde' to $M = 2 \cdot 7$–$3 \cdot 0$ (Boeing and Lockheed projects)).

Take-off and landing performance

The need to operate within the limitations of airfield size and the dominant requirement to provide safe operations after engine failure in all phases of the flight, determines the installed power of most transport aircraft. Other considerations may apply in the supersonic regime. In general the engine rpm are reduced for the cruise below maximum continuous power and it is important for economy of operation that the specific fuel consumption is not sensitive to the selected rpm to meet variations in the cruise conditions.

Take-off requirements, therefore, determine to a large extent the engine-dominated items in the direct cost index. Take-off performance, however, is also influenced by the take-off wing loading which may be decreased together with increased flap settings to give take-off at lower speeds at some penalty in the initial climb gradient. Take-off performance and climb after engine failure may be expected in various conditions to limit the take-off weight, and the payload, wing loading and flap design and setting will strongly influence the landing weight and performance. For economic operations the landing distance required will need to match the likely airports in use under maximum landing weight conditions and with full regard to the ambient conditions (air temperature and wind) and the height of the terrain. Thus a considerable degree of flexibility is seen to be required of a transport aircraft designed to operate effectively and economically in all parts of the world. Maximum operating economy can be achieved by a careful use of the flap settings to balance the limiting factors arising in take-off and in climb. Further, short-haul operations may well allow fuel loads to be considerably less than the maximum required, thereby allowing take-off with maximum payload at less than the gross weight of the aircraft. Water methanol may be used to increase engine thrust or power setting.

Definition of the specification

A number of complex factors in engine and aircraft design will determine optimum solutions to aircraft layout for given operational requirements. If these are well defined then, within the framework set by the payload, range and performance requirements, the final choice of engine, whether jet or prop-turbine, the wing design, its aspect and thickness ratios, its area and sweep, and the fuselage, systems and equipment specifications can be established. Parametric studies of the many design variables aud their effect on the specific direct operating costs will be made. Here we can no more than name the principal problem areas which will be studied in the preliminary design investigation of a typical subsonic jet transport in order to test for the commercial feasibility of the project. These are not necessarily in the order of the work sequence or of priority.

1. Comparative study of the type and number of engines of an acceptable specification which will be available within the time scale of the project.

2. The principal design characteristics of the engine so as to select the optimum by-pass ratio for a given cruising speed, and required ratio of cruise/static sea level thrust.

3. Study of the engine by-pass ratio and its influence on engine fuel economy and weight, and the aircraft operating economy.

4. The engine position and the relative advantages of location on the wing or on the rear fuselage.

5. The effect of wing aspect ratio, wing loading, thickness-chord ratio, and degree of sweep on wing weight and aircraft operating economy.

6. The effect of cruising speed on wing design and airframe cost.

7. The effect of simplification in the structural design on the airframe cost.

8. The effect of aircraft size and payload capacity on first cost and development cost.

9. The effect of variation in the parameters above on the specific direct operating costs.

77

10. The effect of wing flap design on the approach speed and its influence on the results.

11. Economic studies of weight/altitude/temperature and airfield limitations as functions of the design variables.

Beyond these studies lies the effect that the best solutions will have on the marketability of the product. A clear appreciation of the needs of the market is essential, indeed, for an adequate choice of solutions. Each item listed above will be affected by the markets anticipated for the product. Uncertainty as to these markets is a principal cause of indecision as to the major parameters in design.

Arthur E. Raymond,* who was Vice-President, Engineering, of the Douglas Aircraft Company for many years, set down the principal requirements for the achievements of a well-tempered aircraft design as follows:

> A proper environment for design and development.
> Good initial choice of the specification.
> Excellence of the detailed design.
> Thorough development.
> Thorough exploitation and follow-through.
> Adaptability of the design.
> Correct succession and timing for the succeeding model.

His views can be echoed today in the development of later generations of transport aircraft.

A detailed consideration of direct operating costs

A great deal of cost estimating is now regularly carried out on air transport projects, a large part of which is of very doubtful value. Its saving grace is that it is never intended for use as an estimate of true cost but only as an index for comparative purposes. It is suggested that there are three principal purposes for the estimation of cost. These are:

1. For the aircraft designer to optimise his project at various stages in the preliminary design process, e.g. to assess the effect which a modified wing design, aimed to improve handling, minimum approach speed or cruise performance, may have on

* 'The Well-Tempered Aircraft', *Jnl. Roy. Aero. Soc.*, 1957.

direct operating costs and acceptability of the aircraft by the anticipated airline customers.

2. For the airline project engineers and fleet planners to enable them to compare the various competitive designs at an early stage in airline comparative studies. To enable them to assess the effects of alternative proposals and layouts and, in the final analysis, to specify the best equipment introduction programme.

3. For airline operators and development engineers to enable them to develop the flight equipment in service to best advantage, e.g. with regard to operating techniques, selection and integration of services, as well as to achieve engineering objectives such as the extension of component lives and improvement in overhaul procedures on the base.

What is significant about the above objectives is that they can in only a very limited sense be satisfied by a simplified approach such as by means of a formula related to the principal aircraft design parameters. Even in the first item above, the need for optimisation of the overall concept in relation to one variable, or more often to a compact group of design variables, requires a detailed appreciation of many aspects of the operational pattern of the most likely customers' route networks. It requires, moreover, a close insight into the future requirements of the airlines which may not be expressed at all clearly or even be known very precisely, at the time of preliminary design, by the various airline officials to whom access may be available.

The record of successful civil airliners is often a record of close and co-operative manufacturer–airline relations. The well-known liaison between American Airlines and the Douglas Aircraft Company which led from the DC 3 to the DC 7, and the collaboration between BEA and Vickers Armstrong Limited which led from the Viking to the Vanguard, are often quoted in this context. Fresh ideas still need to come in and no arrangement can perhaps remain perfect indefinitely. Certainly the DC 7 and the Vanguard were far less successful than their predecessors and seem to have broken the spells. The input of up-dated airline figures is essential for useful air transport cost studies, but they must be closely applicable to the system and the area under investigation.

The basis on which the principal cost formulae have been built up is discussed below, but it is important to emphasise that the real requirement is a full and exact representation of the cost, which should include all aspects of the operation under consideration, whether for one particular section of one airline's route system or for a wide group of airlines which may be thought to be the potential market for an aircraft project.

It is in the search for simplicity that the need for a formula arises. It is even more because of the importance of unbiassed comparisons that the need for a standard formula, with set levels for the key parameters, still exists. Formulae, however, can take little account of the operating milieu and can suggest only in a very uncertain manner the indirect costs and other airline expenses not directly related to the aircraft itself.

It may be questioned why it is so necessary to introduce a cost index as the final arbiter in these essentially technical comparisons for we are not seeking an accurate statement in a profit and loss account. The balance of forces in the money market is, however, a measure of the wider issues in the economy which can in no other way be so simply represented. Money represents the only complete cross-section of commercial life. Thus the detailed revenue and cost figures of a transport undertaking represent the wide range of sales and publicity, engineering, operations and management functions which can by no other common denominator be so simply represented.

It is then upon this balance of the economic forces which interplay in an operational cost study that we should concentrate. The greatest problem we have to face is that in many areas of air transport organisation there is little relation between the costs incurred (the input) and the air transport product (the output). It is too easy to fall back on the simple formula which may appear to be the only means available. Oversimplified methods of diagnosis, however, may deaden our appreciation of the problem.

The cost of operating a transport aircraft

It is convenient to break down the operating costs into the two principal groups:

Direct Costs
Indirect Costs

The direct costs are those which are principally concerned with the operation of the aircraft itself in a transport system and the indirect costs represent all other operating and promotional costs which concern the management of a commercial airline. There are naturally a great many different interpretations of these two main groups of cost and the dividing line between them. It is doubtful if the fine differences have much significance so long as a clear understanding of the definitions is agreed before making comparisons between aircraft or organisational costs.

At the risk of conflicting with some empirical cost formulae which have been developed to form a basis for analysis, I would like to propose that the most practical basis for establishing cost calculations is to work on the principle that we use the minimum number of cost elements required. That is, we should adopt as a basis for cost comparisons only such items as have a bearing upon the problem under consideration. Thus, in an aircraft design study we shall approach closely to the direct operating costs as a criterion and in airline comparative assessments we would introduce a far wider range of variables.

It is probably most convenient to divide Direct Operating Cost into three elements:

1. Standing Costs, including depreciation of the capital invested in flight equipment as well as the insurance and interest associated with the flight equipment.

2. Flying Costs, including crew, fuel and oil, landing fees and direct maintenance and overhaul costs.

3. Other Costs, which would represent the special costs of significance to the particular exercise in hand.

It is apparent that each one of these items, only broadly identified so far, has a bearing on the large majority of comparative aircraft studies. It is true, however, that they do not relate directly to the standard method presentation recommended by the ATA (Air Transport Association of America) (June 1960) which includes the applied maintenance burden (CAB Account Number 5279.6) and excludes the interest charges on capital as well as the landing fees in the flying operations account. However, the work of the SBAC Operating Costs Panel in 1959 broadly supported our approach and this is the basis upon which the SBAC standard method of estimating cost has now been drawn up (November 1959). It is supported by the current methods of estimating used by BEA and by many airlines who naturally use, wherever possible and relevant, their own more precisely known factors and costs.

No discussion of the apportionment of airline operating costs could be complete without reference to the original and precise contributions to the subject which have been made by Mr Peter Masefield when he was Director of long-term research and development at the Ministry of Civil Aviation and later as Chief Executive of BEA. He also broke up airline costs into two groups, but to him the essential cleavage lay between *basic* and *variable* costs, where basic covered what are in effect the overhead costs, and variable refers to those costs which are directly associated with the hours flown and the number of landings performed. Now on this principle we must accept both basic and variable costs as including important elements which are related both to the aircraft type, called by Mr Masefield the 'A' or Aircraft Costs, and the 'B' or Airline Costs, which he relates to the organisation and standards of the operator, to the location and spread of the operating pattern, and to the characteristics of the individual routes to be operated (1951). A third subdivision of basic annual costs, the 'C' or Promotional Costs, was proposed. This did not apply to the variable costs and these were divided into two groups:

Hourly cruising costs, and take-off and landing costs.

This latter group is not generally accepted now as being necessary in the majority of economic exercises. It will be recognised that the breakdown proposed was designed to be a meaningful and rational method of standardising aircraft type assessment and of controlling airline budgeting and route management. It was based on the simplest economic principles of transport which, at the time, were in danger of being lost in between the project engineer with his concern for the individual aircraft type and its future technical and economic performance, and the accountant with his prime concern for justification of an overall balance between airline revenue and cost over a short period of time.

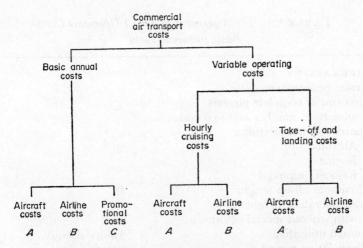

FIG. 2.8. A Breakdown of Airline Operating Costs

The pattern of costs previously proposed by Mr Masefield is illustrated in Fig. 2.8 which is reproduced here by kind permission of Mr Masefield and of the Institute of Transport.

It should be quite clear that for the airline a consideration of the full structure of costs is absolutely essential if it is to identify the significant factors, isolate them and assess the means available to control and improve the total operational situation. To this extent the establishment of a rational airline cost pattern is an essential first step to the control of the economic growth of the business.

In the more general case the fullest data on transport aircraft costs and operations are not likely to be available and concentration must be centred on the direct operating costs of the aircraft itself.

The estimation of direct costs

Table 2.1 shows a useful form of data sheet which may be used for the direct cost analysis. It allows the principal economic and other factual assumptions to be recorded and provides a ready indication of the basis of the computations.

TABLE 2.1. *The Assessment of Direct Operating Costs*
Basic Economic Data

AIRCRAFT TYPE	
Cruise performance data	
First cost of complete aircraft	£
Engine type, number and first cost	
Spares cost per aircraft	
Airframe	
Engine	
Radio/Equipment	
Maximum all-up weight	lb
Basic operating weight	
with/without special equipment	lb
Annual utilisation	Hours/aircraft
Depreciation period	years
Residual value	%
Insurance rate of flight equipment	% per annum
Interest on capital	% per annum
Basis of engineering costs	
(*a*) Airframe engineering costs	£ per hour or
(*b*) Engine maintenance and overhaul	
costs	Man-hours per annum
(*c*) Equipment and component overhaul	
Mean attained period between engine	
overhauls	hours
Maintenance labour rate	£/direct man-hour
Crew costs (No. in crew)	£ per annum
Crew utilisation	hours/annum
Fuel costs	£ per flying hour
Landing fees	£ per landing

Standing costs

This represents the aircraft cost element in the basic annual costs of operation. It normally comprises three parts:

Depreciation of the flight equipment and spares.

Insurance of the flight equipment.

Interest on the capital locked up in flight equipment and spares.

Depreciation of the flight equipment is normally judged to be a function of obsolescence with allowance made for a residual value of between 10 and 20 per cent as a result of the most recent experience available in the disposal of downgraded aircraft. Past experience has been available in the disposal of downgraded aircraft. Past experience has been variable, and some types such as the DC 7 and the Constellation 1649 retained book values within three or four years of their introduction into service which far exceeded their resale value. Demand for demoted passenger aircraft for charter work, inclusive tours and cargo services, however, will more often support higher residual values than the status of the type in the original role would justify.

It is becoming common practice to increase the period of depreciation for first-line jet aircraft. The higher first cost and lower expected rate of obsolescence of the newest types have undoubtedly justified this as well as making it necessary. Even on a ten-year life the standing costs of operation have become a higher proportion of the total direct costs than was usual in the previous generation of transport aircraft which were more usually written off over eight years. Moreover, the utilisation (or flying hours per annum) has tended to increase so that the overall flying life of the current generation of transport aircraft is expected to be longer. This, taken together with the lower overall cost of maintenance and overhaul (per unit of capacity per annum) which is expected for new aircraft, may go some way to alleviate the burden placed upon the operator by the increasing first cost of recent aircraft. There is good reason to be cautious, however, since there is still plenty of evidence that the development of subsonic jet transports is not slowing down. Quite apart from the prospects of the SST, engine development has already created a new generation of turbo-fan transports, and the new 300–400-seat subsonic wide-body transports based on more advanced technology are but one stage in a natural development. Low noise-level engines, auto-landing development, and short take-off and landing techniques suggest that a steady pressure to advance technologically will be exerted on the air operating industry during the next decade. The recent history of this industry indicates quite clearly that the advance will continue as long as the economic case can be justified. From this point of view a period of write-off beyond ten years may be more difficult to substantiate. Indeed, when obsolescence is not the determining factor this limit is likely to be set by other considerations, one dominant factor being the airline growth expectation. Tax allowances may well influence the most economic life period which should be used.

Although a residual value of 10 to 20 per cent is normally assumed in calculations of operating economy, this will depend on the type of aircraft and the experience of the airline concerned. The SBAC method of cost estimation suggests a 10 per cent residual value for the airframe, engine and equipment together with spares, whereas the standard method of the ATA proposed 15 per cent residual value for all items excluding radio, for which the residual value is taken to be zero. It is most usual to consider the depreciation of the aircraft and the spares holding as an hourly cost in the first instance, and this may be written therefore as:

$$C_{sd} = \frac{(C_{air} + C_{eng} + C_{equ}) (1 - r_V)}{L \times U} \qquad (2.12)$$

where C_{sd} is the cost per hour of the depreciation of the equipped aircraft with engines and airframe, engine and equipment spares.

C_{air} is the cost of one furnished airframe with spares.

C_{eng} is the cost of the engines installed in one airframe, and the spare engines together with the engine spares holding per airframe.

C_{equ} is the equipment (including radio and radar) installed together with the spares holding of equipment per airframe.

r_V is the residual value of the fully equipped aircraft and spares after the life period assumed (L years) expressed as a fraction of first cost.

U is the average utilisation per aircraft in revenue flying hours per annum.

The spares holdings here considered are the unconsumed portion of the spares holding which may be considered as a capital element which will be required from the inception of operations with a new type and which will be held more or less intact as an insurance at all times. In practice, the insurance spares holding may decline as experience is gained with a particular type because of the greater knowledge acquired by the airline engineering department of the spares essential to provide an acceptable probability of unserviceability. An important factor is the progressive extension of the life of components which reduces spares requirements as the life of an aircraft type continues. This applies particularly to engines and major lifed components. Our assumption therefore is a conservative one.

The consumable engineering items are included in the materials element of the aircraft maintenance cost.

Utilisation

A large number of variables influence the value of the flight utilisation that may be achieved by a transport aircraft and the most important of these may be summarised as follows for the case of simplified shuttle operations:

D the serviceable operating days in the year
H the usable hours in the operating day
n the number of flights per day
t_a the mean flight time per sector
R the mean distance per sector
V the cruising speed of the aircraft
t_g the average ground time at transit and terminal points
t_l the average take-off, climb, descent and taxi time lost.

Clearly, many of the above items are inter-related. For instance:

$$\left.\begin{array}{l} H = n.t_a + (n-1)t_g \\[1mm] \text{and } t_a = \dfrac{R}{V} + t_l \\[1mm] \text{Also Utilisation } U = D.n.t_a \end{array}\right\} \qquad (2.13)$$

87

It is clear then that $\quad n = \dfrac{H + t_g}{\dfrac{R}{V} + t_g + t_l}$ $\qquad$ (2.14)

and that $\qquad U = D\, \dfrac{\left(\dfrac{R}{V} + t_l\right)\left(H + t_g\right)}{\left(\dfrac{R}{V} + t_l + t_g\right)}$ $\qquad$ (2.15)

This simple relationship can be used to show the effect of the principal variables on aircraft utilisation. Figs. 2.9 and 2.10 have been drawn to illustrate the influence of t_g, V and R on the utilisation of a transport aircraft under the simplified assumptions specified above. An integration factor of 75–90 per cent should be used to correct these figures for problems associated with integration of flights on different sector length, inter-line timings and tag end losses.

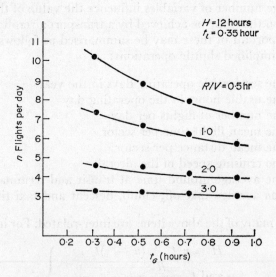

FIG. 2.9. Short-haul Flight Sectors per Day

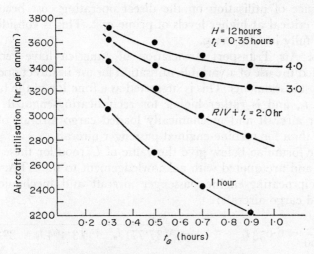

Fig. 2.10. Potential Aircraft Utilisation

It became apparent in the first years of jet transport operation that certain considerations were playing an important part in maintaining the high level of utilisation which was necessary for their economic survival. The number of hours and days on standby or schedule protection was reduced to the essential minimum. The operating hours of the day were maximised by effective scheduling and promotion. Ramp time and turn-arounds were shortened. The potential available is shown in the above figures. The pressure of economic necessity has clearly forced the airlines to work up to the limits of the serviceable hours available to them.

F. W. Kolk of American Airlines (1960) has drawn attention to the time ratios which are of paramount importance in the achievement of high utilisation. These are the ratios of the time spent on various functions to the time spent on service. He studied the time spent on maintenance, the time at the gate, and the time which is spent in schedule protection with service-able aircraft. The waste time during the 24 hours when passenger service is not required is likely to increase as the average block time for given sectors is reduced by aircraft of ever increasing performance. In the case of the supersonic transport this warning will need very special consideration since the influence of utilisation on the direct operating cost becomes more critical at higher levels of prime cost. This is considered more fully in Chapter 9.

The Air Transport Association of America have recommended the use of a variable utilisation for use in direct operating cost assessments. This is suggested as a function of the block time. t_b, and is rather higher for reciprocating-engined passenger aircraft and mechanically loaded cargo aircraft of all types than for turbine-engined passenger aircraft.

The formulae below give the value of $U/1000$ for these two cases and are quoted with acknowledgement to the ATA.

Reciprocating-engine passenger aircraft and mechanically loaded cargo aircraft:

$$\frac{U}{1000} = 6 \cdot 053 \, t_b + 5 \cdot 70 - \sqrt{37 \cdot 771 \, t_b{}^2 + 13 \cdot 494 \, t_b + 32 \cdot 490}$$

$$= 3 \cdot 65 \text{ when } t_b \text{ is greater than } 5 \cdot 0 \text{ hours} \qquad (2.16)$$

Turbine-engined passenger aircraft:

$$\frac{U}{1000} = 3 \cdot 4546 \, t_b + 2 \cdot 994 - \sqrt{12 \cdot 289 \, t_b{}^2 - 5 \cdot 6626 \, t_b + 8 \cdot 964}$$

$$= 3 \cdot 30 \text{ when } t_b \text{ is greater than } 5 \cdot 0 \text{ hours} \qquad (2.17)$$

BEA have suggested for their own short/medium sectors a standard variation of U:

$$\frac{U}{1000} = 3 \cdot 125 \left(1 + \frac{0 \cdot 75}{t_b} \right)^{-1} \qquad (2.18)$$

Insurance

It is standard practice to make an allowance for insurance as part of the standing costs of operation. Thus with an insurance rate per annum on the total equipped aircraft and spares cost of x per cent, the costs per flying hour may be written as:

$$C_{\text{ins}} = \frac{x}{U} \left(C_{\text{air}} + C_{\text{eng}} + C_{\text{equ}} \right) \qquad (2.19)$$

where the other symbols were previously defined in this chapter.

The US practice is to make further allowance for insurance premiums covering public liability and property damage. This is included in the ATA formula. This is also covered broadly in the SBAC formula for which an overall figure of 4 per cent was proposed, including some allowance for the reduction in value of the aircraft with time in service. Where an airline provides its own coverage an equivalent rate based on its own accident/incident record will be used.

Interest

It is not the usual US practice to make allowance for the cost of raising capital when assessing direct operating costs. However, it is believed by the author to be desirable if only to make more realistic and meaningful studies between older types, including converted or re-engined aircraft and new aircraft projects. With the increasing unit cost of transport aircraft, airlines are less able to provide from internal sources the capital necessary to support the cost of flight equipment. Even for the initial payments recourse may be necessary to the banks, insurance companies or equity. It may be necessary to take account of the interest chargeable on the money outlaid in a series of progress payments while the aircraft is in the manufacturing process subsequent to the contract. As an example of European rates, 1 per cent above the bank rate in the country of the capital source would be normal. A further increase for coverage from the Export Credit Guarantee Department (UK) or from the Export-Import Bank in the USA would be necessary when this further insurance is required.

The following method may be used in the interest calculations to allow for a reduction in value of the aircraft with the passage of time. In effect we allow for the investment of the money set aside each year for depreciation and assume that the interest on this will decrease the direct operating expense.

If C is the initial capital requirement per aircraft including spares,

n is the number of years used for depreciation

r is the residual value as a proportion of the first cost of the aircraft and its spares

i is the gross interest rate, per cent

Then the sum of the interest payments over n years is

$$i.C\left[n - \frac{(1 - r)(n - 1)}{2}\right]$$

and the average interest payment per year is

$$i.C\left[1 - \frac{(1 - r)(n - 1)}{2n}\right] \tag{2.20}$$

If now, values of $n = 8$ and $r = 0\cdot1$ as suggested in the standard SBAC method are inserted we obtain an average interest payment of $0\cdot61\ i.C$ which may be used for general analysis. Thus, the costs per flying hour arising from the interest charges may be written as:

$$C_{\text{int}} = \frac{0\cdot61\ i}{U}(C_{\text{air}} + C_{\text{eng}} + C_{\text{equ}}) \tag{2.21}$$

Maintenance costs

The costs of maintenance and overhaul are probably the most difficult to estimate accurately for any type of new aircraft project. It may have been acceptable in the past to work on average figures based on airframe and/or equipment weight or engine output, and indeed the standard formulae of the ATA and the SBAC are derived in this way, but it is highly desirable to provide some greater refinement at the present time. In an airline where similar types of equipment have been in operation there are natural foundations on which to work, and where new projects are in the stage of promotion by the manufacturers, the latter will be obliged to provide proof or at least sound evidence that the cost of maintenance and overhaul of the lifed components and its improvement through the aircraft operating life will show a significant advance on the current situation, taking all the factors into account. In the final issue it is the provable economic improvement that is really required. Sometimes the incentive of a warranty to meet a given maximum cost per unit of transport may so stimulate the efforts of all concerned that major improvements are achieved. Such was the case when American Airlines achieved a 25 pence-per-landing brake cost on the Boeing 707 which resulted from a decrease to less than one quarter of earlier results in the servicing man-hours required per landing.

The regular and rational recording of transport aircraft maintenance and replacement operations and their relation to the aircraft operating schedules are an essential background to the establishment of exact engineering requirements for new projects. This field of activity has developed considerably in the last ten years. The precise definition of an economic need is, however, also closely determined by the state of the design art and by the investment which a particular advance would justify. More consideration could be given perhaps to the joint development of components or equipment by the airframe, engine and equipment manufacturers and by the operators themselves. An approach to the economy of weight and an assessment of the value of weight, and hence of the justification for engineering development aimed to reduce weight, is presented in a later section of this chapter. We may here consider the analogous study of the economic value of research into the development of component life. It is in this development of the period between overhauls of the principal components that the greatest expectation for the future reduction of the specific maintenance costs of transport aircraft must be expected to lie.

If it is our objective to develop the overall operating economy of the new type or to gain a greater insight into the way in which the costs arise so as to bring the necessary effort to bear on the areas most requiring it, we must be provided with the essential data. It may be possible to record this in detail according to a breakdown such as the ATA classification with its systems and sub-systems, but full records will be costly to maintain and are generally acquired only for a specific purpose and for a short period.

For example, the ATA system for landing gear, System Number 32, is broken down as follows:

32 00 General – Landing gear
    10 Main gear and doors
    20 Nose gear and doors
    30 Extension and retraction
    40 Wheels and brakes

> 50 Steering
> 60 Position and warning
> 70 Supplementary gear

It is possible to record costs for these items for particular aircraft types and to obtain valuable comparative as well as factual cost information. It will also provide the equally important data on which the probable cost of new project systems can be based. In the case of the wheel and brake sub-system 32 40 as shown above, it may be possible in relation to established facts on two or more types of current aircraft to assess with some degree of accuracy the probable cost for specified components differing in known respects from the current equipment. When operated in a planned operational pattern the improved equipment would have a predictable influence on the estimated direct maintenance cost (Davis & Curry, 1963).

The approach here proposed is essentially value analysis. The aim is to provide the designer as well as the development specialist with data on which he can work for economic solutions and not only for solutions to new and interesting design problems. Advanced transport aircraft have for a long time been developed up to the frontiers of technical knowledge which has incurred large research and development expenditure. An important aspect of the assessment of maintenance cost is an appreciation of where the system or equipment lies in relation to the 'state of the art'. In effect, fuller margins must be allowed for new and as yet unproven systems. If they do not block the initial airline acceptance of the equipment they may add extensively to the cost under the headings of introduction and training costs, spares holdings, due to low initial life and caution, high replacement requirements and aircraft service delays.

Engine overhaul costs and the TBO

On jet transports the first price, spares cost and the overhaul cost of the engines are major factors in the direct cost and usually control 22–26 per cent of the items that make up the direct costs of the aircraft. The Rolls-Royce Dart RDa3 and 6 engines first established the exceptional TBO extension possibilities of the gas-turbine engine. The rate of progress has been exceeded on the R.R. Conway and the P. & W. JT3 and 4-jet engines installed on the first generation of subsonic jet aircraft. While the early engines required six or seven years to achieve an economic life (3000 hours) more recent development has accelerated the rate of TBO extension, and this period of development has been halved. The installed thrust requirements (T/W) and the engine price per unit of thrust, have tended to increase in recent years and hence engine-dominated operating costs have become significant. In the SST, however, fuel costs will become the most significant airline cost item.

The extension of overhaul life beyond a certain limit (probably 4000 hours) may not provide the gains anticipated because of the increased costs of materials which are a very high proportion of the overhaul cost. It may be advantageous to link the TBO to the seasonal utilisation of the aircraft and/or arrange for winter overhauls. The Boeing 727 engines, Pratt & Whitney JT8D-1, reached a 2400 hours TBO within a year of scheduled operations with Eastern Airlines. However, the combustion chamber overhaul cycle was set at half the engine TBO and this policy of development of the hot sections to maintain a half-life compared with the engine overhaul has been maintained so far as practicable. Thus the life of the hot components may be more important to engine economy than the more widely quoted TBO.

An insight into the pattern of failure is essential to the control of all aspects of maintenance and overhaul economy. The location of sources of failure to identify their nature, whether random or determined by factors of time or use, is today a key activity in maintenance planning. The cost of unreliability, arising from unscheduled maintenance (an engineering base cost), and from delay and dislocation of services (a cost to the traffic department and a possible loss of revenue), stems from an imprecise knowledge of the causes of failure.

It is now perhaps too well accepted to need repeating that the attention to detailed design is a paramount factor in the acceptability of a new civil aircraft because of their high first cost, and the high penalties extracted from an operator for unscheduled unserviceability. The major engine manufacturers now set up overhaul bases for turbo-jet and turbo-prop engines in key world areas. This is a major factor in engine acceptability and is essential to the sales potential of a civil aircraft. Rolls-Royce have bases in Derby, Coventry, Glasgow, Montreal and São Paulo. Various other organisations, including the airlines themselves, are of course equipped to overhaul and test engines. Local overhaul facilities are vital to high utilisation of engines and spares since the capital investment in spare engines and engine spares may become considerable if the turnabout time through the overhaul base, including transport from and back to the airline base, is too long. High aircraft utilisation rate, low achieved life of engines, and a wide-ranging operating network are other factors requiring high spares holding and increased operating costs of the engines.

Landing fees

The landing fee is an item not included in the ATA direct-cost method but is nevertheless a direct operating expense and as such a factor which may be of significance in actual and comparative aircraft cost estimate. An excellent source of information is the Manual of Airport and Air Navigation Facility Tariffs DOC 7100 – published by ICAO and amended from time to time to meet the constant upward trend of airport fees. The largely irrational basis of landing charges is not amenable to very exact analysis. For the most part fees are based on the C of A gross weight of the aircraft, but a number of exceptions to this exist, and international flights and short-stage flights are in some cases liable to special rates.

The comparative effect of the direct cost items

A simplified study of the direct operating costs of a medium-haul jet aircraft of the BAC 111 or Douglas DC 9 class shows that the direct-cost index is principally influenced by eight design and operating parameters. These individually affect the direct cost as shown in the following table:

A 5 per cent decrease in the specific direct operating cost was achieved on the design range by the following:

A 5 per cent increase in payload or in block speed.
16 per cent increase in utilisation.
19 per cent decrease in airframe price.
20 per cent decrease in specific fuel consumption and/or fuel price.
23 per cent decrease in engine cost.
36 per cent decrease in crew salaries.
65 per cent increase in engine overhaul life.

It is thought that this table well illustrates the key significance of payload and block speed increase in improving the operating economy of transport aircraft.

Commercial requirements in aircraft and route selection

The broad commercial requirement in the operation of any transport concern must be the balancing of revenue and expenditure at the highest possible standard of service. Within this general policy are so many varying factors affecting both the level at which the balance may be drawn and the standard of service provided, that a number of considerations must precede all decisions made. Where deficits are incurred, considerable commercial acumen may yet be required to contain them within limits, whether these are set by the future prospects of more remunerative operations (perhaps with improved types of aircraft) or by a nationally sponsored policy of subsidies. This may be in the form of an annual money grant, free meteorological and radio services, or low landing fees at State-controlled airports, etc.

An airline requiring large grants to make good an overall operating deficit may yet be required to make a commercial success of certain profitable routes which are known to generate a heavy traffic. These routes may be required to compensate for high losses on certain essential routes that must be operated throughout the year at some minimum frequency in the public interest. The First Annual Report of the BEA Corporation

(1947–8) had already stated 'internal routes will be confined to those which are likely to prove economic or are provided to meet a special public requirement'. These considerations indicate that there were profitable and unprofitable routes within the sphere of operation of the airline concerned and it is the prime concern of all operators to know clearly what they are and to develop them to the utmost commercial advantage.

Route selection

Route selection must be based on a complex reasoning in which population concentration (industrial wealth and growth), route distance, alternative transport facilities, seasonal travel demand, geographical and/or political barriers and the social–cultural affinities of population centres, all play an important part. The air route planner must be at pains to take a detached point of view and to see not only the present state of the above factors, but their rates of change under the influence of changing economic stresses. He plans his routes with a later, wider development in mind and he endeavours to integrate in space and time with the other modes of transport service, keeping the needs of his own maintenance and overhaul organisation clearly in mind.

The economic value of speed

From the utilisation likely to be achieved on the routes envisaged the number of aircraft required to work the route system may be estimated. Some experience of the degree of integration possible, bearing in mind the layout of the proposed route system and the location of the principal bases, is necessary for an overall estimate of fleet strength to be of value. The integration factor may also vary considerably with the scale of operations, the season of the year and the country of operation. For 30 a/c fleets in Europe, 90 per cent in summer and 75–80 per cent in winter should normally be achieved.

The commercial value of cruising speed must be considered in the light of probable competition from other operators, as advertised schedule times may play an important part in the proportion of traffic obtained. However, much is to be gained by efficient ground handling and punctuality, and in transit stops between short hops five minutes' ground time wasted may correspond to twenty or thirty m.p.h in cruising speed. Under certain circumstances it may even be possible to reduce ground time by a sufficient margin to show an overall improvement in economy when additional equipment or even crew are carried in place of payload. A study recently indicated that below a trip length of approximately 200 miles with modern turbine-engine forty-seat conversions the uplift of a flight engineer may be justifiable. Owing to the difficulty of integrating on international flights, it is possible, on some types of operation, to find speed belts, varying with the length of flight envisaged, between which cruising speeds are difficult to exploit economically. This is closely associated with the fleet utilisation possible, bearing in mind facilities for night services, the landing and communication aids anticipated, and the possibilities of disemplaning passengers in the night hours.

In 1957 Ralph Allen, of Systems Analysis Corporation, described useful approximate methods of combining aerodynamic and economic characteristics so as to optimise operational transport system profit margins (1957). He introduced the principal variables of the aircraft design, the operational pattern and airline economic and administrative policy into a costing method which could be used as a guide to design and to operational planners.

The class of aircraft studied were turbo-prop powered transports with conventional engine-wing attachment and unswept wings. Using a non-dimensional analysis and developing the economics of the system in terms of cost and revenue, it was found possible to establish optimum cruising regimes in terms of stage length, cruising speeds and wing loadings for given input values. The optimum values of these variables were computed to give maximum profit margins. A similar approach had been adopted by the author in a study in 1953 into the optimum conditions for the operation of airline aircraft. Here also it was shown that the economic assessment of direct aircraft costs on a passenger-mile or ton-mile basis does not necessarily give a sufficient indication of the economic merit of an individual type of transport aircraft, nor does it show the best routes for airline exploitation since revenue-earning potential is neglected.

Following work carried out in the UK during this period when the comparison of jet and prop-turbine aircraft was exercising the project departments of the airframe manufacturers and the air carriers alike, it was recognised that the profit margin, or the profit margin per unit of cost incurred, are parameters which are more significant to the air operator than specific direct costs alone.

Now, the equation for the revenue earned per flight is:

$$\lambda f R(Q_0 - Rgd/v)$$

where no capacity limitations to payload are considered, and

λ = load factor
f = revenue fare and rate factor (£ sterling/lb, mile)
Q_0 = payload at zero block distance (lb)
R = block distance (miles)
d = fuel density (lb/gallon)
g = fuel consumption (gallons/hour)
v = cruising speed (mph)

The margin of revenue over total costs per total cost incurred, which we here call the revenue or oncost margin, is conveniently written in terms of the symbols already set out as

$$\mu = \frac{\lambda f R(Q_0 - Rgd/v)}{A + BR} - 1 \qquad (2.22)$$

It can then be shown, by differentiating μ with respect to R, that if λ, the route load factor, is kept constant then the block distance R for optimum operational economy is given by

$$R = \left[\left(\frac{A}{B}\right)^2 + \frac{A}{B} R_u \right]^{\frac{1}{2}} - \frac{A}{B} \qquad (2.23)$$

Thus, the optimum range for providing the maximum revenue margin per cost involved, depends upon the ultimate range of the aircraft R_u and the ratio of the cost factors A and B. Fig. 2.11 shows the variation of the optimum block distance for different values of the ultimate range and of the cost ratio A/B, and suggests that a range considerably less than that giving the

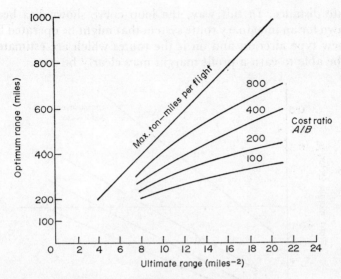

FIG. 2.11. Optimum Operating Range

optimum ton-miles per flight will give the best return for airline operation. It will be noted that the actual load factor does not arise as a variable, but clearly if higher load factors can be achieved on stage distances other than the optimum indicated, some shift in the most desirable stage distance might result. Further, if the ratio of total to direct costs is known to vary from route to route this factor should be considered in the final analysis.

It may be shown that the profit margin per cost incurred μ may be equated to:

$$\frac{\lambda}{\beta} - 1.$$

where β equals the break-even load factor and λ as before is the actual route load factor. Fig. 2.12 shows a plotting of μ for various values of λ, the actual load factor achieved, and β. When the operating costs for each route distance have been estimated for a new type of aircraft, it is possible to plot a curve of β versus the stage distance. Hence, on Fig. 2.12 we may cross-plot the break-even load factor for a given stage distance and the load factor estimated to be achieved on that same route or route distance. In this way, the loop curve shown has been drawn for an imaginary route system that might be operated by a new type aircraft, and on it the routes which are estimated to be able to earn a profit margin may clearly be seen.

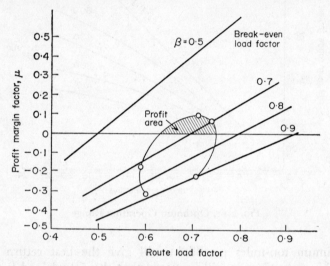

FIG. 2.12. Profit Margin and the Load Factors

Limitations and value of the analysis

The foregoing discussion, although based on a number of simple assumptions and taking no account of the limitations arising on individual aircraft types, does show that the direct or type cost index (pence per passenger- or ton-mile) is not a sufficient measure of transport aircraft economy. A consideration of revenue potential seems to be essential for a proper assessment of economy and the profit margin proposed here is thought to introduce this more exactly and as simply as does the break-even load factor.

The study should assist in comparisons between turbo-jet and propeller-turbine aircraft. Because the two aircraft, one jet propelled and the other propeller driven, each providing the same payload on the same block distance on a similar take-off performance, have different ultimate ranges on account of the difference in their specific air range (miles/lb of fuel). The shorter ultimate range of the jet transport is associated with shorter optimum operating stage length, and generally a a narrower belt of block distances within the specified profit margin. High fuel consumption in this way considerably reduces the economic flexibility of an aircraft. High fuel reserves, also associated with jet engines, not only reduce the transport product in proportion as the route payload is reduced but also decrease further the stage distance for the optimum revenue-earning capacity. The criterion for economic merit given here may not be the one of most value to all airline situations since net profit alone or profitability in relation to capital invested may in individual cases provide a more significant parameter. The principles noted can be applied, however, to any particular case. It is a simple exercise to consider the relation of these criteria to the 'return on investment' which is now becoming widely used as a sales tool to enhance the potential value of a high-cost product.

The use of simplified formulae

There is clearly a great advantage in developing simplified formula for use in assessing transport aircraft operating costs. The standard methods of the ATA and the SBAC do not lend themselves to simplification and are less amenable to the rational analysis which is one prime objective of this approach, expecially in the project stage in the aircraft design or airline planning office.

However, using a formulation of the direct operating costs which was originally suggested by a member of the BOAC project department and modifying it to make it more amenable to analysis, P. L. Sutcliffe found it possible to develop a formula which may be of wider value.

If we write V_B = block speed, mph
W = gross weight, lb
t_B = block time, hours

then the significant weight and thrust parameters may be written as the four non-dimensional ratios

$\dfrac{W_P}{W}$ = Payload to weight ratio

$\dfrac{W_A}{W}$ = Weight of equipped airframe less engines as a ratio to the Gross Weight

$\dfrac{W_F}{W}$ = Stage fuel to Gross Weight ratio

T/W = Sea Level Static Thrust to Gross Weight Ratio

The specific costs are written as:

k_A = First cost of equipped airframe less installed engines (£ per lb)

k_E = First cost of engines (£ per lb)

Using these symbols we may write the specific direct operating costs on long haul operations with subsonic jet transports as d pence per short ton statute mile.

$$d = \left(\dfrac{1}{\dfrac{V_B}{100} \cdot \dfrac{W_P}{W}}\right) \left(0 \cdot 36\, k_A \cdot \dfrac{W_A}{W} + 1 \cdot 64\, \dfrac{W_A}{W} + 1 \cdot 18\, k_E \dfrac{T}{W} + \dfrac{45}{t_B} \cdot \dfrac{W_F}{W} + \dfrac{0 \cdot 6}{t_B} + \dfrac{100\,000}{W} + 0 \cdot 54\right)$$

$$(2.24)$$

Here we may recognise that:

$V_B \cdot \dfrac{W_P}{W}$ m.p.h. is the productivity per lb of gross weight

$k_A\ \dfrac{W_A}{W}$ is the airframe cost per lb of gross weight

$k_E \cdot \dfrac{T}{W}$ is the engine cost per lb of gross weight

$\dfrac{1}{t_B} \cdot \dfrac{W_F}{W}$ is the weight of fuel used per hour per lb of gross weight.

The first three terms within the main bracket represent the depreciation, insurance, maintenance and overhaul costs. The fourth term represents fuel cost, while the last three terms represent crew costs, landing fees and miscellaneous constant items of cost. The costs given by this formula will be found to be higher than those given by the ATA and the SBAC formulae and adjustment may be required for application to aircraft varying widely in type and size. The loading of cost, moreover, is too high for air operations in the USA and those operating on a more restricted scale. However, the analytic form of the equation offers scope for modification to suit a particular operating situation.

Study of a route system

By use of a generalised formula such as the above, it becomes possible to provide rapid parametric solutions to the economy of competitive aircraft operating on a series of routes. This avoids the criticism that an aircraft is designed or assessed commercially on one critical or special route which may provide an arbitrary and inconclusive answer. A full network analysis allowing for the integration of services and giving effect to the local runway and terrain restrictions which may exist at certain points then becomes possible. Overhead costs and the Airline B and C costs (Fig. 2.8) still need to be estimated. Market research must provide traffic estimates for passengers, mail and cargo. Revenue and profit must be computed.

Variations in load factor to account for traffic by routes in each direction and with seasonal effects is feasible in such studies. Moreover, the phasing of the aircraft types in and out of service with contrasting type introduction programmes, then becomes a significant and important final exercise not only to the airline planning department, but also to the project designer intent on gaining the fullest possible insight into the airline problem and the likely reaction of the customer to his final proposals. Simplified formulae of the type suggested above make these steps considerably easier to take.

While ineffective and time-consuming in the past, such studies have now become practical and in our view essential since the necessary computing equipment is available for rapid answers to be made available.

Use of the cost formula in optimisation of design

An original study on which the design of the Japanese twin Dart transport, the YS 11, was based, was reported by H. Kimura, S. Kikuhara and J. Kondo to the International Council of Aeronautical Sciences in September 1960. The basic method required the use of Operational Research to develop from the model established and the set boundary conditions a

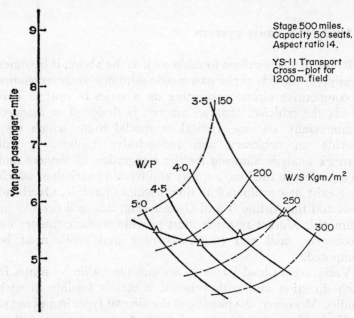

FIG. 2.13. Japanese Short-haul Project. Costs for YS 11 Transport

parametric solution to designs of minimum operating cost. From the combined requirements of passenger seats and effective stage length, systematic calculations of the relationship between W/S (Wing loading), W/P (Power loading) and A (Aspect ratio) provided data from which the economic outputs could be derived. The presentation allowed the conditions for a limiting field length requirement to be cross-plotted. The optimum cost point could then be picked out. Engine-out climb gradient requirements were, in this design investigation, not in fact critical since the take-off field demand was severe. A typical result is shown in Figure 2.13.

Of particular interest in the Japanese studies was the attempt made to assess the seating capacity required in the years ahead in relation to the Industry Activity Index back-plotted to 1952. This realisation of the essential need to combine revenue-earning potential with operating cost so as to obtain meaningful quantitative answers on profitability is characteristic of many recent civil aircraft design studies. Without problematical assessments of the indirect costs of operation, it is still of immense value to estimate the contribution to the overheads which is made when a varying number of passengers, above and below the number required to break even, are carried.

The value of weight in transport aircraft

In the refinement of a design, both in the project and in the development stage, it is essential to be aware of the value which may be placed upon the saving of weight. In the past this has very often been a matter of general interest only and no specific values have been computed. The great increase in the productivity of the modern jet transport, however, particularly its high annual mileage, has increased greatly the significance of the weight control engineer. If this was ever in doubt it can now be no longer, since it is not difficult to show that in the life of one jet aircraft operating over 3000 hours per annum the potential value of 1 lb of equipped weight saved may be greater than £150.

We may separate out two aspects of weight saving, since they affect the economics of operation in different ways. There is the weight saved on an aircraft, probably already in service, which involves negligible cost and perhaps by the removal of equipment (to take the simplest case) enables an increase in bookable payload to be made available. The value of this weight saving may be estimated from the increased revenue potential, the average load factor anticipated and the utilisation and expected operating life of the aircraft. In this case, we should note that the specific direct costs would fall (if the load factor remained constant) and there would be an increased margin between revenue and direct operating costs for each unit load-mile flown. An approximate value of £200 to £300 per lb in the life of an aircraft on medium-range operations can be arrived at in this way, but this will vary directly with the various factors mentioned above and will be greater for the modern high-performance expensive aircraft, with a long operating life, than for the small feeder-line aircraft for which the utilisation if not the life expectation is more modest.

In the second case, we consider an aircraft which in the design stage, or after introduction into service, has weight-saving modifications incorporated which involve extra costs in labour and materials with the object of increasing its bookable payload capacity. The question is how far is the operator prepared to go? What will he pay? The answer given in the first case will be misleading now, for the investment of additional effort may be involved. There is a more expensive aircraft to be insured. Further, the operator is not necessarily now offered a transport vehicle with a lower ton-mile cost. The price that is asked may be too high for him to ensure even equal specific costs (pence per ton-mile).

A study of this problem has shown that the operator will generally be prepared to pay a useful premium for the engineering of lower weight, but it is considerably less than the case first discussed above. Nevertheless, the development cost of weight reduction in many aircraft components and items of equipment could undoubtedly be regained in lowered costs of operation per ton-mile. A practical case here would be the introduction into the design of a close-tolerance light-alloy sheet material which might in fact involve an increase in cost of 3s od per lb of material supplied. Allowing for scrap, an increase in the total cost of material for one particular aircraft of 20,000 lb airframe weight was £900. The cost of the 100 lb weight saving which could be achieved was in fact £9 os od per lb. Revenue earning at this rate through the life of the aircraft is not difficult to prove.

Following our earlier consideration of the principal subdivision of costs, we here divide the direct costs of operation into two parts: *A*, Standing costs, and *B*, Other costs, where *A* includes Obsolescence, Insurance and Interest.

Now A may be written in full as:

$$A = \left(\frac{V.S.}{L} + r + i.S.\right)\left(\frac{C_0 + k(Q - Q_0)}{U}\right) \quad \text{£ per hour.}$$

(2.25)

where V = Aircraft value ratio: $\left(\dfrac{\text{Initial} - \text{Residual}}{\text{Initial}}\right)$

$\quad S$ = Factor to allow for cost of spares

$\quad r$ = Annual insurance rate

$\quad i$ = Interest rate

$\quad L$ = Aircraft life (years)

$\quad C_0$ = Basic first cost of the aircraft before weight saving modifications (£)

$\quad k$ = Development of mod. cost (£) per lb of weight saved

$\quad Q$ = Final payload achieved after weight saving (lb)

$\quad Q_0$ = Original payload (lb) corresponding to basic aircraft of cost £C_0

$\quad U$ = Aircraft utilisation (hours per year)

Clearly, the final cost of the aircraft would be

$$C_0 + k(Q - Q_0)\text{£}.$$

The group represented as B £/hr (all other direct costs) is not further subdivided.

Now if we write V_B = Block speed

and for simplicity substitute Z for $\left(\dfrac{V.S.}{L} + r + i.S.\right)$

then the Specific Direct Cost, pence per passenger (200 lb) mile is

$$p = \frac{48,000}{V_B \cdot Q}\left(B + \frac{Z(C_0 + k(Q - Q_0))}{U}\right)$$

(2.26)

Now k, the development cost £ per lb, is considered to be that giving no change in specific direct cost, so that any lower value than this will give an improvement in specific costs, thus:

$$\frac{d(p)}{d(Q)} = \frac{-48,000}{Q^2 V_B}\left(B + \frac{Z.C_0}{U} - \frac{kZQ_0}{U}\right)$$

(2.27)

or

$$k = \frac{1}{Q_0}\left(\frac{UB}{Z} + C_0\right)$$

(2.28)

Clearly this value of k will vary considerably from one aircraft type to another, and for one aircraft may tend to increase with the length of stage flown (Q_0 decreasing and U increasing). However, for a given specification or with known route-operating costs, a sufficiently accurate value of this maximum permissible value of k can be derived.

It is interesting to take typical values of the constants for two different types of transport aircraft operating on representative length flights.

Subsonic Transatlantic Jet Transport
$W = 320,000$ lb
$U = 3600$ hours per annum
$C_0 = £2 \cdot 3$ million
$Q_0 = 36,000$ lb
$B = 215 \ £$ per hour
$Z = 0 \cdot 23$

Then from Equation (2.26) $k = 157 \ £$ per lb saved.

Small Feeder Line Jet Transport

$W = 45,000$ lb	In both cases we assume:
$U = 2500$ hours per annum	Aircraft value ratio $0 \cdot 85$
$C_0 = £0 \cdot 45$ million	Spares factor $1 \cdot 2$
$Q_0 = 7500$ lb	Insurance rate 4%
$B = 50 \ £$ per hour	Interest rate 5%
$Z = 0 \cdot 20$	

Then $k = 142 \ £$ per lb saved.

The results are rather general and indicate purely the order of the values concerned, but they have some interest in showing that the civil operator can afford to invest in engineering development about one-half of the apparent earning capacity of the increased bookable payload.

Whilst these unit weight costs define the limits above which it is uneconomic to go, considerably lower rates have been possible in the past and must still be the aim of the manufacturer if his product is to stand out above all others. Indeed, if the required standards of transport service are to be maintained at a continually decreasing level of costs, the economic value of load and weight must be considered at all stages of design, and throughout the operating life of the aircraft. It is suggested, therefore, that the principle outlined above could be usefully employed in this way in conjunction with the costs and data provided by the British and American published Airline statistics or with generalised figures evolved from the ATA and SBAC Direct Operating Cost Methods.

Limitations of the cost formulae

It is to be expected that there would be considerable limitations to the value and use of the cost formulae and this is indeed the case. They are restricted to an assessment of the direct operating cost and cannot make any contribution to an understanding of the mechanism of indirect or management costs and to expect more than this is to be misguided. In special studies, however, where an associated element of cost not usually included in the direct costs of operation is under study, perhaps as part of the overall case for a new operating technique, e.g. the use of air stairs on a short-haul operation, then a broader grouping of costs for comparative purposes may be fully justified. The methods of analysis by which the on-cost margin or the contribution to overheads is used as the crtierion, seems to provide the most valuable answers when revenue rates, load factors and some elements of the indirect costs are to be included in a comparison.

It is sound cost accounting practice to prepare estimates in a form which allows a direct comparison at a later date with the records of the actual experience. In air transport this has not always been insisted upon and much valuable knowledge into the causes of estimating errors and the pattern of events has been lost thereby. However, some useful experience has been recorded.

Lord Douglas (1957) in the 14th Brancker Memorial Lecture drew interesting conclusions from the estimated costs and the comparable actual costs after introduction into service of Viscount 701 and Comet 1 aircraft. In both cases the formula costs were greatly exceeded. The formulae were not identical in the two cases considered since they were applied by the

BEA and BOAC project engineers with their own airline operating experience to guide them. The formulae as used by the Corporations at the time provided only the framework on which an aircraft costing could be built up. The cost of the Viscount 701 when well established in service was 21 per cent above the costs estimated some 5–6 years before. These costs were compared at the level of money value existing in 1957. The comparable increase for the Comet in the same period after establishment in service was 35 per cent. The lesson of the cost estimates prepared by BEA for the Viscount 701 was learnt when the Viscount 800 series went into service and the cost estimates were very much more closely maintained in service. Also, of course, prop-turbine operations were more fully understood. The principal discrepancies arising with the Viscount 701 arose under two headings, one was due to increase in costs of aircraft and equipment, especially furnishings, radio and spares, compared with early estimates for the depreciation expense. The other was an underestimation of the engineering cost, probably the most difficult item to establish with any degree of certainty for a new basic type of aircraft. In this case it was the yet untried prop-turbine engine which rapidly improved the overall engineering cost situation and by means of unexpectedly rapid extensions of the life between overhauls contributed to the fine long-term cost record of the Viscount.

From these results Lord Douglas concluded that there was likely to continue to be some differential between the actual/formula cost relationships of jets and turbo-props. He believed this to be primarily because of the jet aircraft's lesser operational flexibility and because of their more 'sophisticated' design which tends to exaggerate the economic effect of engineering changes. This view contributed towards his general conclusion that the turbo-prop transport would have a long and useful 'innings' on the shorter short-haul routes where its block time handicap is small. This conclusion has not been substantiated by the facts, especially when the competitive international traffic factor has been significant. However, the BEA engineering department records can provide strong arguments for the greater economy of prop-turbine transports.

More recent experience of American Airlines has shown the early operating experience with Boeing 707 on US domestic trunk routes in comparison with manufacturers and airline estimates four to five years earlier. It was shown by F. W. Kolk (1960) that the airline was able to approach more closely to the actual operating cost level than was possible by use of the ATA formula using standard and unmodified procedures. The reduced transport productivity through the short-fall in block or ramp speed adversely affected the specific direct operating cost, but it was shown that the generalised assessment of the standing costs (depreciation and insurance) as well as the cost of engineering (direct maintenance) and flying operations, led to a gross over-estimation of formula costs per hour by over 16 per cent. Thus, the errors in block speed and hourly costs tended to balance each other out and the formula costs of 1956 were closely in line with the actuals of 1960.

Early operational study of the subsonic jets gave credit for block (or ramp) speeds which have not been achieved in practice. The overall effect on operating economy is an increase in costs per mile of about 11 per cent. Some part of this has arisen through air and ground terminal delays which are tending to increase year by year and are becoming routine at the major airports through which naturally enough a large proportion of aircraft movements occurs. This problem is a very difficult one to combat, and requires the most careful assessment by the airline analyst in the course of comparative aircraft type studies on a particular route system. Dixon Speas and Associates reported that a survey at a major US terminal showed that the average ramp-to-take-off time was 21 minutes. Recent personal experience on the US trunk routes confirmed that of 18 scheduled jet take-offs, a mean ramp-to-take-off time of 12 minutes was measured with 15 per cent exceeding 20 minutes. This was under summer conditions. A clear-day analysis reported by Dixon Speas at the same airport as that of his previous survey showed an average of 13 min. 50 sec. for 12 departing flights.

Favourable to the development of economic jet transportation has been the general lowering of the price of kerosene in terms of money value over the last five years of operation. The lower actual cost compared with that estimated in the mid-fifties has contributed a great deal to the improved standing of the jet in comparison with prop-turbine transports. Of even greater significance has been the overall improvement in aircraft maintenance (engineering) costs.

Introduction costs

In assessing the costs of operation of new types of transport aircraft the most careful analysis of the cost associated with introduction into service must be made. It is apparent that a large number of items of cost will arise on a 'once only' basis and the length of this list will depend very much upon the extent to which the new design has broken new ground without incorporating engines, systems and equipment already well known to the airline. Introduction costs may be amortised over the life of the aircraft or might, in some cases, be partially reimbursed by Government or other subsidy as a national investment in the airline development of a new project for which overseas markets may exist. It is on record that BOAC in the ten years 1950–60 incurred £18 million in costs associated with the introduction of four types of aircraft into service. BEA incurred costs in this period amounting to £7·7 million.

A study undertaken by the author showed that the costs of introduction can be considered as (*a*) increased direct costs, (*b*) increased indirect costs or overhead and (*c*) reduction in revenue. Under (*a*) were considered the reduction in utilisation, extra direct engineering and spares costs, training and courses for engineers and flying staff, and increased flying costs due to the small initial fleet operating at a lower-than-average level of intensity. Under (*b*) were considered the initial overhead costs of project and development engineering, advertising and public relations, the special ground equipment, simulators, jigs and tools, the planning work in the Flight Operations, Commercial and Accounts Departments and the special services of consultants. Under (*c*) was assessed the revenue loss from low utilisation and a higher-than-average incidence of unserviceability. Late deliveries have been a major source of loss under this heading. It would be unrealistic for a major national carrier to introduce a completely new aircraft type without benefit of long development in service with another experienced operator and without prior knowledge of the principal components (including engines) and equipment, unless a very full assessment of the introduction costs had been carried out. The costs of introduction of a new generation of four engine jet aircraft of intercontinental capability are now likely to be £5–6 million. Extensive promotional campaigns on a worldwide scale could increase these costs by several million pounds. Medium-range transport introduction costs could be about two-thirds of these figures.

In the era of joint airline planning and operation of giant aircraft it is clear that introduction costs may be brought more fully under control. In the KSSU and ATLAS groupings for operation of the Boeing 747 the 'once-off' costs for each airline are likely to be no greater than with the Boeing 707. With this goes an increasing awareness of airline management that minor individual airline preferences must be abandoned in the face of the critical economic advantages of finding a common, readily available, but compatible, aircraft specification.

Introduction of the SST is separately considered in Chapter 9.

BIBLIOGRAPHY

F. M. GREEN, 'Speed and the Economics of Air Transport', *Jnl. Roy. Aero. Soc.*, 1934

LOUIS BREGUET, 'Speeds of Commercial Aeroplanes', *Jnl. Roy. Aero. Soc.*, 1935

E. P. WARNER, 'Post-War Transport Aircraft', *Jnl. Roy. Aero. Soc.*, 1943

R. M. CLARKSON, 'Application of the Gas Turbine to the Field of Commercial Aviation', *Jnl. Roy. Aero. Soc.*, 1946

P. G. MASEFIELD, 'Some Economic Factors in Air Transport Operation', Brancker Memorial Lecture, *Jnl. Inst. Transp.*, Mar. 1951

W. C. MENTZER and H. E. NOURSE, 'Some Economic Aspects of Transport Aircraft Performance', *Jnl. Inst. Aeronaut. Sci.*, Jan. 1940

Standard Method of Estimating Comparative Direct Operating Costs, Air Transport Association of America, June 1960

S.B.A.C. Standard Method for the Estimation of Direct Operating Cost, Issue 4, Nov. 1950

W. J. BAUMOL, *Economic Theory and Operations Analysis*, Prentice-Hall, 1965

H. GLAUERT, *The Elements of Aerofoil and Airscrew Theory*, Cambridge University Press, 2nd Edn., 1947

F. W. KOLK, *An Address to the International Congress of Aeronautical Sciences in Zurich*, Sept. 1960

J. E. DAVIS and R. C. CURRY, *The Cost of Landing an Aeroplane*, Esso Air World and SAE Meeting, Sept. 1963

R. ALLEN, 'Economic Characteristics of Turbo-prop Air Line Transport Systems', *Aeronaut. Eng. Rev.*, July 1957

A. H. STRATFORD, 'Optimum Conditions for the Operation of Airline Aircraft', *Jnl. Roy. Aero. Soc.*, Aug. 1953

LORD DOUGLAS OF KIRTLESIDE, 'The Economics of Speed', Brancker Memorial Lecture, *Jnl. Ins. Transp.*, May 1957

A Critical Comparison of the SBAC and ATA Methods of Estimating Direct Operating Costs of a New Aircraft, I.T.A. Study, July 1960

Operations Research in the Basic Design of YS-11 Transport Airplane, Second International Congress of Aeronautical Sciences, Sept. 1960

ROBERT STOESSEL, *Proposed Standard Method for Estimating Airline Direct Operating Expense*. (Lockheed Co. Report LW 70-500R, May 1970)

ANNUAL OR PERIODICAL PUBLICATIONS:

Air Mileage Handbook, International Aeradio Limited

Book of Official C.A.B. Airline Route Maps and Airport to Airport Mileages, Technical Services: ATA of America

Handbook of Airline Statistics, CAB

Jane's All the World's Aircraft, Samson Low, London

Interavia ABC, Interavia Publications

Shell Aviation Service Availability and International Price Guide

UK Air Transport and Airport Statistics, CAA

New York Airport Statistics, Port of New York Authority

BOAC and BEA Annual Reports, HMSO

Aviation Forecasts, Economics Division FAA

3 Market Research and Passenger Transport

Growth of the civil aviation market

The rapid development of air transport needs no detailed proof today. It is accepted by all, whether actively engaged in civil aviation or not and we have already suggested some of the principal reasons for its explosive growth. The tables and charts below summarise the main features of the expansion. Fig. 3.1 indicates the growth of traffic in passenger-miles and

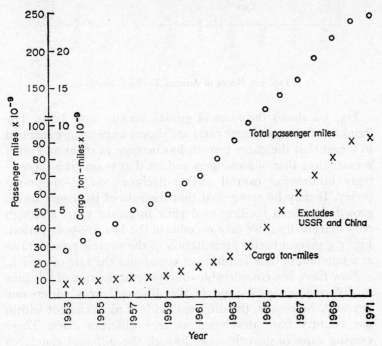

FIG. 3.1. Two Decades of ICAO Traffic Growth

in cargo ton-miles over the last ten years. It is shown as the overall results of the ICAO member states operating on all international and domestic operations. Of the total shown for passenger traffic 59·8 per cent is now carried by airlines registered in North America. The rates of expansion are such that the traffic is doubling in about five years. This approximates to a 15 per cent annual growth.

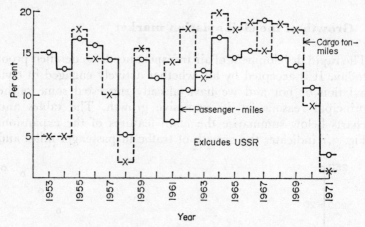

FIG. 3.2. Rates of Annual Traffic Growth

Fig. 3.2 shows the rates of growth on the same basis. The freight and the passenger rates are shown since we are inclined to forget that the cargo growth has become as great and often greater than that of passengers and for that reason it is increasingly influencing overall airline decisions on re-equipment policy. It may be recognised that the rate of passenger traffic growth has been tending to decline in recent years although only marginally if we take account of the last five-year period. Fig. 3.3 gives a useful presentation of the overall growth ratio as a function of time (number of years) and the rate of growth.

Now there is a considerable difference in the rate of advance in different territories and in the different areas within one territory. Moreover, the different fields of air transport within one country have developed at very different rates. These varying rates of growth arise through the different standards of economic development in the countries concerned, the geographical situation of the country, the availability of adequate system of surface transportation and the degree of initial support that is provided by the government for capital airport installations and other facilities and services. Many other

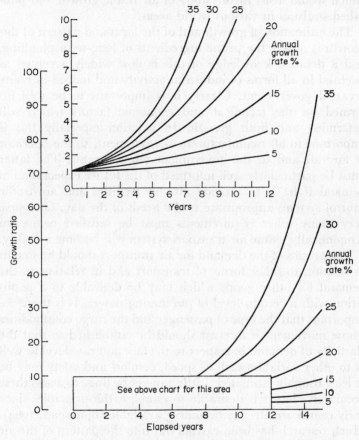

FIG. 3.3. A Chart of Growth Ratio in Terms of Annual Rates

factors also arise. In no other field of transport is political incursion more potent for good and for harm than in aviation. The strength of aviation and its weakness lies in the international arena where it operates with the greatest effect. It may gain sound support from a wise and far-sighted national government or an extravagant boost from a nationalistic regime, but both air operators and manufacturing industry know what it is to feel the cold shoulder and a changed political climate at a crucial stage in the development of a key project. In the Bibliography of Chapter 2 we indicated source material which would assist in the study of air traffic growth and published statistics in various world areas.

The estimation of growth and of the form and pattern of this growth is one of the prime ingredients of long-term planning, and a detailed knowledge of this is now widely accepted as essential in all forms of industrial activity and indeed in many areas of government. Clearly it is important to be well informed on the technical and economic factors which will determine and limit growth. In aviation especially this is important to all manufacturers of equipment, to the operator of aircraft and to the government administrator. The latter must be particularly well informed of the future expectation of demand if he is to provide ground facilities and air traffic control systems appropriate to the needs of the day. Of course very many other requirements must be satisfied before an economically viable air transport system will become a reality.

The origins of the demand for air transport should be sought in relation to other forms of transport and in relation to the demand for other goods which may be desirable to a population with a certain level of purchasing power. It is therefore important that the type of passenger and the cargo commodities whose movement is forecast should be established so that the elasticity of demand in respect to the fare and rate level as well as to other variables such as speed, comfort and safety may be at least roughly estimated. Little can yet be done to assess these accurately, but it is desirable to establish the principles since early results are already becoming available (Bjorkman, 1964). Much research has been carried out into the pattern of the air passenger journey and important recent US studies may be referred to (Lansing, 1964; Caves, 1962; Cherington, 1962). Other references are given. It is to be noted that the large amount of work conducted in the United States is not necessarily applicable in other countries. The results must be tested for the special conditions existing in that country with its great distances, high-class long-distance roads, high GNP (promoting business and tourist travel) and high marginal incomes (pro-

moting the repetitive use of scheduled and private air transport).
The valuable study of Richard Caves (1962) into the US Air
Transport Industry and its regulators is essential reading for a
fuller appreciation of this subject. His findings, however, are
entirely restricted to the US and primarily to the US trunk
carriers.

The large majority of people make a journey for one of three
reasons:

For business, including government and official journeys.
For private, personal or family reasons.
For tourism.

These three reasons are determined by rather different factors.
Business reasons are not self-selected and although senior
personnel and highly paid employees travel more than middle-
and lower-grade staff, nevertheless the income of the traveller
seldom seems to influence directly the frequency of his journey
or the mode or class of his transport. In many areas business
represents about 70 per cent of all air journeys. Private journeys
are generally of an infrequent nature and the use of air transport
is rather more dependent on the income of the traveller and,
of course, on the country in which he travels, as well as the
travel facilities provided. Tourism is now a major source of air
revenue. It is very much more sensitive to the air fare than the
other reasons for travelling. This is accentuated by the tendency
to travel in family groups and because transport is only one
part of the total expenditure to be incurred. It is sensitive to the
journey distance and to the country of origin of the traveller.

All the above groups will be sensitive, to a greater or less
extent, to the other independent variables of air transport.
These are: speed, comfort and convenience, and safety.

Speed

The increase in the maximum cruising speed of commercial
aircraft during the last two decades was shown in Fig. 1.2.
On the same chart is shown the scheduled block times on the
London–New York and the London–Paris routes. On this
chart the year shown is the year of the first introduction into

airline service. We shall develop in Chapter 8 the concept of the value of time which in due course may become a major factor in the use of ultra short-haul passenger air transport, but we should note here that on many short routes (for example, London–Paris) the overall city centre–city centre time has barely decreased at all over the period considered.

Comfort and convenience

This factor may be compounded of comfort in the aircraft and in the airport procedural cycle, as well as the convenience of service, its scheduled frequency, the pattern of destinations, direct flight opportunities and the location of airport and city terminals. These interacting factors are probably more directly appreciated and assessed, often subconsciously, by the travelling public than any other group of traffic-generating factors. Not always in absolute terms but in relation to other modes of transport, the passenger more often than not selects his method of transport by his past experience and by the experience of others of these criteria. Some relevant data are shown in Fig. 1.4.

Safety

Fig. 3.4 shows the ICAO world record of scheduled airline safety. Very detailed reports and statistical information is available from the various government agencies on this subject. It may be claimed that the improving record has allowed the other economic and operational parameters to become dominant in the last decade.

Studies in transport demand

The use of air transport is strongly affected by other forms of transport, especially the motor car. This is not only true of the USA but applies also to Europe and Australia, and indeed to any country where an adequate road system allows full scope for the use of the motor car for private and business journeys. The direct cost of the motor-car journey is less than the tourist-

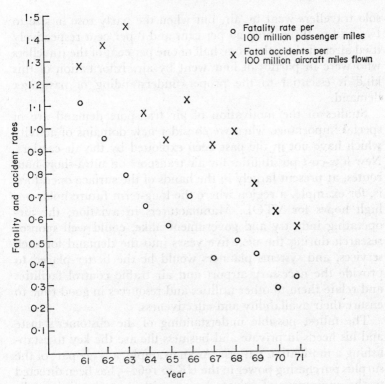

FIG. 3.4. Air Passenger Fatalities and Aircraft Accidents on ICAO World Scheduled Services (ICAO)

class return ticket in most countries of the world, but when the length of the journey requires a night stop or when the longer journey requires a number of *en route* night stops, with associated hotel room and meal costs, then the overall journey costs may often be lower by air. However, when several members of a party share a car it would be difficult to show any direct advantage for the use of air transport. The principal cause for the increasing use of air transport is that the time saved and convenience obtained by the use of aircraft is becoming increasingly appreciated by the business and private passenger. In an enquiry conducted in 1962 by Dr J. B. Lansing, Professor of Economics at the University of Michigan, concerning long-distance non-business trips it was shown that 71 per cent of the solo travellers went by air, but when the party rose in size to two and to three, only 22 per cent and 8 per cent respectively used aircraft. Less than one half of one per cent of the travellers who were in parties of four went by air. Information of this kind is essential to the proper understanding of passenger demand.

Studies of the motivation of air transport demand are of special importance when we consider new domains of activity which have not in the past been exploited by the air carriers. New low-cost possibilities for air transport on ultra-short-haul routes, at present largely in the hands of the surface operators, is, for example, a region where the long-term future holds out high hopes for VTOL. Manufacturers in aviation, the air-operating industry and government alike, could well sponsor research during the next five years into the demand for such services, and systems planners would be the better placed to provide the necessary airport and air traffic control facilities and relate them to other utilities and resources in good time to ensure their availability and effectiveness.

The fullest possible understanding of the customer's taste and his needs in private and business life are the key to estab-lishing a motivation pattern. As an example, a large part of the surplus purchasing power in the UK in 1962–5 has been directed to the equipment of private houses with space-heating appli-ances. This affected to a considerable extent, albeit temporarily, the expenditure on tourist services. A similar annual cost is very probably involved and the competitive element is in strong evidence. The planning and provision of air services require that social judgments, based on such factors as the above, should be taken into account.

Of more obvious importance is the direct competition of surface transport which will fight back with improved equip-ment, facilities, schedules and publicity to hold in check the encroachments of air transport. One example of this is the English Channel Tunnel which must give a significant fillip to our use of the motor car in Europe. A quite realistic assess-ment can now be made of the growth in cross-channel motor traffic, taking account of the principal factors of cost, conven-ience, time and safety. Numerical values can be assigned to all these variables. It could hardly be expected that they will all prove to be correct, but the careful consideration of each factor, its comparative weighting, the recognition of relationships and finally the cross-reference to other case studies with similar objectives, is an essential exercise in technological planning. By setting up what is now known as an 'econometric model' or an algebraic equation representing in an approximate form the relationships between the independent variables and the principal dependent variables it is possible to make a first step towards a theory of the motivation of transport demand.

These concepts were nicely put in a recent report of the ITA in Paris. 'Establish the needs, and we'll put technology to work.'

Transport aircraft requirements and market research

The requirement for transport aircraft may be discussed in terms of a detailed specification to meet the needs of one or a number of operators, or it may be considered in more general terms, with regard to the broad market for certain types of aircraft. It may be looked at moreover, from the manufacturers' and also from the air carriers' point of view. Without being too ambitious in our coverage we shall attempt to touch on various aspects of the subject.

We have already considered the predominant technical and economic factors which have determined the development of the transport aircraft up to the present time. It is necessary now to establish the means that may be used to identify the required characteristics if the maximum economic value is to be obtained by the airline when operating a fleet of the given type and also by the manufacturer if he is to justify the risks involved in tying down his capital resources in a major venture.

Now a very essential starting point is a clear understanding of the product which is under consideration and the conditions of its operation. The first thoughts may in fact have originated from the experience of one operator who foresees a demand in traffic terms which will need to be satisfied some years ahead and which can only be met by the further development of an existing type or the design of a new one. These thoughts may become rapidly formulated in the airline after some amplification in the traffic, operations and engineering departments, and give such guidance to a manufacturer's design department that a design study can be easily and rapidly completed. On the other hand it may often be the case that the action is initiated from the other direction and the design teams, well versed in the 'state of the art' and keen to promote the next step forward in their technology, will introduce a new generation of aircraft, carefully tailored to meet the largest possible market. The close inter-relationship between the relevant specialists in airline and manufacturing groups is of the greatest value in ensuring that the best use is made of both the approaches we have already discussed.

The origins of the demand

It seems to be of the greatest importance, whether looking at the subject from the airline or from the manufacturers' point of view, that we go right back to the origins of the case and seek the pattern of the demand for the transport which all parts of the industry are seeking to supply. We need to know a great deal about the distribution of this demand in location, in time, by age groups and by income group and in the many other ways in which it may be broken down. A greal deal of this is broadly appreciated by the planners in aviation, but not nearly enough effort has been expended in this field of study. People travel and arrange for the transport of goods for very good reasons, be they personal or business reasons, and it is clear that our starting point in any one field of transport promotion should be as precise as possible, and the reasons for and the nature of the requirement for transport should be clearly understood.

The fundamental breakdown of the transport objective and the distribution of its volume can be shown in a simple table as follows:

Objective	Journey length (miles)		
	0–500	500–1500	1500–maximum
Holiday	,,	,,	,,
Private	,,	,,	,,
Business	,,	,,	,,
Cargo	,,	,,	,,

The characteristics of the transport service required is different in each. The demand for speed, comfort (or space), frequency of service, fare level (or rate) and terminal facilities, is often totally different for long- and short-haul flights and the business or holiday traveller on the same stage may have quite contradictory views on the standard of comfort, terminal facilities and block speed which he will expect at a given level of fare. It is interesting to note that the above factors are also of apparent significance, though perhaps weighted differently, for the air cargo shipper. For him the rate, service frequency, hold cube and terminal facilities will acquire special importance.

The elasticity of demand for transport with respect to an important independent variable such as the fare level, has been studied extensively in recent years and in Paris in 1964 the Institut du Transport Aerien convened a special conference to discuss the subject. An important paper by B. Bjorkman (1964) may be referred to for a fuller treatment of the subject as developed up to that time.

A note on the significance of Elasticity as a non-dimensional measure of the variation of traffic flow due to the change of a principal transport generating factor, may be of use at this stage. Mathematically we have been accustomed to consider $\dfrac{-\Delta Q}{\Delta P}$ as the change of traffic Q as a result of a small change of the price or the fare level P, the negative sign indicating that a change of price in a positive direction (or increase) would cause a change of traffic in a negative direction (or decrease). Also the reverse would clearly apply. In the notation of the calculus the rate of change for the infinitely small quantities would be shown as $\dfrac{-\mathrm{d}Q}{\mathrm{d}P}$. In this form the derivative is inconvenient for numerical work since the slope of the curve depends on the scale of values used. To avoid this difficulty the percentage change in the two variables is used so that $\dfrac{100\mathrm{d}Q}{Q}$ and $\dfrac{100\mathrm{d}P}{P}$ replace $\mathrm{d}Q$ and $\mathrm{d}P$.

The numerical and non dimensional ratio of $\dfrac{\mathrm{d}Q}{Q} : \dfrac{\mathrm{d}P}{P}$ is known as the Elasticity E.

Thus $E = \dfrac{-\mathrm{d}Q}{\mathrm{d}P} \cdot \dfrac{P}{Q}$

But the total change in Q or the traffic increase due to change in the principal independent transport generating factors may be considered as the sum of a series of additive terms which might be written as:

$$dQ = -Ep \frac{Q}{P} dP + Ex \frac{Q}{X} dX + Ey \frac{Q}{Y} dY + \text{etc}$$

where the terms including Ep, Ex and Ey respectively represent the independent variables which principally affect the generation of traffic Q. These might be the level of fares or price (P), the block speed (X) or the frequency of service (Y).

The position of air transport in the total transportation field

The historical development of air transport as a competitive element in the total transportation business is very recent and Fig. 3.5 shows one measure of its penetration. From the overall growth during the period, it is seen that air transport has shared very significantly in that growth as well as in the total market. This has been found to be the case in most areas and on both international and domestic routes. In the year 1970, 97 per cent of the North Atlantic passengers went by air.

A study of the domestic travel market within the USA was conducted in 1961 by the Opinion Research Corporation of Princeton, New Jersey, on behalf of four American airlines and two major aircraft manufacturers. Based on a sample of 3680 personal interviews, it was particularly concerned with automobile trips covering 400 miles or more, there and back. Between 1 and 3 per cent of the journeys made were assessed as being the most likely prospective diversions to air transport. 1 per cent of the car journeys made represented about 5 per cent of the annual domestic air carrier volume at that time (Cherington, 1962).

Although 48 per cent of the adults interviewed took a journey of 400 miles or more in 1961, only 10 per cent of them considered the use of air and 64 per cent considered that the possession of a car at the destination was a key consideration in the planning of a trip of this length. As in other surveys of this kind the travellers disposed to the use of air are found to travel alone or in a party seldom exceeding two or three; they have little need for *en route* stops or diversions, and have an inclination to use air for this and other journeys. The percentage of the total passenger-miles generated by scheduled airlines is very dependent on the length of the journey. This aspect of passenger demand has been long recognised as significant from the point of view of the aircraft designer as well as from that of the air carrier.

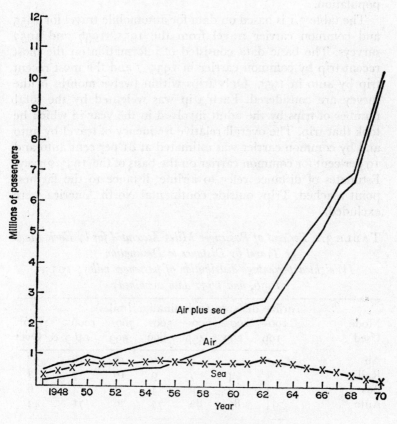

Source: U.S. Department of Justice, Immigration and I.A.T.A.

Fig. 3.5. Penetration of Air Carriers on the North Atlantic

Data of particular relevance of this aspect of air penetration were presented by Dr J. B. Lansing to the International Symposium on Demand Elasticity in Air Transport during November 1964. They are reproduced in part in Table 3.1 by kind permission of the author and the ITA (Lansing, 1964). Use is made of certain data from the National Travel Market Surveys conducted since 1955 by the Survey Research Centre of the University of Michigan for US industrial groups interested in the development of travel. To obtain the information interviews were conducted in the homes of a small sample of the population.

The table 3.1 is based on data for automobile travel for 1955 and common carrier travel from the 1955, 1956 and 1957 surveys. The basic data consisted of information on the most recent trip by common carrier in 1955–7 and the most recent trip by auto in 1955. Only trips within twelve months of the survey are considered. Each trip was weighted by the total number of trips by the adult involved in the year in which he took that trip. The overall relative frequency of travel by auto and by common carrier was estimated at 81 per cent auto and 19 per cent for common carrier on the basis of the 1955 survey. Estimates of distance refer to airline distance to the farthest point reached. Trips outside continental North America were excluded.

TABLE 3.1. *Per cent of Passenger Miles Accounted for by Each Mode of Travel by Distance to Destination*
(Weighted percentage distribution of passenger miles: 1955, 1956, and 1957 data combined)

Mode Used	Airline distance to destination (miles)						
	100– 199	200– 299	300– 499	500– 699	700– 999	1000– 1499	1500 & Over
Air	1	4	9	10	16	18	38
Rail	3	4	7	9	10	7	14
Bus	3	3	2	4	4	4	6
Auto	93	89	82	77	70	71	42
Total	100	100	100	100	100	100	100
% of all passenger-miles	27·4	14·4	14·6	10·8	9·2	12·9	10·8

This aspect of Dr Lansing's study of the motivation for air travel should be viewed as one part only of a broad subject only recently receiving the attention necessary for a fuller understanding of the forces behind air traffic growth.

Of special importance to students of air passenger market forecasting techniques is the work on air travel analysis which has been carried out by the Port of New York Authority. Mr Norman Johnson, chief of the Forecast and Analysis Division developed methods whereby the national market surveys undertaken by the University of Michigan were applied to the estimation of a regional transport market. The objective was the long-range forecasting of the New York–New Jersey air traffic demand. It had been found by the Port Authority that the classical relationships between the transport product (revenue passenger-miles or ton-miles) and isolated economic factors could no longer provide an adequate basis for planning major airport facilities. Instead the competitive aspect of air travel was viewed as the cominant criterion. This leads to the principle that air traffic is the outcome of many carefully weighed decisions by personal and business travellers each of which differ in background, experience, income and taste. The principal factors influencing the volume and/or the mode of transport were found to be occupation, industry, age, income and education, the distance to be travelled and the number in the party. Some aspects of the survey were referred to above and further details are described by Lansing (1964). The work of the Port of New York Authority is published by the Eno Foundation of Connecticut.

Competitive aspects of air transport

An early attempt to develop the relationship between the economic characteristics of a community and its achieved level of demand for air transport was made by the FAA. They used two main criteria for classification: (1) the activity in wholesale business, and (2) the level of employment in mining and manufacturing. Four principal categories of traffic-generating centres were identified as Industrial, Marketing, Institutional and Balanced. Thus, in terms of the type of activity concentrated at each centre, the traffic-generating level per head of the population was calculated. This method has been used in other applications and was employed in principle for assessing the need for air services in the survey of air transport requirements for the north-east of the United Kingdom, conducted by the author in 1963 for the Yorkshire Airport Development Association. In that case, however, the level of incomes, the distance (or time) of the population from alternative airport sites and the length of the proposed journey were also introduced as factors in the analysis.

Studies of demand for telecommunications have been of value in guiding thought on the analogous air-transport problems and, in fact, these may be viewed as elements of a communications spectrum which runs from surface mail through air mail and cable links to the personal visit by car and aeroplane. M. E. L. Spanyol prepared the figure below for a lecture in 1962 to the Institute of Transport. This presents in an interesting manner the position of transport in the whole field of communications.

The Communications Continuum

	Surface Mail	Air Mail	Cable or Satellite Teleprint	Telephone	Personal Visit	Change of Residence
Speed	Poor	Fair	Good	Good	Good	Good
Volume	Good	Good	Poor	Fair	Good	Max.
Cost	V. Low	Low	High	V. High	Max.	High
Flexibility	Good	Good	Good	Good	Fair	Bad

The significance of the four parameters, Speed, Volume, Cost and Flexibility should be noted. The prospect of the great improvement in international telephone and teleprint communications which will be brought about by the use of communication satellites should not lead us to think of a directly competitive situation growing up between personal air transport and the Comsat link.

It is possible, on the contrary, that the two facilities will mutually stimulate each other and separately encourage the development of business and ideas upon which each flourishes.

However, all types of communication, whatever they perform and however they convert energy into a commercial form, are in fact agents of production. The transport product is, moreover, unique in that it is consumed while it is being produced. In this all forms of transport and communication are alike. Moreover, it is economic to produce in quantities far greater than is likely to be required and the demand all too often has a seasonal variance which is most difficult to predict. Now the analogy between telecommunication and air transportation can be carried even farther, and I need mention only one or two international implications which these two areas of human activity have in common to suggest a playground for analogy hunting. One problem, for example, which will impose a limiting tendency to traffic involving any considerable change of longtitude, is the time element, since the difficulty of arranging mutual times for communication will restrict opportunities for discussion, whether by telephone or by personal visit by air. Most significant of all, the intensely high rates of productivity possible by the use of satellites as a microwave link poses the same difficult problems in market forecasting which some of us have been struggling with in the air transportation field, particularly in recent years on supersonic aircraft projects.

Jipps Formula (1961) was an early attempt to provide a practical approach to forecasting telephone traffic between a pair of countries, based on the number of telephones in each country, on the distance apart of the two countries and on empirical factors of language and political association. It was further developed by work undertaken by P. J. Detmold and the author (1962) when we worked on a method using three parameters. This assumed that any change in traffic will be due to one of three influences:

A change in the income of those paying for calls.
A change in the tariff.
A change in the service quality, including rapidity and reliability of the service.

At the present time there is much development of the traffic forecasting methods based on trade since the growth of international communications may be expected to depend very largely on the growth of business.

Airline objectives

To the aircraft manufacturer the market for his product lies in the various airline operators who may be willing to acquire his aircraft for replacement and/or expansion purposes. We should now consider what are the objectives that these customers have set for themselves. We may then the more easily assess their requirements.

It has become clear from the history of transport during the last two decades that profit-making is too simple an objective to be supported rationally as the sole *raison d'être* of Air Transport Operation. While profitable operations are the key to success and are the principal criterion by which airline and management are judged, it is surely in the provision of efficient, convenient and competitive public transport service at a continuously decreasing level of fares with an increasing level of safety that the overall proficiency of the airline will be measured. Without overall profitability, however, the continued existence of an air-operating company will be in doubt. It is certain also that its aircraft selection decisions will be made largely on the basis of profit criteria. We may say then that a primary object of operating an airline is to make a profit, that is to say to earn a higher return on the capital borrowed than that paid for its use. The other political or social objectives cannot unfortunately be analysed to advantage in a general discussion. An airline may sometimes be obliged to operate an uneconomic sector or a lightly loaded route to maintain a service in the public interest, and clearly the principles discussed here are unlikely to apply in this case.

Now the profitability of an airline may have important effects on its purchasing policy. It may also affect the marketability of a project, so that the meaning set upon 'profitability' may have some significance. The word 'profit' is sometimes used to describe any excess of revenue when all operating costs other than interest upon capital have been paid. The word profit is also applied to the balance after financial charges but before taxation, sometimes also to the 'net profit' after taxation for distribution to holders of preference or ordinary shares. It might be supposed that the fluctuating and meagre profits of many airlines would make it desirable to keep loan capital to a minimum. But with many private-enterprise airlines, particularly in the United States, lack of dividends in the past has made it very difficult to raise new funds in ordinary shares. Faced with re-equipment by competitors such airlines face the alternative of losing traffic with outdated aircraft or of borrowing from banks and insurance companies, mortgaging aircraft, buildings and equipment of every kind. Thus, the airline with the greatest need for augmenting ordinary share capital is the least able to obtain it and the worse its competitive position the more it will be driven to a dangerously high loan-to-share capital ratio.

Equipment financing in the jet era

The magnitude of the financing problem for the replacement of large fleets of jet aircraft is of a high order. More than 2,500 three- and four-engine aircraft have been acquired in the last decade with individual unit costs exceeding on average more than £2 million (5 million dollars). These aircraft, moreover, have created a trend of competitive obsolescence in the medium/short-haul fleets which has already stimulated the demand for twin-jet transports of the 50–70-seat-size category which are now developing air transport service with jet speeds and jet age standard in all parts of the world. Small jet transports to meet the need for replacement of DC 3, C 46 and Convair 330 and 440 aircraft are already on offer from manufacturers in the USA, the United Kingdom and France.

It is a central problem in the marketing of a new aircraft project of high intrinsic value, no matter how attractive its potential earning capacity and competitive strength, and no matter how confident the customer may be in its operating economics and the manufacturer's experience, that the financing must be arranged within the resources available to the purchaser. The banking houses will be concerned that the finance required is not excessive in relation to the existing capitalisation, i.e. the debt ratio must be acceptable. The airline may well have cash available from earnings and from depreciation charges which taken together with the sums realised from the sale of surplus aircraft will give him sources of value, but he will almost certainly be obliged to resort to money borrowed from banks, insurance companies and the sale of long-term obligations to the public. Bank investment, because of the need for maintaining liquidity, tends to be short term whereas insurance companies will make loans for considerably longer periods. Longer periods of loan are now becoming essential because of the higher costs of new types of large jet transport aircraft which are less likely to be prone to high rates of competitive obsolescence (Chapter 2).

Six to seven years for the servicing of loans is now becoming mandatory for the sale of transport aircraft in many parts of the world, and the manufacturers, the Export-Import Bank (US), the Export Credit Guarantee Department (UK) and banking and credit houses work closely together to prepare terms and conditions of loan which will provide the individual customer with the facilities he needs.

Leasing arrangements are still not viewed with favour by the aircraft manufacturer, but hire-purchase agreements have had short spells of popularity due largely to favourable tax situations.

It is the experience of some manufacturers that when the requirement for an aircraft is great enough and especially when the overall national economic development justifies it, a considerable degree of overseas government support may be forthcoming. This may not in any way lessen the demand for long-term financing and may even exacerbate the competitive element in the credit terms offered by the export agencies.

The finance houses will concern themselves especially with certain aspects of a possible aircraft purchase and it may be important to recognise what these are:

They will be concerned with the operating cost and economy of operation of the new type, and with its revenue-earning potential. Thus they are anxious to support new and advanced types of transport aircraft when offered by experienced manufacturers to airlines with the capability of operating the type and developing them in service. They know that it costs about six or seven times more money to operate an aircraft for ten years than to buy it, so they are as interested in revenue as in costs.

They are anxious to see the maximum possible utilisation of the aircraft since high productivity means higher earnings and they are watchful of the operating record of the airline concerned, its success with an earlier generation of aircraft, the vision of its management and, of course, the potential for future business, perhaps through new route alignments or pooling agreements which may be open to them.

They are watchful too of the introduction stages of a new aircraft. They like to know who, if anyone, has operated it before, what is the likely extent of fixed introduction costs, the support equipment, tools, training and the possibly long-drawn-out learning stage which some airlines have had to battle with for too long.

Above all, the finance houses look back on the record of technical achievement and management success and look to evidence in the present of imaginative programmes based on careful planning for the future.

The market for private and executive aircraft

The market for the high-performance privately owned executive transport aircraft is only one part of the overall demand for General Aviation which covers:

Transportation of management and business officials.
Private transportation.
Transport of working parties and materials.
Cargo transport (including freight, mail and baggage).
Aerial work (including agricultural use).

This wide range of duties cannot be carried out effectively by one type of aircraft and, indeed, air industries in many parts of the world have been built up to satisfy this wide and expanding demand for aeronautical products. A study of the use to which these aircraft might be put indicates the following principal requirement headings which will determine the specification.

The number of passengers and frequency with which they are required to be carried.

The mean stage length and variance about the mean.

The requirements for speed and flight time on probable journeys.

The airfield limitations (if any) at the home base and the principal destination points.

There exist today a wide range of single- and multi-engine aircraft with piston and turbine engines and with a wide range of seating capacities. To assess a potential market in one part of this field requires a specialised knowledge of the products of the industry and a detailed study of the most favourable territories.

The business house will make decisions for different reasons than those established by the airlines. The operating economy in relation to revenue naturally does not apply, but the first cost and annual cost of operation, which altogether may amount to five times the first cost of the aircraft, will be related to other outlets for capital and annual expenditure. What improvements to the plant could be obtained for the same amount of money? Financing the purchase of a new executive transport is seldom a major problem for an established business, but aviation departments are often cut back when business is bad. Naturally, prestige is a dominant factor in the purchase a business aircraft so far as the board of directors are concerned; to the executive pilot or the flight department of a major business organisation it is, naturally enough, the technical, flight handling, and operational aspects which are prominent in the formulation of recommendations to purchase. These considerations must influence the design, especially the cockpit layout of an executive aircraft. They should moreover set guide lines to the sales approach. Rational methods for the selection of business aircraft were interestingly presented in a paper published by the Society of Automative Engineers, in January 1964 (Smith & Schmidt, 1964). A methodology based on the determination of company travel requirements, examination of aircraft characteristics and the comparative evaluation of key parameters was proposed. Parameters suggested were:

1. Safety
2. Price
3. Operating cost
4. Speed
5. Comfort
6. Flying characteristics
7. Maintenance requirements
8. Compatibility with an existing fleet

It would be difficult to challenge these factors as the principal ones requiring customer satisfaction before purchase. Perhaps operating cost would find it hard to maintain third place.

The organisation and methods of research

We should perhaps consider some of the basic requirements we must meet if we are to carry out competent research in this field. We will touch on some of the shortcomings in the past, and make some suggestions for the future.

We should consider Market Research far more as a continuous process than has often been the practice in the past. In the UK we unfortunately have not always followed this principle and it cannot be too strongly urged that we need to keep in employment a small number of trained staff, so that experience can be continually built up in this progressively competitive business, so that a 'know-how' can be developed.

The related process of analysis should be more fully developed whereby the new project or the developed product, indeed even more so the current product, is continuously measured up against the market for the estimation of its penetration (i.e. sales) potential.

The evaluations and comments of the market research specialist must be fed back continuously to the project designers who will try to introduce the experience gained or the results acquired at the earliest possible opportunity. This is a part of the product development process which includes also the inputs provided by the potential customers, sales staff, design, research and development groups and the national or international research and licensing authorities themselves.

Certain it is that no full and authoritative view of the world aviation scene with its potential markets and sales opportunities can be taken if the Market Research function is a spasmodic and discontinuous process related only to a need for one short-term answer.

Staff required for market research in the manufacturing industry

A mixed staff of qualified engineers and economists has been found to provide a satisfactory balanced group for aviation research of the kind described above. Rather depending on individual qualities and interests, some strengthening by a small number of specialist statisticians, operations engineers and information officers may be necessary. A well-manned and alert intelligence office is of the first importance and should be closely linked to any industrial research organisation.

Although the techniques of Operational Research have an important place in the repertoire of a self-contained Aviation Research Group, these methods are found to be of value only in a limited range of problems. Statistical theory, however, is a basic requirement for the economist who wishes to be fully equipped to handle the large majority of the problems arising, and facility with multiple regression, the various distribution theories, tests of significance and correlation is of greater value than a preoccupation with the theories of queueing and congestion and linear programming. The whole field of operational and econometric research, however, is liable to ransack by the research worker in aviation and only recently some of the fundamental studies in mathematical graphics have opened up to the air transport planner possibilities for future profitable exercise. Econometrics has now become a big field of study on its own. In aviation research it is found that all these disciplines may yield up useful techniques for application. This surely is the true field of operational research, which has been defined as 'the application of the principles and methods of science to problems of strategy'. The science of cybernetics which is concerned with the study of communication and control as applied to organisms and organisations, and playing thereby a 'seminal role' in automation, is likewise a fermenter of ideas in the face of industrial research problems of many kinds. While they have been confined so far to the technical problems arising in the design of control systems due to the need to limit the variables handled, in due course the less amenable operational systems may well become disciplined by these methods. Quality control, design for optimum value (value engineering), and network analysis (the critical path and PERT systems) are all areas of activity which are offering today direct economic advantage. These fields of activity are open to the trained staff of a first-class market research group.

There is in many industrial organisations a lack of confidence in market research and the fault often lies in the vague conception of what market research can do, and what it cannot be expected usefully to achieve. It must be admitted frankly that plenty of indifferent market research work has been done. It is found generally that the consumer product industry has a greater confidence in market research than heavy industry; in aviation, moreover, we have for so long been dependent on Government support through military orders that it is only during the last five to ten years that market research has been seriously considered at all.

Market research must be rigorous and it must be independent; it is of little value if it is a service confined to sales support even though active selling requires constantly the provision of basic information, and an interpretation on products and markets. It is easy for market research to become a side-line of a sales department.

Perhaps we can now take a closer look at what we mean by market research. We can, I think, divide it rationally into three parts, viz:

Information
Interpretation
Investigation

Information, however, is only the raw material for a final analysis of markets and marketing. The interpretation of the facts and the thorough investigation of the problems confronting management in critical decision-making stages of a new project are one of the key functions of market research.

From the above discussion, I believe it can be concluded that market research can provide valuable results on the demand for new aircraft projects, if trained staff are available, so long as there is no unforeseen major shift in technology. Such a shift, the implications of which should perhaps have been more easily forecast, was the introduction of the large subsonic jets in the late fifties. The introduction of the supersonic airliner must be expected to have just such a major effect on aircraft deployment and purchasing policies.

Very numerous are the methods and techniques which are available now to the aircraft industry for market research, but the principal objects are more limited and may be summarised under five headings as follows:

Real economy of air operations against the national background.

The passenger appeal and business growth.

The financial strength of the airline customer.

The competitive need for the type and timing.

Introduction problems.

There is also the paramount need to study carefully the profitability of the particular market for the manufacturer himself.

We continue to develop more economic and efficient aircraft with increasing traffic generating capability. Were it not for the steady growth of traffic, we would long ago have destroyed our own market by our own more productive flight equipment. Today, in the intensive competitive situation in which we find ourselves, we are reaching towards a point of declining production and of reduced profitability. The future is much brighter, if we look at the new fields which are awaiting development. In quite new concepts of transport on short-haul stages, through VTO technology and also in the wide field of air cargo, inroads can be made so much more effectively into the surface transport industries, with the vaster markets which this implies. These changes are almost upon us, and there is plenty of scope for research in design, and in the study of new and more extensive markets.

Interview and questionnaire

In obtaining new information concerning an aviation product it is of great importance to have a carefully prepared questionnaire memorised and very fully understood by the interviewer, who should be of an easy and pleasant personality. There is, quite rightly, a great reluctance nowadays to use a postal questionnaire which is unfortunate, since it is much cheaper and if used with or if completed by the well-informed executive, can give good and consistent answers. The problem lies in ensuring that the right people are interested enough to make time available for the questionnaire, whether by postal method or during a personal interview. Properly prepared questions should not give a lead to the answers required, and it is of crucial importance that the personnel interviewed should be approached in a way that leaves no doubt that their independent and frank views are required, with the numerical replies forwarded at a later date if it is more convenient and/or if it is necessary so as to receive more useful answers.

In the interview with airline personnel which has as its object the comments and views on a new aircraft project, manufacturing representatives need to be very well briefed on the air transport field for which the aircraft is directed, since it is of the greatest importance that a wide range of discussion takes place with a number of different people who will be specialists in airline operations, performance, commercial research and perhaps engine or airframe overhaul problems. Quite wrong impressions have been gained by superficial interviews with a single influential airline representative, who may claim a far wider knowledge of the operational problems of his company than he possesses, and who may have no inkling at all of his own prejudices. The two-way exchange of professional ideas and information on the state of the art is an essential prerequisite for profitable interviews in the aircraft project field.

Certainly well-planned interviews with significant airlines in the principal market areas for a new aircraft are a key to early project design. They act as a probing or testing process when used in conjunction with thorough desk work. Aircraft, however, cannot be designed by interview and questionnaire, however carefully prepared.

The form of a basic questionnaire such as might be prepared for use by market research specialists preparing for interviews with the air carrier industry is shown overleaf in Table 3.2. The information was required for the preparation of an operational study of a small jet passenger transport for a local service carrier in Europe and the questions were for the guidance of the interviewer rather than for direct repetition in the areas where the operational research worker clearly felt the need for confirmation.

TABLE 3.2. *Basic Information Required for Operational Study of a Passenger Aircraft Project*

---

1. What are the current and projected scheduled routes and the minimum acceptable service frequency? What year can we take for the projected introduction into service of the proposed type of new aircraft?
2. What schedule limitations exist for passengers such as arrival and departure times?
3. Is information available on the traffic distribution by routes so that load factors and the passenger and freight capacity can be co-ordinated? What are the peak seasonal demands?
4. What is the mean freight density and the principal types of freight loads carried? What is the free baggage allowance offered on your domestic services?
5. Information is sought on the location and capacity of the airline engineering base and an indication of whether the proposed engines would be overhauled by the engine builder at his nearest base or whether materials only would be purchased from him.
6. Can a growth of passenger traffic be forecast for the next five years? If so, could we be given an annual rate of growth to assume in our analysis? Can we assume that a depression of tourist passenger rates might accelerate this trend?
7. Can you list for us the airfields from which operations would be contemplated? Can you specify alternative airfields so that reserve fuel allowances can be computed? A full list of your current airfield and alternate field data would be invaluable.
8. Could you state whether you anticipate that route and approach facilities would determine that air crew in addition to two pilots with VHF are mandatory?
9. We should be glad of your own figures for the following cost items since otherwsie we would use mean figures which might not apply to your own operations:
   9.1. Crew salaries and expenses (*a*) pilot, (*b*) RO or navigator, if required.
   9.2. Landing fees and other operating taxes (if any).
   9.3. Aviation turbine fuel prices in your area (there are likely to be confidential).
   9.4. The depreciation period and residual value to be used in assessing the standing costs.
   9.5. Are you able to quote an interest rate on capital or is this not to be included in this study?

General statistics

The available information on the market for aviation products, including air transport seat and ton-miles, is strictly limited. It is available in its most accessible form as officially sponsored and published statistics, but some experience in the use of these is highly desirable since the basis on which they are compiled may not be always apparent. An important text by Professor Ely Devons (1961) of London University on British Economic Statistics is invaluable. No strictly equivalent US text is available, but the reference list at the end of this chapter gives a number of valuable US sources.

Statistics of Population and Distribution, Manpower and Industrial Production, Prices and Income, Foreign Trade, Distribution and Transport are the raw material of the industrial market research worker. In aviation outside the USA he is strengthened by the reports of the British Airways Corporations (the BEA annual report is of exceptional value), the annual financial reports of International Air Carriers (of a certain limited value), the reports of IATA and ICAO giving quarterly and annual returns of the member airlines. The reports published privately for members by international associations such as the ITA (Institut du Transport Aerien), the EARB (The European Air Research Bureau) and ECAC (The European Civil Aviation Conference) are of considerable consequence in their special fields.

Many governments publish important statistics of the air transport industry and detailed returns are generally available of passenger, freight, mail and aircraft movements through the principal nationally owned airports. Total traffic figures are also published. The UK Civil Aviation Authority publish monthly figures for movements at state-owned airports. A shortcoming is that it is still not possible to establish the types of aircraft which comprise the movements quoted. However, many valuable papers and reports have been issued and the diligent research worker can find much of value if his enquiry is not too closely confined.

Other important sources are the publications of the United Nations, such as the *United Nations Statistical Year Book* and the

Year Book of National Account Statistics, which provide *inter alia* gross national product values.

A paper in the *Review of Economics and Statistics,* May 1961, provided invaluable GNP projections for selected Asian countries up to 1975. Such source material is invaluable in studies of industrial and trade development which may be presumed to be closely related to the principal factors of economic growth. In research studies on air cargo development we have employed methods using these relations. For other investigations of like nature source material may generally be found.

In the USA a remarkably well-organised body of statistical information is available. It is a requirement of the Civil Aeronautics Board that the Certificated Air Carriers should report their financial and operating results in a specified form for regular monthly, quarterly and annual publication. In a similar form the ATA (Air Transport Association of America) issue returns which are widely published in the US and International Aviation Press (Ref. *Aviation Week* and *American Aviation*). A long list of publications is available from the CAB in Washington and aircraft movements from FAA airports, air fatality statistics and aircraft ownership records are only some of the essential data which are available. References given at the end of this chapter indicate some principal sources which are available from the FAA in Washington It would not be possible to omit mention of the Port of New York Authority which publishes reports and statistics of exceptional value concerning movements of passengers and goods through the airports of New York Papers from the officials of the PNYA have contributed notably to the international discussions on air transport and traffic forecasting for many years.

Factors in transport aircraft selection

It has been already made clear that the selection of a transport aircraft will not rest solely upon one or a series of technical considerations The principal economic and technical aspects have already been briefly noted and we shall now see to what extent the engineering approach can supply the final answers to type selection There are, of course, many requirements which can only be considered generally in relation to the particular set of conditions under which the aircraft will operate, such as the payload capacity or the length of landing and take-off runs, etc., but aircraft type assessment will, in any case, require different methods according to whether a manufacturer, for example, is concerned to find the best design for a production programme planned for a world market, or an operator is requiring to select a design, perhaps in the same embyro stage, but envisaged for a well-established pattern of routes Clearly the aircraft required for the wide market must involve a broader compromise at every stage.

Certain good features of design are likely to be agreed amongst all operating engineers, but may be achieved to a different degree by different manufacturers due to differences in design and/or development experience. The CG limits available and the degree of loading that may be performed indiscriminately are two such design points which will weigh heavily with the operator. Perhaps more important, and yet more difficult to assess, is the value to the operator of the good-will of the manufacturer, his close acquaintance with key design staff and the faith he has in the ability of the manufacturer to develop vigorously both airframe and power plant. The earning capacity of an aircraft is greatly dependent on its potential development or 'stretch': this will effect also its length of useful life and the flexibility of use to which it may be put. It is rare for an operator to be precise as to the pattern of use to which an aircraft will be put more than two or three years ahead.

The operator should be clear as to the aerodrome limits to which he is confined. His plan for future operations and services will take into account both aerodrome length and extension possibilities and the take-off and landing performance of his proposed aircraft operating to the standards laid down by the National or International Civil Air Authority. He may be limited by the weight of his fully loaded aircraft or the maximum single-wheel runway load imposed: he is more than likely to be limited by the maximum size of his aircraft and must ensure that it does not exceed the dimensions of the largest hangars at his overhaul base. All these limiting factors must be considered by the operator in the selection of an aircraft type. The manufacturer also would be unwise to neglect them: he should be familiar with their international implications. The exchange of information between manufacturer and operator is essential to the proper understanding of air transport requirements in the UK and overseas.

The short list below shows how the principal factors in selection may be related in the mind of the operatoı. There seem to be twelve in number. It could not be argued that they are all equal in value: there may be some correlation, as between cost and speed: and in rare cases one of the criteria will not arise at all. In some cases such as the Weight/Altitude/Temperature (WAT) limit, the restriction is temporary or seasonal. However, in few cases of which we have experience have these twelve factors not played a significant part. They are:

First Cost, Delivery and Terms of Payment.
Specific Operating Cost.
Speed and Competitiveness.
Payload and Productivity.
Range and Flexibility.
Potential Stretchability.
After-Sales Service and Technical Training Facilities and Requirements.
Public Acceptability and Marketability.
Operator/Manufacturer Confidence.
Delivery Dates.
Airfield Performance and WAT Limitations.
Introduction Costs.

The importance of these factors is now becoming well known and it is essential for the manufacturer to be able to quote from chapter and verse how he can justify his confidence in meeting all detailed requirements.

Categorisation of Aircraft by Size and Stage Length

It is common practice to categorise transport aircraft into the principal groups defined broadly by the maximum seating capacity and the maximum economic stage length that may be flown with full allowance for fuel reserves. The changing technology and traffic growth has gradually increased the limits of size and stage length and in the early 1970s they may be defined as follows:

	State length (miles)	Seating capacity
Long-Haul	2500–6000	150–500
Medium-Haul	1000–2500	60–150
Short-Haul	150–1000	25–100
Third-Level Operations	25–150	5–25

Such groupings are clearly only of general use and many aircraft types and most airline systems provide examples which straddle two or even three categories. Third-level operations may be defined as those provided by small aircraft feeding major air terminals or providing links between airports.

Requirements for short-range low-cost transport aircraft

Experience of civil project studies and operational cost investigations, suggests that the following items are the most important in minimising the operating costs on a civil transport or, in some cases, in persuading operators that the project is likely to have low cost in service which in some cases may be a rather different thing.

The basic operating weight is tremendously important in its effect on specific costs and often in preliminary estimates of the cost of production. It affects landing fees and engineering cost by formula; moreover, reduction in weight if convertible into payload, gives a direct and proportional improvement in the direct costs per unit of the transport product. The very strictest control of weight is most likely to pay off handsomely and new thinking in this field might lead to most favourable results in operating economy.

To some extent, in conflict with the above, must come standardised equipment and components of accepted reliability and long overhaul life, especially when well known to international operators. Systematic records of reliability and failure rates would be invaluable in backing up claims of the manufacturer and in guiding the selection of components and

149

design. This is a field in which further research and development would pay off handsomely.

High block speed in relationship to cruising speed has a most important effect in the operating economics of short-haul aircraft, both in the formula and in the flight stage. VTO solutions seem to be gaining a good point here but any feasible method achieving this on short-haul by conventional means should be tried. Low cruising altitudes could be suggested but airway limitations and turbulence as well as structural fatigue limits may rule this out. In practice, a wide range of cruising altitude to suit conditions of high payload without a need for speed, as an alternative to *low* payload with a need for high block speeds, would be very desirable in actual operations, although this is difficult to show favourably in a formula. A wide range of climb speed will assist the achievement of high block speeds. In subsonic jets this may approach 350 knots equivalent air speed to give adequate margins on placard speeds. High EAS on cruise at 15,000 ft altitude is essential on congested airways to avoid delays in departure clearance.

The aircraft should have a payload and fuselage capacity which can be readily extended as demand arises or as the market is found to grow, and this factor should be taken into account during the design stage as well as the associated engine power and thrust development which will be necessary with it. A simple modification kit to increase fuselage volume and increase payload and wing strength might be considered in this context. This might enable potential customers to write off the aircraft over a much longer period than is now common practice.

A long-life engine of good repute with adequate power growth expectation and, if possible, with worldwide overhaul facilities already available or in embryo is desirable. An aircraft type which is not solely a replacement type but has a penetration capability in new large markets, perhaps still in the hands of surface transport, is highly desirable. Highly productive aircraft types which replace earlier types of lower productivity cannot always find large markets unless the traffic growth factor is considerable. Where capital is scarce it may be sound economics for airlines to wait and hope to skip a generation. This may not apply in the premium air transport classes, but does in this case. Close consideration of comparable military requirements is self-evident since many of the most effective civil aircraft have been evolved as a result of defence expenditure on transport airframes and/or high-output power units. A compromise design to cover various markets will always help to spread R & D and hence reduce first cost and operating costs.

It seems very desirable in the light of recent experience to design a fuselage for short-haul low-cost aircraft which can cope with passengers and cargo both together and separately. This suggests a high-wing layout in order to simplify payload transfer. The decision on floor width is a critical one. Six-abreast seating is probably desirable between 60 and 150 seats. An 88-inch-wide pallet, however, is most likely to become standard, and allowance must be made for inspection space. There may be a dimensional conflict if the 108-inch pallet is a determining factor. Close consideration should be given to the critical fuselage dimensions of the existing successful aircraft in the class under review.

Market research is essential in order to establish the size of aircraft or the range of size which will be required during a given period on individual route systems. This applies also to the stage length which would be chosen to cover the requirements specific to the stage of development of the route system in a given part of the world. This will determine, in some cases, the type and size of power plants but these again will often play back on the aircraft characteristics to meet a given payload and range requirement. The commercial viability and financial recourses of the most likely customers for the type of aircraft under consideration should be a part of the Market Research exercise. The size of the market and the penetration probability should be studied as quite separate facets of the problem. The time scale of the product in relation to total aviation demand and phasing out of older types needs a careful assessment.

If one could summarise these points it would be to suggest that design for low weight and for stretch of capacity and flexibility of operation within a framework of established components and well-known design features are the key to a commercially acceptable project. This leaves a conflict between low weight and established components and it is not easy to see a simple way out of this dilemma for the project engineer.

Estimated costs per mile, per passenger or per ton-mile and first price of the aircraft and spares, still remain the key parameters in use in airline offices. Crucial to a favourable airline decision is the timing of the introduction into service in relation to phasing *out* of older types. The phasing *in* of other new and perhaps more significant aircraft types, the individual airline's competitive position and the financial resources available are also in need of careful study. The fullest studies of the best alternative projects computed on various route systems and taking account of as many realistic airline cost and revenue figures as possible, should be carried out as early as practicable. The size of the prospective market as a function of date and the penetration probability should separately be assessed.

A separate analysis of long-haul aircraft and the new generation of wide-body jets is provided in the next chapter.

Specialised engine requirements for short-haul operations

The need to develop special turbo-fan engines for short-haul aircraft to be operated on feeder and local service routes has now become recognised. The first cost of these engines must be brought down since the prime cost of the equipped aircraft with spares is a key economic criterion due to the limited utilisation possibility on these operations. Moderate pressure ratios with a minimum number of compressor and turbine stages are required. In spite of reduced sophistication, restriction of the material specifications and the number of components, every effort is made to utilise parts common to other engines in the manufacturer's range. On the RB 172, the 5500 lb two-spool turbo-fan under development for small twin-jet transport and advanced trainers, the cruise specific fuel consumption was to be only two or three per cent worse than that of the Spey although operating at lower cruise speeds and altitudes, and with only half the number of components. It was thought that something better than 0·8 lb/hr/lb at 25,000 ft could be achieved.

It is possible to make reasonable estimates of overhaul cost of an engine of a new type if the design principles are made clear.

More recently the engine manufacturers have provided a fuller account of their thinking on new developments, and the contribution of the engine to airline engineering and capital costs is more fully understood. A first step is the comparison of the major components (their basic design and material of construction) with known operating engines.

Idling conditions are important in the consideration of an engine for short-haul operators. It will determine not only the cost and weight of fuel under idling and low-thrust conditions, but may affect brake wear and assist in the low-thrust conditions of approach and landing.

Engine costs

The development of the approved overhaul life of turbine engines has been remarkable over the last ten years. It has become commonplace for the time between overhauls (TBO) of a turbojet to be extended from under 1000 or over 3000 hours within two years of introduction into airline service. Clearly an assessment of the future extension of the time between overhauls (which will be slightly less than the approved life) is an essential exercise at the commencement of the economic analysis of a transport through its operating life. The future stretch of the overhaul life will determine the total cost of overhauls, the required number of engines to be held as spares and the revenue-earning utilisation of the aircraft.

Eltis and Morley (1964) showed that engine design and efficiency can directly influence 40 per cent of the direct operating costs. Clearly since engine design, including weight, drag and fuel consumption in all stages of flight and on the ground also affects indirectly many factors in the aircraft specification, the overall influence of the engine is even greater than the above figure indicates. With turbo-fan engines on aircraft of the BAC 111, DC 9 and F 28 types, the authors indicated that a 5 per cent improvement in engine specific fuel consumption would result in a 1·1 to 2·4 per cent reduction in direct operating cost for a given engine size depending on whether the improvement was achieved in an aircraft of a fixed design (1·1 per cent) or in a new project on the drawing board (2·4 per cent). If the engine size could also have been reduced to match the saving in thrust required, a further improvement was possible in economy. This was estimated to give an overall saving of 2·8 per cent in direct operating cost.

Development of the Fan Jet engine through the last decade has been remarkable and no immediate pause in the rate of progress is in sight. For the large subsonic transport engine, estimates of direct aircraft operating costs show a reduction per mile of 25–28 per cent between the first generation of low by-pass ratio turbo-fan (1960) and the third generation fan engines with high by-pass ratios operating in 1973–5 presuming constant size and levels of price. Pickerell and Sills claimed (1970) that if engines of the 1964 standard were supplied free of charge and with free spare parts supplied throughout their life, the direct operating costs of the resultant aircraft would still be 13 per cent higher than for the aircraft of the present generation using the more advanced engine. In spite of such a comparison the noise certification requirements of the 1970s demand that the new engine are some 10 db quieter.

Less dramatic advances have been made with the smaller sizes of jet engine for medium haul transports.

The contribution of the engine manufacturers to the continually improving economy of the whole spectrum of transport aircraft is not least in the area of noise, which now shares with weight, drag, cost and specific fuel consumption the concentrated attention of research and development. Jet engine R & D is considered farther in the next chapter.

The cost of transport aircraft development and production

The principal elements of cost in the development and manufacture of transport aircraft may be summarised under three headings:

Aircraft design, Test Tooling and prototype flight development up to the Certificate of Airworthiness (C of A) stage.

Development, Modification and Product support after issue of the Certificate of Airworthiness.

Unit manufacturing cost. This is a variable cost which should decrease as a function of time and of the scale of production.

It may be assumed in general terms that the first item above is the launching cost, although the educational costs, which may overload the costs of early manufacture, are sometimes considered as part of launching costs. The launching costs may be spread over the whole production or sales quantity and hence become a dominant cost factor in small production runs. It has often been noted that launching costs as a proportion of the cost of the product itself for specified types of aircraft are higher in the USA than they are in Europe. This is probably because the anticipated market is greater and the decision to proceed is made only after this larger market is assured by firm undertakings and/or adequate market research, and also because of the heavy cost of high-grade research and design staff employed on the scale believed to be essential in US industry.

Figures have been published in the USA reporting that the non-recurring cost of design, development, tooling and launching of the Lockheed 141 type was approximately £60m. The equivalent figure for the Boeing 727 has been quoted as £30m. These launching costs for transports covering a wide range of specification and unit cost, represent about twenty times the first cost of the product. Launching costs for the Hawker Siddeley Trident and Sud Caravelle are about two thirds of the above figures in relation to the unit costs of the aircraft.

The realistic estimate of launching costs for a new project with its own special characteristics of design, manufacturing requirements and developmental lineage can only be undertaken by the engineering and planning departments of the manufacturing organisation concerned. The scale and rate of planned production, the record of previous products of comparable complexity and the experience with advanced modern manufacturing techniques together with the 'bought out' equipment required will be principal factors in determining the cost.

The control of cost is a problem of the first magnitude, and loss of control of the launching cost had been the ruin of many fine designs of transport aircraft.

The control of cost starts with control of the timing of the programme, for a programme on schedule is a programme whose planning was sound. Delay lies at the origin of most of the growth in costs of a production programme. In the control of design and development, it is found that the following items must be carefully watched.

1. Aircraft design, test and tooling

The minimum use of special materials and processes, especially those for which difficult test procedures are required.

Control of the list of materials available to designers and provision of criteria for the assessment of the value of weight saving.

Use of the value engineering approach to design for production. Control of the cost and specification of bought-out equipment and establishment at an early date of a complete and realistic specification.

Designs for simplicity with a close understanding of the operational conditions likely to be encountered and the incorporation where possible of proven components with a long-established record of reliability. The design of tooling should relate to market expectations.

Establish the test programme in relation to other experimental work at the National Research Establishments, and integrate with other tests, structural, aerodynamic, as well as systems, so as to achieve the maximum coverage at minimum cost. Especially avoid semi-developed components during the flight-test stage.

2. Development, modification and products support after C of A

The development programme should be exactly followed. Time lost will add proportionally to the cost.

Modifications must be strictly controlled. They also add to the learning costs. The desire to reduce learning costs often conflicts with technical merit.

Full consideration might also be given to the commercial

advantage of selling some prototypes of high-cost transport aircraft. Such aircraft types however require long-term development for which the flight test prototypes are always essential.

3. Unit manufacturing cost

It is essential to maintain first-class liaison between the design department and production at all stages of a project. Clear objectives and standard layouts with the minimum of special requirements will always ease the production run.

Critical path analysis should be considered when planning for production which must be dislocated to the minimum extent.

Airworthiness and its influence on cost

Mr Walter Tye had defined airworthiness as that quality by which an aircraft makes its contribution to safety of flight. He thought that this made it dependent also on a number of other qualities such as controllability, stability, performance, structural strength and stiffness, reliability of moving parts, adequacy and accuracy of instruments and so on. He also included the ability to offer protection to the occupants of an aircraft in a crash (1956).

Now airworthiness is not an absolute level of safety below which the contrary state may be said to exist. Nor is it possible to reach, by a rational determination, anything more than a relative level of adequacy for the qualities given above. Overall safety in the air must in general be gauged in relation to safety in other human activity. Clearly the level of safety will be likely to depend to a great extent upon the effort expended by Government and operator and the economics of the matter quickly appear as an important determining factor. In short the rapid approach towards a condition of very nearly absolute safety, or let us say, a ten-fold improvement in the overall statistical record, might require a public investment in research and development together with an increase in the costs of operation which the taxpayer and the air travelling sector of the population might not be prepared to accept.

Estimates have been made of the economic gain to be achieved by designing to lower levels of safety thereby reducing the cost of the aircraft and the provision of service, and while not negligible it is clear that the loss of goodwill from the public and industrial user, as well as the very steep rise in insurance costs, would be such as to force the standards of safety to a level very close to those achieved today. Insurance and the cost of maintaining the service, will tend to fall with increase in safety and reliability. Only the cost of development of the equipment and the maintenance of higher safety standards will rise. A total cost curve plotted against the level of reliability of critical components shows that minimum costs may be achieved at a level of safety and reliability which is rather greater than that at present achieved. Calculations have indicated that this increase would be small and probably less than a five-fold reduction in risk.

It is in the balance of operational realism and air safety that the airworthiness requirements have achieved a notable advance in the last fifteen years. For example, in establishing the levels of flight performance under various adverse conditions so that these do not inflict an economic burden on efficient operations, and yet do not give rise to an untoward number of incidents due to a deficiency of performance, the airworthiness authorities in Europe and USA have been highly successful.

Value engineering

This technique of engineering management is an economic discipline for relating the cost of design, manufacture and operation to the purpose and objective of the product.

The first stage is to assess as precisely as possible the function which the item is required to fulfil. It may be necessary very often to do this in great detail since a number of subfunctions may be identified. Some may be rejected for various reasons or alternative means of execution found. It is a basic feature of this approach that a money value should be assigned to the function, and that design and production or any other action involved should be provided for a cost which is related to the final output of the function.

Value engineering underlines the significance of cost and aims to identify promptly and efficiently any redundancy or any unnecessarily complex approach to the problem. It is claimed that the discipline contained in value engineering must be learnt and is not completely incorporated in other disciplines such as economics, operational research, organisation and methods and cost accountancy, although it may touch them at many points.

Originating with the work of Value Analysis Inc., of New York, the use of value engineering has been required by the UK Ministry of Defence in major aircraft development contracts. As a general concept it has in fact been applied in airline project departments for more than a decade.

Special requirements for the US market

Where a product is judged to be suitable for the US market, it is a first task to investigate the advisability and possibility of seeking design, development, manufacturing or sales agreements with a suitable US manufacturing organisation. For this purpose we must first of all know very intimately the market and the customer. Clearly, if a product is already available it will be fully appreciated at an early stage whether it closely meets the needs and whether only nominal modifications may be required to satisfy the market. However, the preliminary market research studies should have established the requirement in detail, and only if the requirement is highly variable should the reactions of the customer be in doubt. Unfortunately, it is rare for the requirements of a large number of airline customers to be standard to any great extent. This is where a close understanding of the customer's business is essential. This can be based on an intelligence service or a constant flow of debriefing sessions from the manufacturer's representatives and specialists in the design and operational field, or best of all a compound from both these sources. The operational development unit of a major manufacturer should keep well-documented dossiers, continuously updated from all sources, on the personnel, operations, route applications and new permits, aircraft introduction and problem status as well as the financial position of the world's major carriers, 60 per cent of which are in the USA and Canada.

Close contact with the potential US customer on his home ground and in conference is essential if only to keep abreast of the air transport situation in the earliest forcing ground which still lies in North America. The importance of carefully assessing the best US equipment for installation in the product to be marketed in the USA is perhaps obvious, but if this is what the customer wants and if he represents 50 or 60 per cent of the world market it may be justifiable to adopt such equipment in all production. Compatibility of equipment is of crucial importance to all operators. This applies to flight equipment and systems as well as to ground equipment. The fullest possible knowledge of the inventory of all equipment in use is desirable for optimum decisions and type selection.

It has often been suggested that the airline departments and personnel should be marked by the manufacturers like the players on the football field. This is a game played by both sides, and the airline project manager should be no less anxious that his senior professional engineers and operations staff should be in step with the rapid movement on the manufacturing side of the field whose designers, research workers, market analysts and operations engineers are at pains not so much to sell another aircraft but to develop their ideas, their new projects and their current products into the most useful form. The motto for both sides of the aviation business must be 'know your opposite number' and the outcome will be almost totally good.

In view of probable financial pressure on US airlines to buy American, even the attainment of a technical lead will not, on its own, ensure the success of a new project in the US market in the face of competition from domestic manufacturers. The recent history of European products in this market suggests that a future project would find success in the United States only if its technical lead were matched by the prospect of delivery at least two years in advance of an American product. As there is an inherent risk of delay in the development and production of a technically advanced aircraft, marketing in the US is likely to remain hazardous.

In recent years the high design and development cost of

increasingly complex aircraft has increased the cost advantage of the long production run. As this trend is likely to continue, the large domestic market may well prove to be of increasing advantage to the US manufacturer who may be able to offer aircraft for sale outside the US at prices below the cost of small-scale European production. One possible solution to the problem would be to concentrate upon specialised types of transport aircraft with market potentials of less than about 100 aircraft, including sales to foreign air forces.

Market sharing agreements

For projects with larger market potentials there seems to be a strong case for negotiating market sharing agreements with a US manufacturer. This would need to be done at a very early stage when a major technical lead could be clearly established. In such an arrangement the American company might obtain the licence to build a project in return for some contribution to Research and Development costs and for an agreement dividing the remaining world market into areas.

If neither of these courses is followed, and an attempt is made to market an aircraft with a large potential demand in direct competition with US manufacturers, risks will be high unless the capability for rapid development and production were adequate to maintain the initial technical lead over the USA for a further two to three years.

Development time

The elapsed time between the production go-ahead decision and the first commercial flight is generally shorter in the United States than in Europe. In spite of this the Argosy and the Viscount 700 development times of little more than fifty months are amongst the shortest on either side of the Atlantic, whilst the Boeing 707 development time of seventy-eight months is amongst the longest. It is notable that the DC 8 and the Electra, which started off so well, each had a long period of flight development subsequent to first airline service in order to correct substantial engineering faults.

It should be emphasised that the Viscount, which is the only British aircraft to break into the US civil transport market through achieving a substantial technical advance, did also achieve a notably short development time. The Britannia also appeared to have achieved a comparable technical lead over rival American products at the time of the north-east airlines negotiations in 1956–7, but in this case the problems in power plant development seriously damaged its initial market success.

Production cost

Though it is popularly supposed that long production runs of large aircraft are produced at lower cost in the United States than in Europe, there is no reason to conclude that if both industries tool for a similar run of over 100 aircraft there is any substantial difference in costs. There is, indeed, every reason to believe that for the production of runs of less than 100, costs in Europe are substantially lower than those in the United States. The real advantage to the USA arises from the considerably greater production runs that have been possible with the associated economies made possible.

It has been inferred that European production methods are inefficient because the British and French industries use more man hours than the US industry to produce a given weight of aircraft. Such a conclusion is not necessarily justified: as the cost of labour in US industry is very much greater than in the UK and as interest rates have for several years been lower, it is only to be expected that the ratio in which capital and labour are used should be greater in the US than in the UK. Studies to assess the optimum relationship between the use of capital and labour might be well justified by the European manufacturing groups. It is, moreover, very significant that research design and development costs appear now to be increasing at a faster rate than production costs. The advantage of long production runs is therefore continually increasing and final decisions on the few key projects are more than ever crucially dependent on good marketing analysis.

The Elstub Committee

Following recommendations of the Plowden Committee which had enquired into the UK Aircraft Industry 1964–5 (Cmnd 2853), a Committee under St John Elstub reported in 1969 on the productivity of the national aircraft effort especially in relation to that of other countries.

Associated Industrial Consultants Ltd were employed to make a survey of the productive effort required in the various stages of design, development and production of seventeen British airframes and engines, the data to be so far as possible comparable to that prepared by the Rand Corporation in an earlier research study of the US aircraft industry. This study had compared the Boeing 707 and the VC 10, had shown the latter aircraft to have needed 9 per cent fewer design man-hours and 41 per cent fewer tooling hours, but in manufacturing man-hours the VC 10 was 41 per cent higher per unit of weight.

The British consultants, however, found that in the design, tooling and manufacture of airframes, direct man-hours in the United Kingdom are respectively 14 per cent, 43 per cent and 25 per cent greater than the results that would be predicted on the basis of the American records and current practice. Thus the Elstub Committee concluded that when taking full account of the shorter production runs encountered in European industry, the overall advantage to US in the value added per man may reach a ratio of 3 to 1. It is because of this that Britain loses all of the advantage inherent in low wage-scales, but it is in no way differently placed than the French aircraft industry which faces similar problems.

The Committee found that in the design, development and manufacture of turbine engines the US and UK industries were comparable, it being concluded that this might be due to engine components being built in much larger numbers than the airframes which they matched and that the advantage of UK wages and salaries might then balance out the US advantage of larger orders.

Such industry-wide comparisons have some validity and may provide guide-lines for action in a broad field of decision, but should not be applied without caution to an individual project. The lesson of the Rolls-Royce RB 211, for which the cost of development including research into new materials and their applied engineering were to escalate and test management beyond its immediate resources, is one not to be forgotten in any industry.

The US market for a new project

In this section we will consider in some detail the type of analysis which would be undertaken if it were necessary to study the marketability of a new type of medium-haul jet aircraft of a size suitable for international scheduled operators and also for the US trunk carriers. A hypothetical type of second-generation jet has been assumed and to provide guidelines for the study, a general specification has been suggested below:

A second-generation compact jet

Payload	100 passengers or 24,000 lb
Maximum take-off weight	120,000 lb
Crew	5
Design range	1000 statute miles
Take-off distance	7000 ft
Wing loading	80 lb per sq ft
Cruise speed	$M = 0.88$ at 34,000 ft

The specification of the aircraft will be precisely defined in technical and commercial publications which are too numerous for one man to carry with comfort. In summary, the following aspects of the project are prescribed:

1. The principal characteristics, dimensions, weights and loadings.

2. The performance, under various conditions of flight and in terms of weight, altitude, temperature and configuration.

3. The design criteria, principally critical weights, speeds and limiting factors.

4. The structure. Its description, materials of manufacture and design features.

5. The interior accommodation and layout.

6. The flying controls, systems control and locks. The Autopilot System.

7. The power plant and associated fuel systems. Description and functions.

8. The hydraulic and electrical systems.

9. Radio and electronics.

10. Instruments.

11. Cabin pressurisation and ground conditioning.

12. Fire protection, ice protection and oxygen systems.

13. Ground handling equipments. Its design and operation.

14. Maintenance and services. Interchangeability, accessibility, treatments and recommended practices. Equipment schedules.

15. Guarantees.

To limit the scope of this study we shall cover only the market in the US since it is there that the largest part of the demand is likely to reside. This study might be expected to show that there is a substantial requirement in the USA for a new jet aircraft of this type if certain advances can be established. Such would be a considerable improvement in the direct operating cost or in the standard of accommodation provided or perhaps in the level of airfield take-off and landing performance. The immediate market may be presumed to arise from the shorter sectors (short-haul services) of the trunk carriers where compétition is strong and where the traffic development justifies a high-class service with an aircraft of the selected size. Although the above specification indicates firm figures for size, range and performance, a very important part of such a study is likely to be not only the investigation of the demand for the vehicle, but also the sensitivity of this demand to changes in the key design parameters of which the seating capacity and design range are paramount.

It is generally agreed that the US aircraft industry can only provide aircraft at the same cost as the British industry when it can be assured of a market which is considerably greater than that available to a European manufacturer. This is because a break-even production quantity of at least one hundred and fifty or two hundred aircraft is required. The study would therefore need to discover whether a sufficiently large demand existed for an aircraft of the new type so as to make it likely for production to be warranted by a European manufacturer or for joint production to be warranted by a European manufacturer or for joint production and sales by an American/European consortium. On the other hand, the results might indicate the high likelihood of an American manufacturer entering the field. Already first-generation medium-haul aircraft are being manufactured on the West Coast and competition is strong from at least two European manufacturers. The US market probably comprises about 65 per cent of the world total and already the principal airlines likely to be in the position to meet the financial burdens involved, are orientated to jet operations on short- and medium-haul routes so that the field under discussion is intensely competitive. US local service airlines are already experienced in the operation of advanced aircraft of this type. This, therefore, is not a market dependent only upon the big league. The significance of this and the level of the risks involved in invading such a market will not be lightly discounted.

It is evident that there must be considerable marginal competition between the new project which we are here considering and the aircraft in current operation many of which will be under further active development. Competition will arise also from the larger and smaller aircraft of quite different specification which might be introduced before the new project is ready for airline service, or which might be under development at the same time. The competitive situation between the Boeing 727, the Douglas DC 9, the Hawker Siddeley Trident and the BAC 111 are illustrations of this from the mid-1960s. Cases may well arise where the larger and smaller aircraft could be operated together as has happened with the Viscount and the Friendship.

The choice of an engine is a critical matter in the marketability of any new project of this kind. The availability of the engine within the required time scale, with first-class and well-sited overhaul facilities and with an initial overhaul life requiring minimum spares holdings, are all factors of the greatest importance. In our new project, which might need to be based on an engine of a new and advanced design, this factor may be of special significance and it is possible that for the American market, an American engine would be given urgent preliminary study by a European manufacturer before finalisation of a specification.

We should study with special attention the financial position of those operators who would, on technological and operational grounds, be the most likely initial customers for this project. We would particularly consider their financial strength, their sources of capital, their recent operational and financial record, and the prospects of ready access to new sources of loan capital for a major aircraft purchasing programme. The potential market which might be established in our study would need to be weighted strongly by the probability of the necessary funds being made available to them.

The comparative operating costs must be a key factor in the market assessment and the most detailed study of the aircraft operating competitively on the route systems of the potential customers would be analysed so as to assess realistically the attractiveness of the manufacturer's proposals. The specification would be viewed in relation to the developing route pattern of the airline, its licensing position, its competition and the expected traffic development during the life span of the new project. The comparative costs per mile, per passenger mile and per ton mile would be computed. Of special importance in this stage of the study would be the competitive price, terms of sale and attractiveness to the travelling public of the product in relationship to the current aircraft in operation and the new projects most likely to be offered during the period of evolution of this aircraft by overseas and US manufacturing groups.

One approach to an airline study

The first essential task is to establish the existing traffic on the routes of the individual airlines under study. The recent trends of traffic on these routes and the relevant sector information such as the aircraft type being operated, the competitive types, the frequency of service and load factors achieved seasonally, is of the greatest significance.

Now this information is not readily available because of its commercial importance to the airlines operating in an intensively competitive business, and although the capacity and frequency provided can be computed from the published schedules, the traffic achieved is not issued as public information, except in the case of special reports, or, from time to time, in the public hearings before the Civil Aeronautics Board. Nevertheless, the most precise estimates of the traffic development by individual sectors should be made, and recent Origin-Destination figures of the key routes must be acquired if a realistic analysis of the developing traffic situation is to be carried out.

For many of the airlines under consideration it is likely that the aircraft in operation will cover a wide spectrum of sectors of short, medium and perhaps long haul. We do not need to define these here, but clearly the types of aircraft operated by the carrier will be integrated so that the overall pattern of operation is capable of achieving the maximum overall profitability. A careful study of the current situation should allow the operating and scheduling policy of the airlines to be apparent and the reasons for the existing flight planning programme to be understood.

The principal factors which determine the operational policy of the airline are dependent upon:

1. The traffic density already achieved on the routes operated and its variation through the network seasonally.

2. The competition on the various sectors and its location and distribution.

3. The rate of traffic growth and new route opportunities (e.g. licences, business and tourist trends) and the national industrial expansion envisaged.

4. The recent business success and present capital resources of the Company.

5. The traffic stimulating capacity of its existing flight equipment.

If our new aircraft project is to be given full consideration by the US airlines it is clear that it must be able to provide in a striking degree proof of its capability in strengthening the airline position in one or more of the above categories. Our own hypothetical project may need to be operated in conjunction with the well-established main-line trunk jets and it may need to be considered in a number of different configurations. The estimates of traffic growth over the period considered (probably six to ten years) is a next stage in our study. Following this the scale of operation in the life of the new project with each potential airline customer can be computed. A chart showing the development of the airline and the growth of its transport capability as a function of time may then be drawn. To find its location in this programme our new project must show its application and prove its economic potential.

The economic capability of our project will depend on several prime factors which are subject to discussion with the airlines.

The Interior Plan: Density of the seating (seat pitch and two or three abreast seats).

Variation in the catering standard (weight and space).

Flexible interior layout. (Perhaps movable partition to vary cargo/baggage space.)

Economy may also depend on a basic design variable for a project aircraft which is not yet fully specified.

Design Payload Range: Fuselage length may be flexible at this stage and extension may be feasible with increased zero fuel and/or Landing Weight Limits.

Increase Range may be available with increased Gross Weight Limits.

Alternative power plants, or engine development may provide an answer to meet airline needs in a critical case.

In the most likely configuration the new project would be integrated on an *ad hoc* basis with the other airline equipment so as to establish a probable service pattern. If the load factor is found to be unrealistically high compared with the existing practice in this class of operation, we may need either to consider reallocation of routes to introduce the main-line aircraft on some high-density sectors or the possible fuselage extension may be proposed.

Such fuselage extension may widen the application of the aircraft, but this can be assessed only after an extensive assessment of the market as a whole. As we have noted above, the costs per mile would be increased only marginally and the specific direct operating costs for a given load factor would be improved unless major design changes beyond a structural extension in the fuselage were involved. An adverse effect on landing field performance is one factor which may well follow fuselage extension to provide increased payload on short sectors. Any modification to the wing and secondary design changes to improve the situation by re-balancing landing and take-off requirements is virtually certain to be economically undesirable.

It will be apparent at an early stage in this analysis whether the airlines concerned are likely to have a need for the new project as proposed or in a slightly modified form. Is there a replacement task, taking account of the state of obsolescence of current equipment, or is it a traffic expansion programme which provides the principal stimulant to the demand? In many cases these two factors acting together will create the demand. In the final stage of our study the frequency of service necessary for the proposed sectors will be established to meet the needs of traffic promotion, and the required fleet strength can then be computed for a number of years subsequent to the introduction into service.

Future needs in undeveloped areas

For many future decades an urgent need is likely to exist for aircraft to provide the means of transport for people and goods in remote and inaccessible parts of the world. The need for transport necessitates the use of the cheapest, sometimes the only, vehicle available irrespective of its actual operating economics, its size or its performance limitations.

Since the end of the Second World War, between 800 and 1000 Douglas DC 3 and Dakota aircraft have been operated in such areas because of their immediate availability and low first cost. Even in the USA 172 were still operating with local service operators in early 1964 compared with 63 Convair 340/440 and 180 larger piston aircraft. Many attempts have been made to launch acceptable aircraft designs on these markets, but unfortunately without success since no manufacturer has been able to build to a price which these countries can afford. The market, moreover, is too restricted to offer the large scale of production necessary to spread the cost of a new development and to justify testing for a long production run. In spite of the recommendations of many observers, the needs of the under-developed areas have been poorly satisfied (Cartaino, 1962).

Some of these areas have special needs. For example, Africa has few airfields but ground is cheaply cleared since labour is freely available. Temperatures are high and terrain adverse especially in the south and east. The requirements of aircraft to meet the needs of these areas have, however, many common characteristics. Foremost of these are rugged design without the necessity for advanced maintenance facilities. Their thin traffic and low revenue yield demands low first cost and low operating costs even at moderate rates of utilisation. Also essential is a capability for take-off and climb without payload loss from high and hot airfields.

The ability to operate without complex ground support is highly desirable. On the other hand, no great priority for high cruising speeds is likely since surface competition is negligible. Pressurisation, however, is desirable because of the higher temperatures and humidity in some areas and because of the need to operate at altitudes above turbulence. Without much doubt the prop-turbine seems the most suitable power plant for this type of aircraft. As an example, we may cite the requirements for a transport aircraft to operate economically in the many low-density routes of India which are not generating adequate traffic for the HS 748 or the Fokker F 27.

Out of the million or so passengers carried in India in 1963–4, nearly a quarter were transported by Dakota aircraft on short low-traffic routes on which the passenger average was 12–13 per flight. An average sector length of rather more than 200 miles is flown and since scheduled surface competition is weak the need for a high performance aircraft is doubtful. The largest number of passengers is carried on stages between 100 and 200 miles in contrast to the peak uplift in the 700–800 mile group representing the trunk traffic between the major cities, principally Bombay–Delhi, 707 miles, and Calcutta–Delhi, 815 miles. Cargo traffic has declined in India since the mid-1950s.

A similar situation exists in many other countries such as those in South America and Africa and the Far East. A more complex problem exists than the direct replacement of the Dakota by a more advanced and economic aircraft. The model 'T' Ford was not replaced by one type of car and the classic aircraft of an earlier generation needs to be followed by a wide range of types, some of which must be aimed at the restricted markets now existing in the undeveloped areas.

BIBLIOGRAPHY

E. DEVONS, *An Introduction to British Economic Statistics*, CUP, 1961

N. A. H. STACEY and A. WILSON, *Industrial Marketing Research*, Hutchinson, 1963

EDDISON, PENNYWICK and RIVETT, *Operation Research in Management*, EUP, 1962

J. B. LANSING, *The Motivation of the Demand for Air Transport*, ITA International Symposium, Nov. 1964

BO BJORKMAN, *Methods of Research into the Elasticity of Demand for Air Transport*, ITA International Symposium, Nov. 1964

G. DESMAS, *Methods of Market Research in Air Transport*, ITA Studies, 64/11-E

R. E. CAVES, *Air Transport and its Regulators*, Harvard U.P., 1962

M. H. SMITH and H. P. SCHMIDT, *A Rational Method for Selecting Business Aircraft*, Proceedings, Society of Automotive Engineers, Jan. 1964

Statistical Handbook for Civil Aviation (Annual), FAA

Federal Airways Air Traffic Activity (Annual), FAA

Aviation Forecasts, Port of New York Authority

National Airport Plan (Annual), US FAA

R. HORONJEFF, *Planning and Design of Airports*, McGraw-Hill, 1962

P. W. CHERINGTON, *The Domestic Market for Air Transportation*, Connecticut General Life Insurance Co., July 1962

A. JIPP, 'Estimating the Volume of Traffic by a Simple Formula', *Journal UIT*, Jan. 1961

A. H. STRATFORD, 'Economics of Telecommunications Systems', *Jnl. Roy. Aero. Soc.*, June 1962

D. J. LAMBERT, *Specialized Design for the Short-Haul Jet Transport Role*, Society of Automotive Engineers, New York, April 1962

T. F. CARTAINO, *Technological Aspects of Civil Aircraft for the Less Developed Areas*, Rand Corporation, July 1962

A. A. LOMBARD, *Engine considerations for Transport Aircraft*, South African Division, Royal Aeronautical Society, Oct. 1964

E. M. ELTIS and F. W. MORLEY, *The Engines contribution to Economic Short-Haul Jet Transport*, SAE Los Angeles, Oct. 1964

W. TYE, *Philosophy of Airworthiness*, Advisory Group for R & D NATO, Aug. 1956

Magnitude and Economic Impact of General Aviation 1968–1980 (R. Dixon Speas Associates, 1970)

P. M. S. JONES, *Technological Forecasting as a Management Tool: Programmes Analysis Unit*, HMSO, 1969

D. J. PICKERELL and T. D. SILLS, 'Design and Cost Considerations for large Subsonic Transport Engines', *Proceedings Roy. Aero. Soc.*, May 1970

PETER SMITH, *Market Research Methods in Aviation*, ASA report 142

4 The Development of Jet Transportation

Decade of the Jet engine

The development of Air Transport since the early 1960s has been dominated by the jet engine which allowed the aircraft designer to offer to the air carriers both increased performance and greater vehicle size. After a period of continuous engine development with increasing by-pass ratios, operating temperatures and improving specific fuel consumption, the aircraft provided exceptional operating economy. Nor were the US aircraft designers prepared to compromise the economy of aircraft such as the Boeing 707 and Douglas DC 8 by limiting their wing design and engine thrust to suit the shorter runways then available.

We have considered in Chapter 1 how the jet transport was a natural outcome from the pattern of civil aviation growth as it had unfolded from early years, and in Chapter 2 how the 4-jet formula, and later the 2- and 3-jet formulae met the key criteria for economic transport services. In this chapter we shall consider the development of the jet transport over the period 1960–70 and consider the factors critical to its recent development, and significant to its evolution in the present decade.

Gas turbine development

The extrapolation of size, essential to meet the continuing traffic growth of the late 1950s and desirable in the interests of improving specific direct operating costs, was well nigh impossible with the piston engine which was by that date already requiring double contra-rotating propellers and had reached the practical limits of development in the larger sizes. Propeller-turbines were already posing similar problems in power transmission, nor were solutions to be found in compound designs such as D. Napier & Son evolved in the UK (1945–50), even though able to achieve a remarkably low fuel consumption, since they inherited similar problems in growth and transmission efficiency. Development of the axial flow and centrifugal type gas turbine engines in the post-World War 2 period led to a series of prop-turbine engines, especially in the UK, where the most active work on the gas turbine had been carried out during the War following the pioneer work of Whittle at Lutterworth and Constant at Farnborough. The most successful of these developments was undoubtedly the work at Rolls-Royce, Barnoldswick, where the Dart engine with a centrifugal compressor and a basically simple 2-stage turbine was actively developed through the 1950s and 1960s as the engine for the Viscount 700 and 800 series, the Fokker Friendship, Handley Page Herald, Avro 748 and AWA Argosy aircraft. A parallel prop-turbine engine of more limited success was the Proteus developed by the Bristol Engine Co. and later by Rolls-Royce. Avon, Conway and Spey jet engine developments at Rolls-Royce progressively offered the aircraft designer increasing thrust at decreasing unit weight for a specific fuel consumption which is rapidly approaching the levels finally achieved by the piston

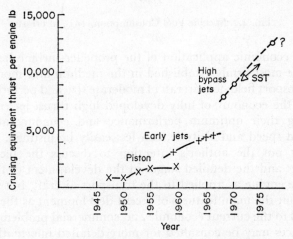

FIG. 4.1. Cruising Thrusts, 1945 to present

engine in its full maturity. Figs. 4.1 and 4.2 show the principal features of these developments which have generated the high capability and economy essential to the jet transport aeroplane.

In the most recent development stage there have been created several families of high by-pass engines to meet the special needs of the civil airline industry which have provided even yet more remarkable results in low fuel consumption combined with the lower noise level in the airport environment which has now become a key criterion.

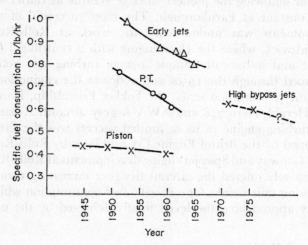

FIG. 4.2. Specific Fuel Consumption, 1945 to present

The economic application of the propeller-turbine has now become most firmly established in the medium and short haul air transport field, for aircraft of moderate size and performance where the economy of fully developed high thrust jet engines, offering their optimum performance and economy at high forward speed and altitude, can less easily be justified.

It is not the author's intention to discuss the technical features and the detailed stages in the development of the gas turbine engine as applied to the transport aircraft, but rather to set out the main features of recent development as the background to the current economic and commercial problems. The references may be consulted for more detailed information.

The introduction of jet aircraft into airline fleets increasingly

dominated the air carrier capacity through the 1960s and Fig.
4.3 shows the changing picture from 1960–70. The fan jet
engine which introduced the improved fuel economy and reduced take-off and landing noise characteristics of the high
by-pass engine gradually modified the position so that by 1968
a major part of the jet fleets were engined by the improved
equipment of the second generation.

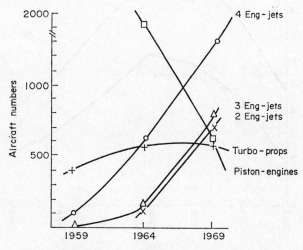

Fig. 4.3. World Airline Fleets by Engine Types, 1959 to present (IATA)

The acquisition of jet aircraft during the 1960s by the world's
airlines was a remarkable revolution in transport, carried
through with much heart-searching. The competitive need to
acquire up-graded fleet equipment spurred many an operator
with limited resources to extend his credit to bursting point,
and traffic growth, as in the years 1960/61, was unable to keep
up with increased capacity, thus causing widespread anxiety.
Intensive marketing, and the promotion of economy class fares
and international tourism, succeeded in encouraging the required rates of growth, and load factors which had taken an
unnerving dip in the early 1960s rose again. Fig. 4.4 shows the
markedly improved situation of the IATA carriers in the mid
1960s. By that time the large four engine jet transport, especially

the Boeing 707 and the Douglas DC 8, had become the greatest money spinners in the history of air transport, having achieved intensive use with operators both large and small in most countries of the world.

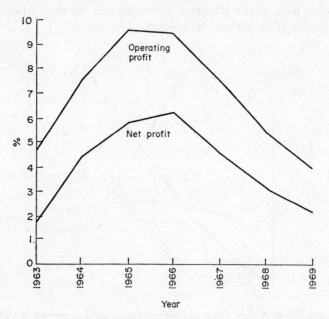

FIG. 4.4. World Airlines' Operating Profit and Net Profit (as % of Revenue), 1963–9 (IATA)

The short-haul jets

The medium and short-haul jet transport has had a record of development almost as long as the four engined jets. Preliminary studies of the twin jets in the UK and in France preceded those in the USA, and the Caravelle (Sud Aviation) and the BAC 111 found a market in many parts of the world (including the USA itself). Several years elapsed before McDonnell-Douglas and Boeing took active steps to meet the world potential for the short-haul jet. We have already considered in Chapter 3 aspects of market research which are related especially to the short-haul transport. In this chapter we shall concentrate largely on the medium and long-haul market which has raised the greatest problems to the aircraft industry and operators alike.

The medium-range tri-jets

To meet the increasing specialisation of the air transport market in regard to sector length, traffic scale, and growth, the three-engine jet was developed in the early 1960s. The first of these to fly was the Hawker-Siddeley (originally De Havilland) Trident which was rapidly followed by the Boeing 727. A comparison of these aircraft may not be out of place since the remarkable success of Boeing in overtaking the Trident in production orders has been widely discussed. The reasons for this may be analysed in a manner which reflects the deliberation of airline management in many hard-fought arguments in the late 1960s.

The payload and range of these earlier and small tri-jets (not to be confused with the Lockheed L 1011 and McDonnell-Douglas DC 10 tri-jets) is shown graphically in Fig. 4.5 where their relationship to other aircraft in the medium haul jet transport field may be seen. A more detailed comparison is shown in Table 4.1 where the key parameters may be noted. Available at an earlier date than the Boeing 727 and with many superficial resemblances, the Trident has eventually been developed in the two marks 2 E and 3 B although BEA originally took delivery of the Trident 1, a smaller capacity and shorter range aeroplane. The Boeing 727/200 as subsequently developed has provided an increase in payload which has made it one of the most formidable jet transports of two decades. To compare aircraft with similar characteristics is always difficult. When one type has rather a greater capacity more nearly matched to a growing international market and has the backing of the world's largest and most successful air transport design and development team, an airline management may be tempted to discard the detailed engineering assessments and to make selection on the most rudimentary criteria subject only to the terms of sale.

That the frequency of service could be increased with a smaller aircraft and that such a fleet might more precisely match the demands of many traffic patterns was clearly a great asset in favour of the Trident, but it became clear to an increasing number of airlines that very strong individual ties to the manufacturer were required to attract them away from the formidable Boeing organisation at Renton.

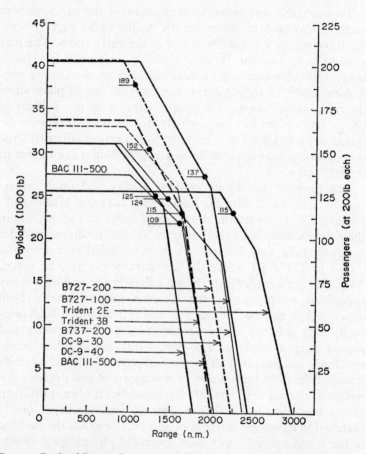

FIG. 4.5. Payload Range Comparison of Transport Aircraft on Medium Haul Assuming (*a*) Economy layouts: 30-in. pitch. (*b*) Fuel reserves: 100 n.m. diversion and 45-min. hold. (*c*) Long-range cruise technique. (*d*) Still air, ISA, 30,000-ft altitude. (*e*) Passenger weight 200 lb.

Meanwhile a powerful incursion into the market for the medium-haul tri-jets such as Trident and 727 had been achieved by developments in the short-haul field. Notably the introduction of the DC 9–50 presented a challenge because of its extended payload/range envelope and its lower first cost and remarkable d.o.c. record.

From the other extreme, the down-graded early mark 4-engine jets such as the Boeing 720 and early 707 series have been

TABLE 4.1. *Comparison of Trident and Boeing 727*

		Hawker Siddeley Trident		Boeing 727	
Aircraft Model		2E	3B	100	200
Length Overall	ft	115	131	133	153
Wing Span	ft	98	98	108	108
Wing Area	sq. ft	1,461	1,493	1,700	1,700
Engines 3x		RR Spey RB163-25	RR Spey* RB163-25	P & W JT8D-7	P & W JT8D-7
Thrust/Engine	(lb)	11,930	11,930	14,000	14,000
Weights					
Maximum TO	lb	143,500	150,000	142,000	172,000
Landing	lb	113,000	128,000	135,000	150,000
Zerofuel	lb	100,000	115,500	111,000	136,000
Fuel Capacity (Imperial Galls)		6,400	5,620	5,974	5,974
Maximum Passengers		100–115	140–152	125–137	160–189
Cruise Speed	(kts)	518	523	525	517
Range with reserves (max. payload)	(nm)	2,200– 2,400	1,200– 1,300	1,900– 2,000	1,400– 1,500
Take-Off distance to 35 ft	(ft)	8,500	7,500	7,450	8,000
Landing from 35 ft	(ft)	5,250	5,920	4,700	5,100

* With RR RB162–86 Boost Engine 5,250 lb thrust.

appearing on the used aircraft market, offering at a very low first cost many of the characteristics provided by the tri-jets. In the author's assessment of the potential market for jet transports which is presented later in this chapter the tri-jets are not thought to require individual replacement in the late 1970s other than by twin jets and wide-body aircraft of larger capacity.

Introduction of super jets

As traffic developed on the world's major trunk routes it became apparent to the large air carriers that aircraft larger than the Boeing 707 and Douglas DC 8 would be required in the 1970s. The steady growth in commercial air traffic through the 1960s has made this apparent also to the aircraft manu-facturers who had for some years been assessing the feasibility of military freighters in the 400,000 to 600,000 lb, gross weight bracket. This eventually led to the Lockheed L 500, a civil freighter version of the C 5 Galaxy military cargo aircraft, and hence in the passenger transport market to a series of important aircraft which are expected to dominate the world's trunk air routes through the 1970s. Their principal characteristics are summarised in Table 4.2 below which includes also the Concorde (Pre-production model) and the Boeing 707/300. On the key long-haul trunk routes such as New York–London, and Chicago–Los Angeles, frequency had already reached such a level that a doubling or even trebling of size posed few ap-parent economic problems. The economics of size still holds out hope for further gains, and new technological advances through the period 1958–66 offered important potential advantages to the operators. Most serious of all problems was recognised to be the immense resources required by airframe and engine manufacturers to launch the projects and to cover, hopefully with government aid, the R & D necessary. Perhaps no less serious were to be the difficulties presented to the air-lines in the raising of finance to meet the costs of purchase and of provision of associated facilities no less than the cash flow required in the phases of introduction and initial opera-tions.

TABLE 4.2. *Main Characteristics of the Wide-Body Jets*

		B747B	DC 10 Srs 20	L 1011	A300B	Concorde	B 707/ 300
Length (*L*)	ft	229	182	176	167	204	153
Span (*S*)	ft	196	161	155	147	84	146
Wheel Base	ft	84	73	70	58	60	59
Wheel Track	ft	36	35	36	31	25	22
Minimum Radius of Turn	ft	151	123	121	103	127	116
Floor Height	ft	16	16	15	16	15	10
Max. Payload	(1,000 lb)	143	102	84	74	31	46
Max. Pax.		490	345	330	259	144	189
Gross Wt	(1,000 lb)	775	548	426	291	385	334
Max. Pax./ $L \times S$/1,000 sq ft		10·9	11·9	12·2	10·8	8·5	8·6

Differentiation of the super-jet market

Market research had established that several distinct markets would persist for the developing jet transports, and that to attempt to meet the full demand with too few individual types would be unrealistic. In Chapter 3 we have considered the broad delineation of the long, medium and short-haul markets and their differing requirements for aircraft capacity. In the new generation of super jets it was also recognised that similar differentiation would exist. The Boeing Company, well established in the long-haul inter-continental and US domestic trunk market, had assessed the growth pattern and investment potential as adequate to support a very considerable increase in passenger and freight capacity. McDonnell–Douglas and Lockheed, as well as the British Aircraft Corporation who eventually were unable to find the financial backing required, were convinced that their position was better secured by designing for the medium-haul market where they believed a larger potential demand would emerge through the 1970s. The European Air Bus Consortium sought a less obviously competitive market in the medium-haul project which was well within the joint resources of the countries concerned (France, Germany and Holland).

Critical super-jet layout characteristics

The most fundamental decision in any commercial aircraft design is that concerned with the principal fuselage cross-sectional parameters. A breakaway from the dimensions of the Boeing 707 and Douglas DC 8 fuselage was clearly essential although many alternative arrangements could be envisaged. Double-bubble cross-sections with two passenger decks, were considered, as well as passenger and freight decks, and wide fuselage arrangements in many permutations and combinations. The fuselage cross-section is critical to the operator since it limits his seating arrangements in First and Economy class and is keyed to seat and gangway width; it is also crucial for the manufacturers for it is a virtually unchangeable parameter unlike fuselage length, wing span, seat pitch and engine thrust. Other critical factors in design which bear upon airport operating flexibility are considered in more detail in Chapter 10.

The lesser flexibility of the larger aircraft is a factor which has given anxiety to many operators. Nor is it only the small operator who is thus concerned, for the major carrier may also have critical low-load sectors, especially on long inter-continental routes, and the economic advantage of the wide-body jet on the key trunk sectors may be eroded on thinner sectors which call for no more than 100–50 seat capacity. Indeed two airport authorities in South East Asia have expressed to the author fears that 'Jumbo Jets' may encourage the leap-frogging of all but the key traffic points to avoid the costs of low-load sectors. Since this will encourage feeder air services, increased air movements at major airports will ensue, and increased end-to-end costs for many air journeys may result.

Typical of the need to elucidate such problems was a study carried out by the author when it was required to assess and select the jet fleet which offered the best cost-effectiveness on a system of routes in South East Asia under development for tourist promotion.

A study of air transport demand in South East Asia

This study brought out the remarkable variation in air traffic development in one relatively compact world region. The scale of future demand was established from an extrapolation of the trend pattern of the growth of tourism from those principal areas from which tourists had originated over the preceding five years. This showed that Japanese, US, Australian and West European visitors were the predominant groups, and their record of travel through the region had increased over the period as a simple function of their respective gross national product *per capita*. This provided the basis for a traffic demand pattern, modified albeit by the competition, which justified 4-jet transports with 150–80 seat capacity in the period 1973–5 but clearly made Super-jet operation uneconomic on several grounds.

Comparative calculations showed that an initial fleet of two aircraft in used condition but with an effective operating life of 20,000 hours and with ducted-fan engines of recent mark, offered the most favourable economic solution. The new generation of wide-fuselage jets, in this case the McDonnell–Douglas DC 10 and the Lockheed 1011, were clearly of greater operating economy if the traffic could be generated at an equal level on all sectors and with some uniformity throughout the year, because of the significantly lower direct operating cost index with these larger aircraft. But the wider practical operating problems were to prove the dominant issue.

The ultra short-haul jet

No reference has been made as yet to the jet aeroplane on very short routes, and with smaller capacity than those exemplified by twin-engine jets such as the DC 9, B 737 and BAC 111. In effect an economic case has not yet been made out for the jet transport of less than 60 seat capacity operating on stages of less than 200 miles. Projects have been put forward and some individual airlines have indicated keen interest but a market of adequate size to justify investment by the manufacturing industry has not as yet been established. Meanwhile

Viscount (of later production), Friendship and Avro 748 still operate with considerable success and economy and it may well be that we must wait until the mid 1970s before the need is urgent enough and sufficiently widespread for the small jet to be a financial proposition. The inherent disadvantages attached to the small jet are easily recognised. First cost and operating costs are high, and the essential ingredients of good airline economy are notably lacking in the typical operations of the small airline operator. These are adequate revenue yields, high and reasonably uniform load factors, seasonally and through the day, and a high potential utilisation through the year. The relative freedom of the lower cost prop-turbine aircraft from the necessity to achieve high utilisation in order to depreciate the fixed operating cost elements is the main obstacle to replacement by the small jet transport. Field performance and noise in the airport environment are secondary factors which are well on the way to improvement in the current generation of jet-engined transports of all types; but these have, to date, been unfavourable in comparison with propeller driven aircraft. It should be added moreover that the extra comfort and freedom from vibration of the jet aeroplane is a bonus less essential to the passenger on very short flights, on which moreover the value of jet speed is difficult to realise in practice on scheduled operations.

More successful have been the efforts of the manufacturers to build and sell the executive jet transport to wealthy corporations and businesses in all parts of the world. A small demand in the charter fleets has also been found. While the economic principles apply no less in this case than in any other, the weighting of the factors is entirely different. We indicated in Chapter 3 that the business house will base its decision and priorities on a set of criteria different from those of the airline. In essentials the use of the business jet depends on the saving of time – that of executives and of most grades of labour for the business itself, and also for the potential customers; this is at the root of the demand for this relatively hign cost transport. Table 4.3 summarises the aircraft in the executive jet fleets in 1970/71. The principal characteristics of the US and European types are shown. Some decline in sales was apparent in 1970/71 in common with other executive aircraft, but the industry specialising in this field is anticipating an expansion in all fields through the 1970s.

TABLE 4.3. *Executive Jet Aircraft 1971*

Manufacturer/ Name	No. and type of engine	Max. TO weight (lb)	Max. Cruise speed (kts)	Range (nm)	No. of seats
Grumman Gulfstream II	2 × RR Spey 511–8	57,500	491	3,000	19
Lockheed Jetstar	4 × P & W JT 12A-8	42,000	495	1,840	10
Dassault Fan jet Falcon D	2 × GE CF 700–2D	27,335	465	1,910	8–14
HS 125 400	2 × RR Viper 522	23,300	443	1,530	6–12
IAT Commodore Jet 1123	2 × GE CJ 610–9	20,500	470	1,259	10
MBB HFB 320 Hansa	2 × GE CJ 610–9	20,280	446	1,278	7–12
North American Rockwell Sabreliner 60	2 × P & W JT 12A-8	20,000	489	1,736	10
Dassault Falcon 10	2 × AiResearch TFE 731–2	16,135	486	1,820	4–7
Gates Learjet 25C	2 × GE CJ 610–6	15,000	473	1,759	8
Gates Learjet 24D	2 × GE CJ 610–6	13,500	464	1,702	6
Cessna Citation	2 × P & W JT 15D–1	10,350	347	1,213	5–6

The economic trend in air transport

The foregoing indicates the hierarchy of jet transport vehicles which are now available or are under development for commercial operation through the 1970s. Their success in exploitation will depend on the enlightened management of manufacturers and operators alike, and on their ability to assess the fine balance of the economic forces affecting air transport, and to foresee their changing direction.

Serious economic difficulties are currently challenging the scale and growth assumptions of the airline industry and it seems important to identify the principal causes of these.

In the years 1965–9 the profitability of the air transport industry as represented by the members of IATA has taken on a progressively unfavourable look. This was illustrated in Fig. 4.4 which showed how the operating profit and estimated net profit turned down in the last half of the decade. When the total of all non-operating items such as the interest payments, taxes and subsidies are included the resulting net profit in 1969 fell to 2·1 per cent of revenues. In the last years of the decade a decline of about 1 per cent per annum in the net yield was aggravated by an increase of about 0·5 per cent in direct operating costs, thus creating a squeeze which has not been alleviated by the immense investment programme already in progress or contemplated by all the major carriers for their fleet re-equipment. In the USA the position was particularly serious and the 12 major scheduled airlines as a whole registered losses in 1969 and 1970 in spite of reduced employment and scheduled capacity, and the exercise of a strict control of costs.

It seems clear that the dominant factor was the incipient recession in the USA which still generates a high percentage of the originating air passengers in most parts of the world.

The shape of the changing demand for air transport

We have already indicated in Chapter 1 that tourism has become a major factor in the growth of air transport. Defining tourism in accordance with IUOTO who consider it to include any person travelling for a period of twenty-four hours or more in a country other than that in which he usually resides, we find that over the past five years tourism has provided the principal sources of air transport growth. Our difficulty here is that the definition includes traffic with many different travel incentives (including business) and this presents problems in the analysis. Clearly to the airline operator the length of the stay at each point is of less significance than the transport itself, but the purpose of the journey may dictate the fare that will be paid, who will pay it, and the methods of promotion most likely to sell it successfully. For more than a decade it had been apparent that scheduled air services had been supported predominantly by the business community. In spite of a fairly general rise in discretionary income the private individual could, in 1970, rarely afford to pay air fares at a level exceeding 2 new pence (5 US cents) per mile.

It is for such reasons that certain air operators first looked at the possibilities of selling combined air transport and hotel accommodation as one package for the holidaymaker. This indicated a sound understanding of the nature of the traffic demand and the intent to provide for its needs. The inclusive tour, now a well-accepted and very rapidly growing sector of the air transport industry, has reached the degree of specialisation where a large number of separate airlines are catering for this one market alone. This has led to a well-marked differentiation between scheduled and non-scheduled or charter operations, the former often calling upon government support and protection, the latter being restricted in favour of the scheduled service operator. A number of major scheduled air carriers, especially in Europe had by the early 1970s set up their own I.T. subsidiaries and many others are actively pursuing the idea. Nor has it required the easy availability of down-graded transport aircraft to maintain the economic viability of I.T. operations. From beginnings in the UK with prop-turbine aircraft such as the Britannia and the Viscount, jet aircraft beginning with the Comet IV and the BAC 111 were rapidly acquired by the airlines.

Already wide-body jets are on order and the economic potential of the largest available jets holds out high prospect of the I.T. operators continuing successfully throughout this decade. Thus the most signal contribution of the large jet transport to the current airline economic situation is its matching to the requirements of the growing I.T. business. Table 4.4*

* Ref. European Charter Airlines November 1970.

TABLE 4.4. *Western European Inclusive Tours and Charters*

Country	Passengers 1969	Fleets 1970		
		4-engine Jets	Other Jets	Prop Turbines
Austria	190,000	—	5	—
Belgium	110,407	—	2	—
Finland	165,278	1	2	—
France	336,000	1	3	—
W. Germany	1,634,000	5	15	—
Italy	360,000	4	—	—
Holland	620,000	4	7	—
Scandinavia	1,863,616	3	20	3
Spain	1,675,726	7	7	4
Switzerland	242,000	1	—	3
United Kingdom	4,380,613	12	36	36
Yugoslavia	204,725	—	2	—
Total	11,882,365	31	99	46

shows the European Independent Airline Charter Fleets at the beginning of 1970 for the 12 principal Western European States. The leadership of the UK, Scandinavia, Spain and Western Germany is there shown. The UK alone generated 39 per cent of the total I.T. and charter business in 1969, and no less than the other European countries will become increasingly dependent upon US equipment for its I.T. operations through the 1970s. Pugh has estimated that British carriers handled 40 per cent of the North Atlantic charter traffic in 1970 compared with 37 per cent in 1966. A report published by McDonnell–Douglas in 1970 gave a forecast of non-scheduled intra-European air passenger traffic in 1979 as 56 billion. This would represent a mean annual growth of 12 per cent over the 10 years from 1969. This is to be compared with our own forecast annual growth of 8·5 per cent for the European scheduled air traffic, and indicates one interpretation of the current growth trends in the charter (including the I.T.) side of air transport. But we must note that inter-continental Inclusive Tours are only as yet beginning their likely upward swing, and the potential here for transatlantic as well as European–Middle

East and Far East tours is not less bright. For such we would expect the long-haul wide-body jets to be ideally suited both in specification (payload and range) and in operating economy.

The inclusive tour charter business

The three basic forms of charter operation must first of all be recognised. These are Inclusive Tour Charters, Affinity Group Charters and Private (including single entity) Charters. The last of these may of course be applied as much to cargo as to passenger operations, and very small as well as large transport aircraft types may be employed. The Affinity Group, which has been discouraged by some States, allows bona-fide members of one group or association to charter an aircraft for an individual return flight to an overseas destination. Though widely practised especially on the North Atlantic this method of whole-plane charter is much abused and requires strict control by the government allowing it.

The basis of the inclusive tour on the other hand is the provision of a 'packaged' holiday, usually for a 7 or 14 days, period, at an 'all-in' rate to include travel, hotel and gratuities which is considerably below the total cost of scheduled airline excursion fares and equivalent hotel charges. The remarkable difference in the fare levels generally causes surprise, but this can be reasily understood when the principal characteristics of scheduled and non-scheduled services are compared.

TABLE 4.5. *Comparative Factors in Scheduled and Non-Scheduled Operations*

	Scheduled	Non-scheduled
Aircraft types	Becoming very comparable	
Direct costs/seat mile (d.o.c.)	Very comparable	
Load factor %	50–60	85–95
Indirect costs/seat mile (d.o.c.)	1·25–1·5 × d.o.c.	0·75 × d.o.c.
Utilisation (hours per annum)	2,500–3,500	2,000–2,750
Fare restrictions (International)	IATA and Government	Government
Special fare reductions	Extensive	Negligible
Seasonal capacity control	Negligible	Complete

As Table 4.5 shows, the principal advantage to the non-scheduled operator lies in the high load factors he can achieve, arising largely through his ability to switch flights and control capacity as demand dictates, in a way not open to a licensed scheduled operator. Moreover the charter operator can call upon his passengers to accept departure times for holiday journeys and even a destination change when booking which would not be acceptable to the scheduled airline passenger whose programme is most likely to be linked to a business assignment and an uncertain return date. In this way the utilisation of the 'non-scheduled' service aircraft can be maintained well above the essential minimum level. To insure this utilisation the extension of the holiday season has been actively pursued by the I.T. operator. The most effective means of doing this has been the winter sports holiday tour in central Europe (from the UK and to a lesser extent from Scandinavia), and the 'Shoulder-Season' short tours. Typical of the latter are Easter and Whitsun Tours to Paris and Amsterdam, the bulb fields of Holland in May, fishing trips in October and 'High-Time' weekends in an increasing number of 'permissive' European capitals.

No less important to the lower rate structure of the independent air operators is the stricter control of indirect costs, including management, promotional and station costs, which has been achieved. Promotion of the holiday tour itself has been separately and very efficiently handled by the tour organiser largely through mass media, television and the national press, as well as through the High Street travel shops. The Supermarkets have already entered into the business. Thus the charter airline provides capacity as and when required and has concentrated its expertise where it can be most effective.

It is significant that the hotel trade have been able to concentrate likewise upon provision of space over a lengthening season at a high load factor and with negligible promotional cost.

To a public with a gradually increasing discretionary income and a taste for sharpened experience with clearly defined costs, the inclusive tour has offered a much needed outlet. Certain limitations are inherent which effect largely the choice of destination.

TABLE 4.6. *The Make-up of the Inclusive Holiday Price*

London–Palma	TWO WEEKS' TOUR	
Based on	Aircraft Charter	15·50
Load factor of 90%	In Flight Catering	0·50
	Hotel (13 nights)	20·00
	Transfer transport	2·00
	Commission	3·40
	Promotion	2·00
	Overheads	1·80
	Net Profit	2·00
	Cost per head	£47·20
Frankfurt–Bangkok	THREE WEEKS' TOUR	
Load factor of 85%	Aircraft Charter	80·00
	In flight service	4·00
	Hotel (19 nights)	36·00
	Transfer transport	3·50
	Commission	11·50
	Promotion	1·50
	Overheads	2·50
	Net Profit	5·00
	Cost per head	£144·00

That the remarkable reductions in costs have opened up air holidays to an ever widening public is a social factor of immense significance, for the air holiday is in the consumer market in competition with a new car, stereo, central heating or a new electric cooker. Its growth moreover is strongly susceptible to the techniques of promotion and the vitality of the national economics in many countries.

Table 4.6 shows how two typical inclusive air holiday prices were made up from the ingredients of travel costs, hotel and other expenses. It shows for comparison the content of two different categories of holiday tours, a Spanish Mediterranean Holiday from London and a South East Asian Tour from Frankfurt. An important current development is the extension of the holiday areas, for which in the first stage the trend is towards North Africa and the Eastern Mediterranean. Operation of the wide-body jets, such as the Boeing 747 by Condor, a subsidiary of Lufthansa, is a clear indication of the broadening horizons of the charter operator in the 1970s, and West Germany has already become an important starting point for inclusive tours to the key centres in South East Asia – Bangkok, Singapore, Hong Kong, Taipei, and Bali.

The restrictions imposed by many countries upon the price levels charged for inclusive tour holidays have generally been introduced to protect the nationally controlled scheduled airlines. Typical has been the Provision 1 control of the UK Government which required that the charge for the total package should not be less than the lowest applicable fare of the scheduled services for that particular route. Restrictions on the total value of currency taken abroad would of course apply to all holiday journeys. In West Germany, Austria and Switzerland no restrictions were in force in 1970/71, but restrictions in France and Italy applied principally to North Atlantic charters. In the UK overseas currency restriction may actually have encouraged the bookings for Inclusive Tour charters in the 1960s especially in the lower price categories.

The political implications of the restrictions of foreign tourism have often been discussed. Restrictive foreign travel allowances and minimum limits set upon holiday tour prices are unlikely to be viewed favourably by electors in democratic states. Freedom in tourism moreover is generally favoured by the host countries and may be an important source of foreign exchange. Hence comes a general tendency towards the freedom of inclusive tour operations in Western states.

In the less advanced countries tourist expenditure has been a factor of critical importance in the economy and active steps have been taken to encourage the services of international airlines by providing airport facilities, landing rights, minimal customs and immigration formalities and more hotels. The rapid growth of air travel in the Pacific area where overwater distances encourage the use of aviation, and where the active economics of the USA, Japan and Australia are stimulating factors, is of particular interest. Already in Taiwan (Formosa), Thailand, Singapore and Indonesia (especially Bali), tourist expenditure has reached or exceeded 50 million US $ per annum, and is growing at rates between 15 and 25 per cent in 1970–1.

Thus, the charter airlines have come of age and are now entering a period when their collective stature entitles them to greater recognition. The aircraft industry is already considering the significance of this for the design requirements of new generations of jet transport aircraft. A first essential is the need for a full realisation of the payload/range capability of the aircraft in high density layout and very rapid load/unload capability.

The pattern of transport aviation is therefore being considerably modified by the impact of inclusive tour operation by charter airlines. The IATA carriers have been obliged to restructure air fares so as to encourage ITX (or holidays tours on scheduled services) on the inclusive tour principle, and the rates of revenue have thereby been depressed for the industry as a whole.

The viability of the scheduled airline has been challenged largely because the rate of growth of tourism has considerably exceeded that of business and personal travel. There is little doubt that the justification for the wide-body jets is dependent upon the tourist business, and the potential yield from these aircraft will be linked to the group fare rate rather than to the fare paid by the individual business passenger. Of greater uncertainty is the question whether the impact of tourism will modify the basic organisational structure of the major air carriers. Can a major segment of separate non-scheduled airlines meet the needs of the time, or is a more drastic reorganisation of the structure of the whole air carrier industry called for? From various published studies it seems clear that a major reorganisation of the industry will in due course be required, and that by the end of the 1970s the IATA membership will be considerably modified. It may already be concluded that the cost of the unfilled seats on the scheduled airlines is extracting too high a price for the highest service standards which are now provided on the main trunk routes. It must farther be recognised that the cost of management, promotion and handling of the high capacity jets on the key routes could be very drastically cut if the industry were rationalised, and if an integration of scheduled and non-scheduled organisation and technique could be achieved.

It is apparent that in the near future the air transport industry must become market-orientated rather than capacity or production-orientated, as it is at present, with its sharp divergence between scheduled and non-scheduled services. Through price differentiation it must become possible to provide satisfaction for the more demanding needs of the business traveller and the less exacting wishes of the holidaymaker. No early solution to the organisational problems can be seen, however, unless economic pressure and inflationary forces set the pace.

The US supplemental air carriers

In the USA the development of inclusive tour charters was held back for many years by restrictive legislation designating operational freedom only to a small number of carriers in limited geographical areas (e.g. two supplementals in 1964 on the North Atlantic). In 1966 however ITC authority was granted by the CAB to supplemental carriers for a five-year period although challenged by the scheduled airlines. Jet equipment was acquired by the supplementals when their franchise was extended, and the military transport contracts for US forces in Europe and in Vietnam gave them the opportunity to invest in high-productivity aircraft. The status of the supplementals grew in proportion to the increase in their operating efficiency and their profitability through the 1960s. The 1970s must offer an immense opportunity since the less restrictive legislation and the rise of per capita incomes in Europe and Japan as in the USA, encourage a world wide tourist market.

Revenue yield

The need to develop air traffic on the major routes has led the members of the IATA in conference to propose a formulation of fares to encourage the tourist group at the expense of the business traveller who in 1969 lost even the concession of a 5 per cent on his return fare. Such methods of traffic stimulation which have been accelerated by the competition arising from the independent charter companies (Europe) and supplemental air carriers (US), have caused a fairly steady decline in the airline yield (i.e. the net revenue per passenger-miles performed) and must be some part of the explanation for the declining revenue of the IATA carriers. We should remember however that the reduction of the fare level has been a notable characteristic of international air transport since the end of World War II, and the introduction of economy fares in 1962 was only one of a number of steps taken in this period to maintain air travel demand through periods of over-production and rising costs.

An ICAO report (*The Economic Situation of Air Transport,* 1968), demonstrated explicitly the rate of decrease of the average fare for the member countries' scheduled airlines from 1957 to 1967. This overall trend should cause no surprise since the increase in transport aircraft productivity in the period considerably outpaced the unit aircraft operating costs especially after the introduction of the jets in 1959–60. Thus operating costs per ton-mile were depressed at a rate of about 1 per cent per annum from 1951 to 1960 and at about 5 per cent per annum from 1960–9. In the words of the report, 'it seems probable that the rate of increase in operating costs per hour will again be not so great as the increase in aircraft productivity. In the case of the SST hourly costs are expected to rise more than productivity, particularly in the case of the first generation, but this will be more than offset by the effect of the Boeing 747 and the various types of "airbus" whose volume of operations will probably be greater than those of the SST's at least until after 1980.'

In the author's view this overall result is unlikely to be achieved, and the inflationary movements in the period commencing 1970–1 will be carried forward into the mid 1970s thereby restraining the downward price trend for a consolidating period while the wide-body jets settle down into more profitable operation. These factors may as a result have a dampening effect on air traffic growth. The annual growth has been considerable and the percentage increase in the capacity ton-mile performed by IATA carriers has ranged from 14·6–18·6 per cent between 1964 and 1969. As in Europe, the ITC work of the US supplementary carriers predicates high load factors and the curtailment of overhead costs. This includes marketing which is handled, as required by the CAB, by the tour promoting organisation. It is important to note the special requirements of the CAB when approval for ITC tours are sought. A plane load or split charter may be arranged and the tour must include stops in at least three cities which are 50 miles or more apart. The tour must be at least seven days in duration. The price, which includes hotel accommodation and surface as well as air transportation, must be no less than 110 per cent of the lowest available scheduled service fare over the same routes.

Operating costs of the principal jet transport aircraft

We have considered in Chapter 2 the principal criteria for the selection of transport aircraft to meet the critical airline requirements. It was shown there that the increasing size of the transport vehicle offered potential advantages in operating economy if the level of traffic justified the investment and if the many other criteria – including service frequency, integration with existing fleets, flexibility in airfield operation, performance and noise could be favourably assessed. Such assessments, it cannot be repeated too often, require a full and detailed analysis of a fleet of aircraft operating in an integrated pattern often with other aircraft types on a system of routes. All these considerations, however, do not contradict the fact that the prime parameter for initial analysis is the specific direct operating cost. If only for reasons of simplicity it is a first requirement that the d.o.c. of a transport aircraft should be considered in comparison with other aircraft on some equivalent basic. Thus arose the demand for the standard formulae for d.o.c. which were described in Chapter 2.

The difficulty often arises that comparable data is not available and approximations may invalidate the basis of comparison. For this reason, properly controlled airline results have immense value for the comparison of aircraft already in service if only to emphasise to the uninitiated the influential factors which typify and segregate the operating costs of the various air carriers and their framework of operations no less than the aircraft types themselves.

It is instructive therefore to study the direct operating costs of the principal jet transports in service in the year 1969–70 from the results published by the CAB in 1970 and hence to prepare a comparative analysis of aircraft type costs and airline economic results. A very wide variation in cost levels is immediately apparent, and in the case of the twin-engined jets the specific direct operating costs per passenger mile vary in a ratio of 2·6 to 1·0. The principal factors which were found to determine this were:

1. The aircraft capacity (size), installed power and engineering complexity.
2. Average sector length flown.
3. The time the aircraft has been in service.
4. The intensity of operation.
5. The seasonal variation in utilisation.
6. The mode of integration with other types.
7. The financing policy. Purchase or Lease.
8. The expertise of airline management.
9. The load factor achieved.
10. Size of the airline concerned.

The total operating costs for three important twin-engined jet types operating on US domestic routes in 1970 show remarkable contrasts in the critical economic factors. No simple model could be made to represent these factors and their interrelations, but the student of air transport economics can gain considerable insight into the factors involved by seeking to establish relationships in more limited areas by a farther analysis of the published data from the CAB.

Airline management

It would be too facile to believe that the differences in the recorded economic results are due to the aircraft and its scheduled operating pattern alone. The quality of management skills in some sectors of the air transport industry has not kept pace with the rapidly changing technology, and the flexibility of mind which responds to the immense growth of scale, and defeats complacency in a time of restricted competition and financial strength, has not always been apparent. Imaginative developments have moreover not been notable in the large airlines. Car ferry operations and Inclusive Tour Charters, to take two European examples, were activated in the relatively weak and unprotected UK 'independent' air transport industry. There is a certain rigidity in the organised airline industry which stems from the heavy investment in aircraft, ground equipment and staff. This already affects the indirect and over-head costs of many airlines and might infect the new critical areas now about to present themselves for clear thinking and decisive action. Fig. 4.4 showed the trend in recent profitability which almost certainly has been aggravated by these airline management difficulties.

Probably the area of indirect costs lends itself to management control more than any other. It is still the most primitive part of the air transport business and lends itself to new approaches and new techniques, and to less conservative and extravagant practices. Aviation men have led the classical advance into air transport from the engineering sciences and from the flying services. We need now an injection of new talents and ideas from the many disciplines which have been little imbued with the aeronautical idea. Passenger handling, reservations, baggage and cargo control might well repay extensive replanning in many airlines more especially at this time when the new large jets will introduce flow control problems not readily amenable to the scaling up of conventional methods. Reliance upon computer techniques is not an adequate alibi for traditional methods of working.

Impact of the wide-body jets on operating economics

The estimated direct operating costs per mile of the Boeing 747 and other wide-body jets in comparison with the 707 and the DC 8 are shown in Fig. 4.6 for the year 1975. In comparison Fig. 4.7 shows the direct operating costs per passenger-mile in that year in relation to the number of passengers carried for the B 747 and B 707. These figures, based on the ATA operating cost method (1967) and adjusted to account for likely changes in the pattern of international operations in the period

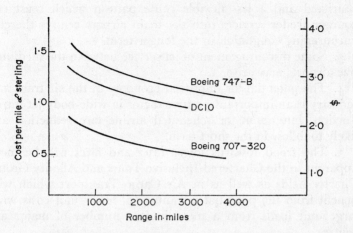

FIG. 4.6. Direct Operating Cost related to Range

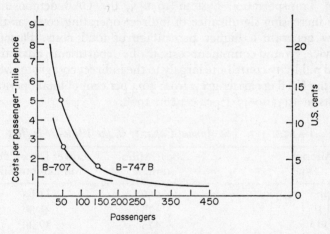

FIG. 4.7. Direct Operating Cost related to Passengers

1967–75, illustrate the critical characteristics of the wide-body jets. In essence these may be stated to be:

1. The very large increase in available capacity offers a high potential for reduced direct costs per seat mile, but requires higher passenger loads per flight to break even.

2. The high unit load requirement carries with it a more

restricted and a less flexible route pattern which must encourage feeder services into the main airport centres thereby encouraging congestion in the longer term.

3. Some discouragement of jet service between the medium-size airports may arise.

4. The potential for improved economy in the air transport industry is an important positive factor in wide-body jet introduction, but no major scheduled airline fare reduction are likely to follow in the short term.

5. The trend towards lower rates and fares will be most apparent in the Chartered Inclusive Tours and Affinity Group Charter fields as well as in Air Cargo Transport which will benefit from the potential advantage of lower unit costs with large unit loads from a more limited number of major air centres.

In their report 1969 on the impact of New Large Jets on the Air Transportation System 1970–3, the CAB demonstrated the increasing significance of indirect operating costs, as these now generate a higher percentage of total costs. Passenger service, ground equipment costs, traffic departments, advertising and publicity contribute largely to the indirect cost group which on the US flag carrier grew from 40·3 per cent of total operating costs in 1957 to 47·4 per cent in 1968.

TABLE 4.7. *The Annual Capacity in the Wide-Body Jets*

Aircraft Type	Seat Miles (million)	Lower Deck Cargo (million ton-miles)
Boeing 707 300	250	11·63
DC 10	475	21·38
L 1011	475	20·99
A 300 B	425	
Boeing 747	681	45·00

Note: International Routes, 10 hours per day.
Source: CAB and ASA.

There may be an accelerating trend in this direction with wide-body jets which may adversely affect the impact that lower d.o.c. may have on fares and rates. These effects will be enhanced and abetted by rising costs in an increasingly competitive market-orientated environment actively concerned to oblige air carriers to meet every item of readily-allocated cost. The costs of congestion are also increasing direct costs well above the forecasts of manufacturers and airline project offices. The price of noise which had become high in the late 1960s will be paid in full by airline and by air traveller in the 1970s. Table 4.7 indicates the immensely increased capacity of wide-body jets in comparison with the earlier 4-jet aircraft such as the Boeing 707 300 series.

The position of the SST in the development of air transport

In Chapter 9 we study in some detail the operating characteristics and the economic implications of the SST. Prejudging our conclusions from that chapter we must consider at this point how the new SST projects will fit into the transport picture of the 1970s. An account is given later of the Anglo-French Concorde, the Russian Tu 144 and the Boeing 2707. It must be presumed that these aircraft will proceed and that the many alarums and excursions of the 'environmentalists' will in due time run their course and that all three aircraft in some developed form will reach airline service. In mid 1972 the situation of the Boeing project looks grim indeed, but it is inconceivable that the USA by wilful act can hand over the technological leadership for a sustained period to Europe and to the Soviets. Supersonic transport in the author's view is more inevitable than many other forms of advanced technology transport, and we have surely witnessed in the early 1970s no more than a phase for pausing in the development of transport at Mach 3·0. If it were economically incompatible with the needs of the airlines, it might well be justifiable to cancel the project, but such was clearly not the case any more than it has been shown to be with the Concorde project in Europe.

It must be recognised, however, that the supersonic transport, Mach 2·0–2·7, is not an economic proposition in the same sense as the wide-body jets or the aircraft which have preceded them. This is not only because of the immense government backing which has been essential to solve the technological problems and which cannot be fully recovered by a 'call-back' of funds from the manufacturers as sales progress: it is related basically to the operational parameters of a supersonic transport and the size of the vehicle. Thus the Concorde operating at a load factor comparable to that of the fan-jet Boeing 707 Douglas DC 8 and BAC VC 10 could not operate at the same fare level without subsidy, and cannot be considered as a direct replacement aircraft for any existing types. Replacement has rarely been directly recognisable in the history of air transport, largely because of developing technology and the constant demand for increasing unit size. It has been well said that no motor car exactly replaced the Model 'T' Ford. Even more dramatically has the pattern changed in Air Transport. Thus the SST must be expected to create its own individual demand even though an important part of its utilisation may represent an encroachment upon the conventional jet domain. While it might be claimed that a Mach $2 \cdot 7$–$3 \cdot 0$ aircraft built of higher grade materials (principally titanium) and of considerably larger size than Concorde or the Tupolev 144, might if eventually built, provide an improved operating economy, it is now generally accepted – as is argued in the next chapter – that the likely return on investment, though higher than for Concorde does not compare with the early 4-engined jets, still less with the wide-body aircraft now in service. Nevertheless it can be shown and has been effectively demonstrated by the British Aircraft Corporation and Aerospatiale, that the joint operation of SST and high capacity subsonic jets provides a combined service in speed, comfort and cost which more effectively meets all sectors of the total market and increases the profitability of the airline.

No reference to the place of the SST in the air transport scene can discount the serious problem of the boom which for some years will exclude SST operations (above M–$1 \cdot 15$) from most overland routes. Thus sectors across the USA and Canada may be totally curtailed, as also many important European stages. Some authorities feel confident that the boom problem will be solved, but at the present time it clearly forbids our consideration of any existing SST projects as direct replacements of subsonic aircraft. Moreover the straight jet engine still essential to optimise in one design flight performance in all stages of flight, introduces airport noise as a fundamental obstacle to universal acceptance of the SST in all communities. We reserve this subject to Chapter 10 where airport noise is considered.

Potential for V/STOL

We also reserve for a later discussion in Chapter 8 Vertical and Short Take-Off and Landing (V/STOL) operations, and their special contribution to the future of air transport. Vertical Take-Off (Helicopters), and Short Take-Off aircraft (Third Level or Feeder types), have been in service for a considerable time, but their development into major elements of air transport organisation has been slow and might in some areas be called static. The essential obstacle to progress has been the small vehicle size and the apparent high unit operating cost of all technically feasible projects. New technical solutions now seem likely to change the situation and progressively towards the end of the century it is probable that conventional take-off and landing modes will be fully replaced. It seems most unlikely that a major impact will be made by Vertical Take-Off aircraft (VTOL) until the 1980s, but the development of Short Take-Off and Landing (STOL) is almost certain to make an early impact on the pattern of air transport services. We consider the influence of STOL aircraft upon the airport situation in Chapter 10 where the possibility of new concepts applicable to the airport congestion problem is explored. The economic case however has still to be demonstrated. In this section we shall discuss the likely effect on airline operations in Europe and the USA if STOL aircraft types can be effectively developed on the lines now being proposed by the major manufacturers.

The larger airlines in the first years of the decade, 1970–80, were not encouraging the approach of manufacturers and government research groups on the subject of new STOL types for passenger operations. The reasons were self-evident. The key routes were remarkably well provided with airport facilities (perhaps with the exception of cities such as New York and London), and the need to provide duplicated buildings, equipment and staff was a major deterrent to a consideration of STOL services if operating from alternative airfields. Of all the design studies which have been analysed none had claimed a parity in direct operating costs with conventional jets even with equal payload capacity. Most designs, moreover, if only because they were early projects not initially conceived for trunk line service, were of smaller size, seldom exceeding 90 seats, and the direct operating costs were well above current jet transports in the short-medium haul field. Perhaps most important of all, the manufacturing industry especially in the USA – was marketing an expanding range of conventional jet aircraft of increasing economy and capability so that new STOL projects were, in effect, in head-on competition with the products of the same industry and in many cases of the same firm.

Government research and development funds, even though the prospects of use in defence work might be small, have nevertheless been available on a limited scale for the STOL and VTOL project work in the USA as in Western Europe, and the hope for world sales and the expectation of expanding technological 'know how' has matched private industrial support in countries with an aircraft industry especially in the UK, West Germany, and the USA.

The courses of airlines and Governments may for some time remain well apart, but in parallel, with the manufacturer gaining more encouragement from the latter than the former. The inherent stability of a growing transport industry arising from a past need to invest heavily in capital equipment, with some disregard to the forces promoting change might seem surprising in aviation, but in fact at the root of the matter is not conservatism so much as caution and a sense of responsibility at a time of shrinking profit margins, worldwide cost inflation and decreasing yields. Two facts, however, have modified the outlook of the major carriers and have obliged them to go over very carefully their long-term project plans. These are the ever-increasing competition, and the environmental position. The competition, most fierce in the international field, has encouraged the acquisition of the high capacity jets (with higher comfort standards and lower direct operating costs per seat), and has maintained the pressures for supersonic transports (higher performance but higher d.o.c.). This competition has not at the same time stimulated interest in an expansion in the short-haul market where most total transport is generated (low yield and very high d.o.c.) and where it may for some time be left to small air carriers willing to take high risks with the promise of only minimal profits. Airport congestion might, however, modify this situation quickly and favourably.

In the airport environment, the airlines have found themselves in an increasingly adverse position largely because of obtrusive aircraft noise and supposed pollution. An emotional pattern of public action triggered off by some very reasonable local reactions, has been established which all airline and airport authorities are obliged to consider seriously in project planning. Noise legislation and operational controls are at the same time introducing economic penalties which airlines at present are little able to bear.

STOL transports are now engaging the attention of aircraft designers in all the manufacturing nations. Fan-jet engine and prop-turbine designs have been proposed and new operating patterns, new STOL sites and new approaches to land use and regional planning have been put forward to meet the congestion and environmental problems.

The work of Breguet in France, Douglas in the USA, BAC in the UK as well as Canadair, has concentrated on STOL designs which would provide short-haul services on metropolitan routes using peripheral airport sites thus relieving congestion in dense near-city areas, and by-passing traffic from large airports like New York (JFK) and London (Heathrow). The need is now so intense that potential sites have been established at a number of US and European cities, and draft specifications for STOL ports have been drawn up in the US by the FAA.

To forecast the impact of STOL aircraft operations on the future development of the conventional jet aircraft is as yet a formidable task, but airline project departments in all countries will be wise to take account of the likely arrival of such aircraft on the market from the mid 1970s. Initially 60–90 seat capacity and 400 statute mile range will be the likely limits of capability but by the late 1970s 150–200 seat STOL transports in the 1500–2000 mile range of the spectrum will be almost certainly available.

The future of aircraft demand

The changing aircraft types which have been discussed in the last sections of this chapter arise from the incentive to meet the ever more stringent requirements with advancing technology. Eventually they will be put on order if the airlines believe they will offer higher overall profitability, provide features which will attract custom, and ease the constraints of the air system infra-structure. In addition, size, performance and passenger appeal will be dominant parameters in selection, for the advancing technology as well as the pressures of economics and competition will surely continue to encourage the introduction of new projects. Moreover, one aircraft type operating a sector will bring influence to bear on other routes and sectors and the equipment that serves them. Thus an interactive pattern of change is continuously emerging. Far less likely is a continuing downward trend in airline operating costs per unit of transport produced. Air transport with the new projects is at last approaching a mature and hence more stable stage in its ultimate development and further reduction of operating costs will be difficult to achieve.

Forecasts of future jet aircraft demand

Such forecasts have become routine work in the aircraft manufacturing industry for many years and provide the basis for investment appraisal of specific projects seeking penetration into particular markets. Forecasts are built up from the separately estimated growth expectations in various world areas prepared by the major air carriers allowing for competitive factors (mergers etc.), and with many assumptions as to the critical economic parameters.

The gradual retirement of transport aircraft as they become obsolescent or are replaced by more economic and generally larger aircraft is a source of great difficulty in forecasts beyond about 10 years. New factors are continuously emerging to confuse the trends, and it is now apparent that public demand for lower noise levels in the airport environment will cause

earlier retirement of the early jet types than was at one time
anticipated. An insight into the significant trends in design and
development is no less essential for success. In due course
sophisticated econometric models may well be available which
will relate the future aircraft demand pattern to the needs of
the travelling public and the freight shipper as they will unfold
in a future period of years, but the relevant data is unavailable
today and may never reach the degree of detail required to
provide a basis for sound traffic forecasting using modelling
techniques.

To the manufacturer, to the airlines themselves, to airport
authorities and to research bodies, refined results of market
research are to be highly prized, since investment of many
millions of pounds (or dollars) may be at risk, and undue
caution through lack of confidence may be as costly as over-
boldness.

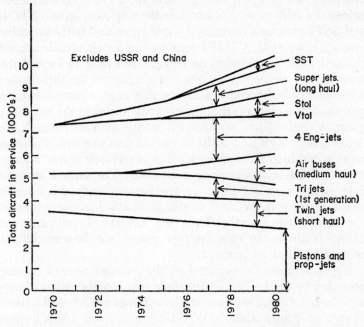

Fig. 4.8. World Airlines' Demand for Transport Aircraft: a forecast for
1975–80; showing likely changes in composition of world fleets

Forecasts prepared by the author in a private project (1970) are shown in Fig. 4.8. For the purpose of this figure the original data was extended to include twin-jet aircraft and the declining prop-turbine market. From such a pattern of growth and decay the manufacturer must build up his product market and seek to define his market share. Upon the accuracy of his estimate of the market share will depend his financial success or failure. At the earliest possible stage in the development of a new project discounted expenditure and revenue calculations should be made which will test the sensitivity of the profit (or loss), to variations in the estimated market share and to the discounted expenditure which might be incurred by the project and its production.

The figure shows an estimate up to 1985 of the eight principal air transport type groups, although the figures beyond 1975/6 are to a great extent problematical. Based on the known fleets up to the summer of 1971, and from manufacturers data on firm orders at that time, the emergence of the air buses is characteristic of the mid-1970s. We presume the origins of serious STOL and SST operations in the mid – late 1970s and fairly extensive operations by 1980. VTOL operations on a serious scale are not thought likely until the early 1980s. Such data as formed the basis of this figure is the point of departure for the market research of all the major airframe and engine manufacturing groups. It is significant that the gradual decline in the use of the 3 and 4 engined jets of current design is forecast through the decade, the major part of the growth in fleet size by 1980 being represented by high capacity aircraft of bus type and to a lesser extent STOL and supersonic transports. The growth in total fleet strength is not great in comparison with the forecast passenger growth because of the gradually increasing size of the individual aircraft. Thus the average investment per transport aircraft in 1980 (at 1970 prices) will be some 88 per cent higher than in 1970–71.

Fig. 4.9 shows for comparison the average aircraft seating provided by the IATA carriers since 1959 together with a long-term forecast based on estimates taken from a study undertaken in 1971 on future traffic at West German airports (ASA Report 155).

The author's figures are on a slightly different basis since

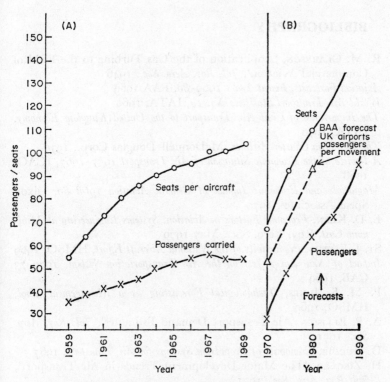

Fig. 4.9. Seats and Passengers, Worldwide IATA Members: (A) Actual Averages, 1959–69. (B) Forecast, 1970–90 ASA West German Airport Study)

they refer to transport aircraft operating through major European airports and are not representative of many IATA carriers who may be confined to the USA and other parts of the world. The forecast trend towards 1980 has included an allowance for a reasonable increase in overall load factors representative of the increasing impact of tourism and inclusive tour operating methods in the years ahead. At every stage of our analysis we find tourism, especially in the context of holiday tours, taking an increasingly significant part in the future pattern of air transport. It is for consideration whether this is a force acting in the interests of a more stable future for the air transport industry or a long-term danger inhibiting the traditional scheduled service characteristics of the business.

BIBLIOGRAPHY

R. M. CLARKSON, 'Application of the Gas Turbine to the Field of Commercial Aviation', *Jnl. Roy. Aero. Soc.*, 1946

Aviation Forecasts, Fiscal Years 1969–80, FAA 1969

World Air Transport Statistics No. 14, IATA, 1969

The Importance of Civil Air Transport to the United Kingdom Economy, IATA, 1970

The European Charter Airlines, McDonnell–Douglas Corp., 1970

A Review of the Economic Situation of Air Transport 1957–1967, ICAO, 1968

Magnitude and Economic Impact of General Aviation 1968–80, Dixon Speas Associates, 1970

E. D. KEEN, *Economic Factors in Aviation. Systems Engineering at Minimum Cost*, Roy. Aero. Soc., May 1970

ST. J. ELSTUB, *Productivity of the National Aircraft Effort*, HMSO, 1969

Impact of New Large Jets on the Air Transportation System, 1970–73 CAB, 1969

P. M. S. JONES, *Technological Forecasting as a Management Tool*, HMSO, 1969

A. P. ELLISON, 'Air Transport Demand Estimates', *Jnl. Roy. Aero. Soc.*, 1971

D. HUDDIE, *Economics of Propulsion Systems for Air Transport*, 1967

H. ZIEGLER, 'The Major Development Trends in Air Transport', *Jnl. Roy. Aero. Soc.*, 1971

J. E. STEINER, *Aircraft and Air Transport Development in the Next Ten Years*, Roy. Aero. Soc., Johannesburg, 1969

The State of the Air Transport Industry, IATA Annual Report 1969

A. T. PUGH, *Holiday Traffic*, Roy. Aero. Soc., May 1971

B. A. BOTTING, *Market Research – An Economic Necessity*, Roy. Aero. Soc., May 1970

PICKERING and SILLS, *Design and Cost Considerations for Large Subsonic Transport Engines*, Roy. Aero. Soc., May 1970

M. O. WILMER, *Aspects of Optimisation in the Design of Civil Aircraft*, Roy. Aero. Soc., May 1970

Aviation Forecasts, Fiscal Years 1969–80, FAA, Jan. 1969

E. E. MARSHALL, 'The Role of Aircraft in Future Transport Systems', *Aircraft Engineering*, May 1969

M. R. STRASZHEIM, *The International Airline Industry*, The Brookings Institution, 1969

5 Air Cargo Operational and Economic Problems

Introduction

At the present time there are many conflicting thoughts on the subject of air freight development and it is hoped to establish the significant factors in the following discussion, giving reference where necessary to recent published work. Air cargo commenced from very small beginnings in the post-war period, and it was for long believed that when specialised aircraft became available many of the problems would disappear. We have now, however, a wide range of aircraft designed specifically for cargo: these range from the small Short Skyvan through the Hawker Siddeley Argosy and the Canadair CL 44 to the Boeing and Douglas subsonic jet transports, culminating in the Boeing 747 Super Jet Freighter and the Lockheed L 500 which provide, with differing emphasis, most of the features which have long been recommended. A range of performance and capacity is available which can meet most airline requirements, but it is still argued that the long-awaited breakthrough has not been achieved and the relatively high cost of air transport deters many industries from its regular use. Others, however, contend that the breakthrough has already taken place and point convincingly at the growth figures and the orders for new all-cargo aircraft and convertible types.

Various aspects of the problems and prospects for cargo aircraft development and operation are studied in this chapter, and we turn in the next chapter to mechanical systems of handling cargo and load transfer which are now receiving the keen attention of the air carrier industry and equipment manufacturers. The conclusion of many recent investigations into the air freight business is that the specialised aircraft and the systems development associated with it can provide only a part, even though an extremely important part, of the final drive towards the growth of air cargo into a viable economic industry. It is held that the selling of air transport as part of the production and distribution process is the key to success in this sector of air commerce and much attention has been given to economic research in this field. Work undertaken in the UK and in the USA is described in Chapter 7, and we are led to conclude that this activity should be pursued even more vigorously because of the apparent success of the methods employed in the stimulation of traffic.

Air cargo is different from the other forms of air transport which have developed before it. It requires the systematic and commercial approach which has been less obviously to the fore in the development of the passenger business. It may be thought that in air cargo, with its immense potential for growth, there lies the greatest hope for a well-balanced and profitable air carrier industry.

TABLE 5.1. *Regional Air Cargo Traffic Growth and Distribution*

Region	5 Years to 1965	5 Years to 1970	1970 Share of Traffic %
North Atlantic	3·48	2·83	23·9
USA Domestic	2·57	1·86	33·2
Intra-European	2·05	2·15	4·0
Other Regions	2·35	2·19	38·9
			100·0

Source: ICAO.

The economic development of air cargo

The growth of air cargo transport has been exceptional over the last five to ten years and is running now at a rate higher than in most other fields of transportation. On the North Atlantic route where aircraft provide a great time advantage which may exceed four weeks the scheduled IATA carriers have achieved traffic increases over the previous year of 38·8 per cent in 1969 and 33·2 per cent in 1968. The carriers reporting to the European Air Research Bureau on their intra-European services record percentage growth figures for the five years to 1970 of less than half those figures but achieved a doubling of cargo traffic in five years. Now a growth rate of 15 per cent per annum corresponds approximately to a doubling of traffic in five years, and by this standard the future of air cargo operations is likely to be of the very greatest significance and may increasingly influence the business structure of civil

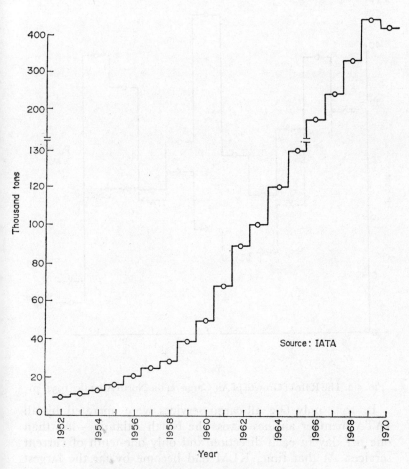

FIG. 5.1. North Atlantic Air Cargo Growth.
Scheduled and Charter Operations, 1952–70

aviation.* Already on the North Atlantic routes 61·5 per cent of cargo was in 1969 carried in all-cargo aircraft, and a major network of services with specialised aircraft was in operation. Recent studies which are discussed in Chapter 7 indicate that the disparity between the growth rates of cargo and passenger traffic may be expected to continue and to lead to the carriage of an increasing proportion of traffic on all-cargo services after a brief pause in the early 1970s, while excessive capacity on the 747s is utilised.

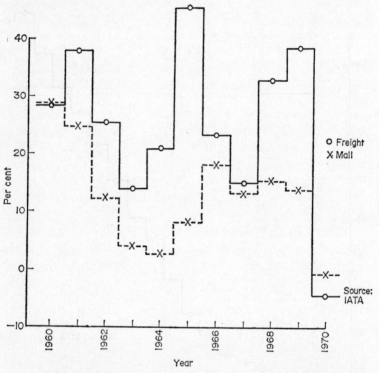

FIG. 5.2. The Rate of Growth of Air Cargo on the North Atlantic, 1952–70

In 1954 only 662 all-cargo services were operated by all IATA member airlines across the North Atlantic – less than one per day in each direction and only one-tenth of current services. At that time, KLM had become by far the largest operator of all-cargo services, supplying nearly half this capacity

* Note Chapter 3. FIG. 3.3.

and carrying almost a quarter of all North Atlantic cargo on this specialised service and in passenger aircraft. Pan American, whose share of the market had declined in the recession following the end of the Korean War, countered this competition by doubling its all-cargo capacity and embarked on a vigorous sales campaign to such effect that by 1955 it had regained its lead in North Atlantic cargo traffic. 1955 and 1956 saw the start of scheduled services by three important freight carriers, Seaboard, Lufthansa and Alitalia, who together now account for more than one-quarter of air cargo traffic. Despite this upsurge in competition, Pan American and KLM retained between them a third of the traffic throughout the late fifties.

Over the last fifteen years the North Atlantic air cargo traffic has grown thirty-fold. Fig. 5.1 illustrates this growth. Throughout the US recession in the early 1960s this traffic continued to grow at around 35 per cent per annum and even the growth rate increased in 1960. Fig. 5.2 shows the rate of growth and Table 5.2 shows the percentage distribution of freight traffic between the IATA carriers on the North Atlantic routes in the year 1970.

TABLE 5.2. *Cargo on the North Atlantic*

	% Share of the Market. 1970
Pan American	15·65
Seaboard	13·72
Lufthansa	9·62
TWA	9·44
KLM	8·52
Air France	7·20
BOAC	5·91
Air Canada	5·33
Alitalia	5·00
SAS	4·85
Sabena	3·84
Swissair	3·19
Irish International	2·24
El Al	1·79
Iberia	1·04
	97·34 % of Total

Excluding Airlines carrying less than 1 % of Traffic

It will be seen that the principal European Air Cargo carriers on the North Atlantic, BOAC, Lufthansa, Air France and KLM retain 31 per cent of the business: the recent growth of Lufthansa's share of the traffic has been at the expense of its Northern European competitors. Similarly, Seaboard's growth has drawn traffic from the two principal USA international carriers, but altogether the US carriers retain some 40 per cent of the trade. Air France, SAS and Sabena have managed to hold their market shares, but such airlines as Swissair, Sabena, Quantas, Air India, El Al, Aer Lingus and Iberia, despite their growth of capacity, have seen their combined share squeezed to little more than 10 per cent.

TABLE 5.3. *The Top 15 Airlines in World Wide Air Freighting, 1970*

	Ton-Miles
Aeroflot	1,420,000
Pan Am	728,332
United	545,102
American	462,984
TWA	449,855
Flying Tiger	390,211
Lufthansa	334,700
BOAC	263,685
KLM	257,654
Seaboard	255,137
Air France	243,300
Air Canada	193,331
Alitalia	187,352
Japan	185,808
Air Lift International	163,714

A report by G. Besse published in 1963 by the Institut du Transport Aerien, entitled *Comparative Examination of Some Air Freight Forecasts*, concluded that because air freight traffic was still comparatively small, precise forecasts, though essential, are particularly difficult to make. A factor of importance was that, freight being a much more diversified business than passenger transport, it required a study of the world market to be built up from a series of separate studies concerning different categories of goods and different geographical areas. With this view, we must concur, and we shall later consider methods which have been developed for a more rational approach to the estimation of future demand. An early study concluded that on the North Atlantic routes with the development of marketing methods backed by distribution costing and with more advanced aircraft design and load transfer technology, the traffic in cargo should overtake that in passengers by the mid-1970s (Whitworth Gloster Aircraft Limited, 1962). In general, the revenue per ton-mile generated by freight is little more than one-half of that generated by an equal weight of passengers, passenger accommodation and service equipment, even at tourist rates; thus the equality of total revenue from cargo and from passengers would not be achieved until perhaps a decade later.

TABLE 5.4. *Passenger Freight and Mail Revenues on World Scheduled Airlines*

| | Revenue from Passengers, Freight and Mail | | | | | |
| | 1965 | 1966 | 1967 | 1968 | 1969 | 1970 |
	Millions of US Dollars					
Passengers	7,378	8,399	9,671	10,862	12,584	14,512
Freight	904	1,052	1,167	1,371	1,648	1,694
Mail	404	492	531	561	592	619
Non-scheduled services	469	669	860	851	863	709
Incidental	217	758	302	348	422	487
Total Operating Revenues million $	9,372	10,870	12,531	13,993	16,109	18,015

Source: IATA Annual Report No. 15.

The slow start of the air cargo business was undoubtedly due to the high operating costs of the early types of aircraft converted from passenger use. Cargo, however, is a different and more difficult form of air carriage than passengers. The essence of the difference lies in the strongly commercial factors which determine its structure and its needs. In the selection of aircraft, the handling of traffic, and the forward-looking aspects of sales and commercial research, the exploitation of air cargo is likely to encourage new approaches to management and organisation in the airline industry.

The freight charge for the air transport of goods may still be between two and twenty times higher per ton-mile than the fastest surface competition can offer. Moreover, the frequency of service is still often inadequate and door-to-door service not always available. It is not surprising then that air cargo services have taken so long to become widely accepted. Even today we are carrying only a modest proportion of the most suitable higher-value goods available. The old transport problems continue to arise, though in a new guise, for with light traffic loads neither high-frequency services nor the more economic larger vehicles can be operated. The natural and convenient stop-gap for this early phase of air cargo development has been the use of the passenger plane to carry goods in its lower holds or in place of some passenger seats. Cargo then becomes secondary to the requirements of the passenger as to the routes flown and the schedules planned. At present the majority of passenger aircraft provide considerable cargo space which can be sold with only marginal added cost and with minor loss of passenger revenue. Large volumes are available on the long-range jet passenger aircraft such as the Boeing 707 and Douglas DC 8, but considerable restriction on the size of load is imposed because of the poorly shaped holds and the awkward access under the main passenger floor. Space provisioning for cargo on the medium-haul jets such as the Trident and the Caravelle is even more restrictive. In the Caravelle, less than 500 cubic feet of baggage and freight space is available outside the passenger cabin. The Boeing 727 is better provided in this respect.

This aircraft is also offered in a Q-C or quick change version which can be rapidly switched from a passenger to an all-cargo or mixed passenger-cargo version by use of rapidly removable seats, movable partitions and easy-to-load pallets.

Both all-cargo and passenger/cargo air operators are increasingly adopting unit load devices as the principal means of handling air cargo. The original basic unit was the standard pallet of lightweight construction measuring 88 × 125 in.

Goods loaded were generally constrained by netting. Non-structural shapes were then developed to hold the required pallet contour, creating the familiar shape of the igloo container which is commonly used on all combination and all-cargo jets.

The introduction of the Boeing 747 with its large under-floor holds has given rise to the development of new container shapes such as the lower deck half-container. This container is of an aluminium-faced honeycomb sandwich construction in one approved design and is lockable. Such containers used on the Boeing 747 have not yet brought about the door-to-door industrial distribution revolution that was forecast nor are they fully interchangeable with ground modes of transport. Aircraft design still dominates the container size and shape and full 'inter-modal compatibility' is still some time away.

The eventual introduction of even large all-freight aircraft, such as the Lockheed L 500 in the late 1970s should introduce an era of compatible containers. On the L 500 for example, the tilt-up nose door will allow 8 ft $\times$ 8 ft containers of length up to 40 ft to be loaded.

The increasing scale of air cargo movement thus makes it imperative to operate separate all-cargo aircraft with the necessary capacity (and adequate hold and access dimensions) on frequent scheduled flights. This makes possible not only the acceptance of the larger loads, which in practice form an important, if small, proportion of air cargo traffic, but allows fuller use to be made of the load transfer and handling equipment which must be properly integrated with surface transport, warehouse and aircraft systems. The need for 'inter-modal compatibility' has now become widely recognised as essential for the economic development of the transport industry in the future. In other words we need easy load transference between all kinds of vehicles.

In a lecture in 1962, Professor Crocco said that air cargo transport cannot develop in proportion to its true prospects unless it became differentiated at every stage and in every way, from the passenger side of the business. This view is strongly held by many specialists in this field who believe that the different operating techniques, types of aircraft, commercial methods, airport requirements and customer relationships are in need of segregated effort and concentration in the two sectors of air transport. To expect a full and effective exploitation of air cargo from predominantly passenger carriers may be optimistic but the increasing significance of air cargo revenue on the balance sheets of European and American air carriers will surely provide the best means of persuasion.

Table 5.5 shows how the cargo aircraft fleets of the world's airlines have adapted themselves to make fuller use of the jet transport in the last decade. Estimated by the ICAO statistics section it shows the composition of All-Cargo aircraft and convertible passenger aircraft including the total aggregate payload capacity of such aircraft. The capacity increase of about 4 to 1 in this period can be seen to have been provided by an increase in aircraft numbers of only about 50 per cent.

TABLE 5.5. *Cargo and Convertible Aircraft in Fleets of Scheduled International Airlines*

TYPE OF AIRCRAFT	1960 No. of Aircraft	Tonne Capacity	1965 No. of Aircraft	Tonne Capacity	1970 No. of Aircraft	Tonne Capacity
Turbo-Jets	—	—	77	3,362	563	19,033
Turbo-Props	—	—	74	1,122	124	1,692
Piston-Engined	674	5,555	441	3,369	270	1,793
Total	674	5,555	592	7,853	957	22,518

Source: ICAO Bulletin, April 1971.

Air cargo traffic in Russia

Soviet air transport was re-organised in the 1960s under a Ministry of Civil Aviation, after having been for many years a combined transport administrative and operational system within Aeroflot. It still seems to be viewed primarily as a State service subdivided under headings of function. The principal subdivision of operations is determined by the existence or otherwise of alternative surface communications. Where railways exist it is primarily urgent medical stores (e.g. isotopes), consignments of key technical equipment for industry, and essential agricultural and fishery supplies which move on combined and all-freighter services. Transport cost does not yet seem to have become a predominant factor, time-saving being the predominant criterion for use. Where water routes are frozen in winter, an important use for the cargo aircraft exists; in such cases, seasonal fluctuations of air traffic are, of course, considerable. Use of the hovercraft is increasing in these applications. Forms of air cushion craft, without sidewalls, are likely to be developed at the expense of hydrofoil ships, because of greater year-round capability over lakes and rivers.

Freightage of perishable goods, vegetables and fruit is now common by air, especially from the warm south to the northern areas, often across the lines of principal rail communication. Such services have been encouraged so as to maintain adequate living standards in the harsher terrain of the north and east and to meet an increasing purchasing power of the population in the areas. Already over 48 per cent of the freight traffic in the USSR domestic system is reported to be moving on routes within Central Asia, Kazakhstan and the Urals. Moscow, Leningrad, Kharkov, Sverdlovsk and Kiev are the principal points of air cargo uplift.

The design of specialised cargo aircraft has now become of importance in the USSR. The Antonov AN 10 (1957) and 10 A (four Ivchenko turbo-props) were designed primarily for passenger use (up to 126 seats) but now exist in the passenger/ cargo and the all-cargo role (up to 32,000 lb). The AN 12, a military version of the AN 10, which was re-designed with a new upswept tail with rear door and ramp, is now in extensive use in the USSR. These aircraft have been in operation in India, and also in use with Ghana Airways for civil freighting. The AN 26 (AN 24 T) a civil and military freighter with a large rear-loading door has been in operation in the USSR in the late 1960s. Twin turbo-prop engines each of 2,830 ehp power this aircraft which has a maximum payload of 11,000 lb and range of 700 nm. An earlier type the AN 22 Antheus, an immense aircraft with a payload exceeding 200,000 lb and powered by 4 × 15,000 ehp engines (the Kuznetsov NK 12 MA) has not been in extensive civil use so far as is known. The development of very large all-cargo jet transports is now known to be in hand in the Soviet Union.

Military air cargo transport

In most parts of the world military transport is operated under conditions which are in important respects different from the civil counterpart. This may lead to basic differences in the ideal type of aircraft to meet the requirements of the operator. There is inevitably a different approach to the economic criteria for selection.

The mission of the military air transport service must be: (1) to ensure that under war emergency conditions the total demand for airlift and its immediate deployment can be met; (2) to provide the most effective and efficient service in the normal peace-time situation, so as to implement the air staff requirements with maximum flexibility and at reasonable cost.

The capability to meet a high peak demand is generally a high cost requirement and the maximum possible use needs to be made of the potential airlift of an air transport force in peace-time conditions through training and by economic use of logistical services. Some conflict may arise here in that a major emergency may dislocate the less urgent, but still essential, supply lines of military support. It is for this reason that the US Air Material Command introduced the Logair Transport System which is operated by civil airlines within the USA for logistic support. Since these services are operated on a scheduled basis, their continuation is assured. This system has not been attempted elsewhere, although a case can probably be made for tri-service support in other areas of the world. The UK Government perhaps could operate between the British Isles and Cyprus a shuttle service which, with support from trooping revenue, would justify economically the high-speed supply of all but the heaviest items of equipment. The case could only be made if the total costs of supply were taken into account, with reduced inventory due to rapid and frequent air support. But the physical location of military stores at key supply points would need to be reduced in bulk otherwise it is unlikely that an economic justification can be made. Here lie prospects for the longer-term utilisation of the aircraft of the British Independent Air Operating Industry.

The specification requirements of the aircraft for military

use can be very different from those of the civil aircraft, even though common types have been extensively used both in the USA and in Europe. The economics of this are clear enough. The market for specialised civil or military cargo aircraft has been up till now so small that the costs of development become extremely high and too large a proportion of the direct costs of operation. As a result, the military air service has generally adopted a basically civil passenger or cargo aircraft, e.g. the:

> Boeing KC 135 and VC 137
> Lockheed L 1049 H. (Constellation)
> Douglas DC 6 A
> Boeing C 97 C
> Handley-Page Hastings
> Hawker Siddeley Argosy C. Mark 1

The outstanding exceptions arose through a specialised type not being available on the civil market, or the larger requirement justifying a new design:

> Douglas C 124 (Globemaster)
> Douglas C 133 (Cargo master)
> Nord Noratlas
> Lockheed C 130 (Hercules)
> Hawker Siddeley Beverley (Blackburn)
> Lockheed L 141

For these specially designed military transport types, it is notable that no civil counterparts have been successfully evolved, although hope exists for the development of the Lockheed L 500, which was initially designed also to meet civil requirements. It has been the general view that the specialised military cargo aircraft is not economic as a commercial freighter. Cross-sectional dimensions, especially the height of the hold, have been tailored for wheeled vehicles and military stores, and only recently have predominantly palletised loads introduced a common factor in the dimensions of standardised pallets and containers which in time may bring the military and civil requirements more closely together (Keen, 1959).

Other factors which demand compromise between the civil and military functions of cargo transport are: (1) cargo density;

(2) overall airlift capacity as a variable with respect to sector length, airfield length and altitude, and (3) economic stage length capability for the maximum payload in weight and volume as well as the ferry range of the aircraft under positioning flight conditions. We should note that the military transport aircraft will be required to operate under a wider range of unexpected operating conditions. A fuller consideration of the density requirements for all types of cargo transport aircraft is given in a later section of this chapter. We shall discuss the requirements for mechanical handling of military cargo loads in the next chapter. Here it should be noted that the armed forces have pioneered the use of the pallet both for rapid load transfer in the interests of aircraft utilisation and operational economy, and also as a means of effective direct air delivery. Technology and the need for standardisation of pallet dimensions, as well as the means of restraint when airborne, has been influenced by the intensive development sponsored by the US Air Force. Strength requirements such as the bending case during air drop are, however, more stringent and therefore weight creating to meet the military case. The USAF load-transfer and air-delivery system known as the 463.L, is of special importance in this field of development.

The approach to an economic criterion must be less precise than is necessary for the airlines, if only because the military transport operator has a captive market. The objective is likely to be to achieve the maximum utilisation of his equipment with high load factors and with a paramount concern for capability to meet a peak demand with minimum delay. Perhaps the difference between the prime military and civil objectives can be most simply considered in terms of output ratios. The military advantage is to be measured in terms of the maximum/mean ratio of the output from all available resources. The civil operator is aiming broadly for a fair profit, that is a favourable output/input ratio, that is output minus input divided by input.

The handling of many items of cost in the military and the civil operation is different. The major differences arise in standing costs (depreciation, interest and insurance) and crew costs. The standing costs of operation (Chapter 2) are generally not included in military air transport costs, however, the Defence Budget must be limited, and Parliamentary or Congress approval has to be obtained for capital investment in aircraft and equipment so that the overall decision on an aircraft specification will be based inevitably on multiple cost characteristics which only marginally differ from those of the civil transport. Military cost accounting varies from Air Force to Air Force. For example, the US Military Air Transport Service rates varied from under 25 per cent to 65 per cent of the common carrier general rates according to one study of the USAF. Transport Service published in 1960 (Brewer and Ulvestad, 1960). The Air Forces have, with few exceptions, been obliged to operate a large proportion of obsolescent aircraft types of multi-purpose design which have not, therefore, been of high economy. Until more recently there was a tendency to consider the operational cost of the military transport vehicle as best measured in terms of manpower input. For example, Sir Ralph Cochrane (1947) wrote 'In the Service the currency is man-power and the problem is to get the maximum output of useful transport work from the resources allocated.' Fuel costs, taxes and station handling costs have in the past been based on quite different concepts of price and assumption. These things are changing. The increasing sophistication of the new flight equipment and the more common requirements of fleets with standardised civil/military equipment such as mechanical handling systems is likely to encourage common costing and funding systems.

Methods of comparison for cargo aircraft on commercial operations

The most important thing to be said about civil air cargo operation is that it must be based very clearly on principles of sound economics. We are not now interested in a peak output with minimal warning nor in the glamorous aspects of a high-performance aeroplane; performance is important only from a safety and economic standpoint and few design characteristics are known to the customer, who is generally the agent or the shipper; this individual will seldom even see the aeroplane for himself. General du Merle put this well in a lecture to the

Royal Aeronautical Society, when he remarked that with the freight aircraft everything is dealt with by the initiated. In other words, the basis of judgment on cargo operations will not be distorted by popular appeal and the manufacturer and operator have the greater confidence in their predictions because technical and economic criteria will be predominant in determining success or failure.

Before drawing attention to the main differences between cargo- and passenger-carrying aircraft and their operation, we should mention the less obvious economic factors which underly the discussion.

Firstly, the aeroplane is by no means the only thing that matters in the transport of cargo by air. This does not contradict the fact that the aircraft must be the best and right for the job. Transport is, however, only one stage in the whole cycle of production and consumption, but it is the capability of aircraft to introduce economy through speed and facility which affects to such an important extent even remote parts of the cycle of production. Thus, in a sound economic analysis aircraft operating costs are not to be simply compared with the costs of surface transport. The other well-recognised factors such as packaging and handling, insurance and loss through delivery delay and damage, and, finally, inventories and the warehousing question, have all to be considered and assessed. It is, unfortunately, only too true that many organisations have no exact knowledge of important components of their production costs, particularly in respect of transport and inventories, and they are not, therefore, in a good position to make a true comparison of air and surface transportation.

The most common basis of comparison is still the cost per ton-mile for all means of transportation and it would follow from the previous discussion that we should seek to include the broadest possible area of costs not only through the transport regime, but both before and after, indeed whenever any differential factor arises. This is not often easy to carry out. Seldom in practice are all the differential factors self-evident, even when they can be extracted from the records. While it is clear that the case for air transport will be based on the overall economy achieved, and not upon that of the aeroplane alone, at the same time the reasons for many of the associated economies are based on the prime characteristics of the aeroplane itself. I would like to summarise these as speed and facility. Let us look more closely first of all at what we have called 'facility'.

This quality of transportation is not readily measurable in economic terms. It is the capability of direct delivery which the aeroplane possesses; its independence from terrestrial barriers, the reduced distance often possible with an airway. It is the lessened load transference, the airport-to-airport convenience with its associated economy of immobile time and of manpower. It is worth noting that the quantitative analysis of cargo transport by air tends to be conservative. The many associated factors, some of which have been mentioned above, are rarely antagonistic to the case for air transport even though difficult to quantify. High standards of facility are costly to maintain and may require national investment in airports and air traffic control systems, cargo 'towns' and terminals and even motorway links between centres of industrial and residential importance.

The value of speed

The value of speed or the element of time in transportation depends on the significance attached to time by the shipper and upon the fact that certain costs are directly proportional to time. If the time of transport and its associated periods of load transference are considered as a period of suspended satisfaction of customer demand and of capital idleness, then the speed of transport is a very important quality indeed. It may be noted that even before the air age higher speeds of transport commanded higher rates: it may then be logically assumed that the proportionally higher speeds now possible in the air will often justify higher total costs of operation, but the true quality of air transport cannot always be evaluated. This theme is well developed in *The Time Element in Transportation* by Herbert Ashton (1947). Clearly, if time were of no significance then low-cost canal transport would dominate the situation.

The economic importance of time cannot always be made evident. It may, often, however, have a significance beyond the more obvious factors which are susceptible to measurement, such as cost, availability and exchangeable value which may be isolated and assessed. On the other hand, the value of time is not invariable, nor is it inevitable. It has, therefore, a mercurial quality which is unlike that of dimensional length and its products, or additive cost. Modern techniques may in fact modify the value of time, e.g. refrigerated ships and supersonic flight, especially where considerable change of longitude is involved. In many cases, it is clear that the higher speeds of transport could introduce a serious problem since the transport vehicle in the past has often served as a form of storage. While the operator will gain considerably and the community as a whole may well receive advantage, the customer or user may suffer a measurable loss and for him higher speed in transport will create disutility. Even the railways today are seriously concerned at the cost of storage in mobile trucks and containers which provide in some cases a great convenience to shippers.

Speed may be thought of in time and distance. The value of certain goods depends upon their condition on reaching the market. This is a function of time, and, clearly, many goods will require the speed of air transport to reach particular markets. Generally, the market restricted in space and in time needs higher speeds in transport; this minimises the risk of failure to reach it. This is often, moreover, the means of opening up new markets. The time factor of perishability may be attached to the goods or to the demand for the goods, for the value in time is seldom constant. Thus, the value of speed will vary with the time that it is available. This is less true of the cost of providing the speed since it is primarily the additional costs of overtime for certain labour elements which will affect the aircraft operating costs. The air operator must at all times be critically conscious of the importance of correct timing since his high-quality product may not have equal value at all times.

On longer term, the value of speed in transport increases steadily as the value of time increases. The latter increases as the rate of production increases so that the value of speed will increase with the degree of industrialisation of communities. The increased division of labour and specialisation of production which follows industrial development augments this trend towards higher-speed transport, since centres of production and markets become more widely dispensed. Finally, higher speeds of transport have effects upon the expeditious handling of commercial transactions in general. Since the speed of a transport system must conform with the average tempo of the community, we must expect this demand for higher speeds to grow. The implications of a continuing increase in the value placed upon time must be interpreted as the growing demand for air transportation, particularly in the foreign trade wherever comparable total costs can be anticipated. These factors and influences, though difficult to recognise in the day-to-day operation of transport systems, are undoubtedly at the root of the steady expansion of the use of the private motor car and of scheduled air transport in the post-war era.

It is now becoming rapidly apparent that the most important advantage of air freighting as a means of transport lies in its powerful influence upon the economics of production. For the true advantage of air transport is high speed and independence from terrestrial barriers; its aim is to achieve for the products of industry a market or objective which is more profitable or more useful than those achievable with the slower means of surface transport. The factors determining the choice of transport will vary widely with the products, the sources of raw materials and the markets to be sought. The principal criteria may be summarised as follows:

1. The value of the goods. The higher cost of high-speed transport can be borne more readily when it is a small percentage of a high-class product (Scientific instruments).

2. The perishable nature of a product may be such that it must reach a market within a short period of time, or it must be flown to the market to provide an adequate display time there (Flowers and Fashion goods).

3. The market may be extended in area by the use of higher speeds of transport (Flowers and Fruit; Newspapers).

4. The higher cost of high-speed transport may often be mitigated by the reduced cost of packaging and insurance (Scientific equipment and Motor parts).

5. The cost and delay due to actual loss or damage may be minimised by direct air delivery (Radio, Electronic instruments, Household appliances). Insurance costs are lower.

6. Sales revenue can be stimulated by improved marketing (Industrial spares and New models for overseas).

7. Delivery might otherwise not be possible at all (Berlin Air Lift).

8. Pilot schemes of national importance to reduce capital outlay on rail or road may be justified (Air beef).

9. In some cases the cost of transport is lower by air (Supplies in Northern Canada and Alaska).

10. Studies of the distribution pattern of a company's product outlets may show that by use of air transport overseas stores may be so reduced that a far more economic system can be set up.

At the rates now prevailing for air transport, most commodities have been moved for one or more of the above reasons. One must conclude that with a gradual reduction in the freight rates made possible by the introduction of larger and more economic aircraft, with improved airline operational techniques, and with more scientific marketing, the schedule of goods moved by air and the reasons for the use of air transport will be extended progressively.

Surface and air transport costs

We have seen the need to rationalise the significance of the speed and facility provided by air cargo services, and have already suggested that the overall costs of operation should be carefully analysed rather than that the simple cost comparison between various modes of transport should be made, lest a wrong conclusion be drawn. Now there is some danger that these points may appear nebulous and that the aviation protagonist may be accused of adopting specious arguments to support his case. It could be said that there are only two reasons to use the aeroplane for cargo; one is when urgent loads are to be carried great distances, in which case the high cost of air transport in relation to the time saved is likely to be readily acceptable, and the other case is when spare capacity for cargo is available in the holds of passenger aircraft which can therefore carry the extra load with a very small additional cost. The cases cited are indeed significant factors in the use of air cargo transport, but principally in the formative era. We are now rapidly passing out of this stage and other more significant issues are beginning to direct the development of the business. It is generally wise, when studying any air transport problem, to be wary of extrapolating recent practice.

Let us look at some actual cases. Plate 5(a) shows part of a load of light engineering and automotive parts which were transported to the Continent from London. We should note the simple form of packing, light in weight and cheap; the load transfer system consists only of pallets, a light-weight nylon net and/or webbing and frame with foot fixing and a light roller conveyor. The operators can at all stages see what they have to deal with. The total costs of delivery to the cities of northern Europe are generally less when using air transport for such commodities except in the very largest consignments. The table below gives figures from one comparative study.

Two Monotype Machines Weighing 200 kg Sent From London to Amsterdam

	Surface	Air
	£	£
Collection and delivery at dock or airport	1·60	2·50
Packing	15·00	0·75
Freightage	4·50	6·65
Customs clearance	—	0·66
Total	21·10	10·56

This is a typical case taken from many examples in which the higher cost of the packaging necessary for surface transport can provide a ready-made case for the choice of air transport. In the transport of industrial spares and of 'knock-down' parts or sub-assemblies for the motor industry, it is possible to show a considerable economic advantage for the air even when, with the use of ships, the most advantageous dock-side warehouse facilities are already established. In one study completed for a motor manufacturer in the South of England, the unit costs of total transportation to the Netherlands of components for a current product was £22 when using surface methods of transport. By air, using specialised freighter aircraft, the average costs were estimated to be £16·50. This was made up as follows:

	£
Road transport	0·93
Direct aircraft operating costs	9·31
Indirect airline operating costs	4·89
Ground equipment and palletisation	1·33
	£16·46

Other associated cost savings accruing to the manufacturer through use of air transport are not accounted for. A total saving of over £8 per unit or approximately 32 per cent became possible. These costs were dependent on return loads being available. The absence of these, however, caused the project to be abandoned.

The comparative costs of air and surface transportation requires consideration in any study such as this, and a combination of modes will occur more often than not. Air transportation can seldom be affected without road or rail transport also, and even in passenger carriage an increasing interest is being shown in the provision of mixed transport, particularly on road/air operations. British Rail have recently become very alive to the possibilities of encouraging road/rail links between the Midlands and the North and the London airports.

The total cost concept

It was the conclusion of a widely quoted report of the Harvard Business School Research Division that the fullest use of air transport in the United States was made rather by the younger and more alert industries not yet tied to conventions of organisation and supply. It was found that many organisations had, in fact, no exact knowledge of important components of their production costs such as warehousing and were, therefore, in no position to make a true comparison of air and surface transportation (Chapter 7).

It was emphasised that inventories (storage) usually entered into the final issue as to whether air freight was to be used or not. The well-planned business organisation may be expected, therefore, to make an increasing use of air freight while the dire emergency – now a main source of cargo traffic – will not increase to the same extent. The use of air transport to meet the predictable crisis situation already generates a major category of traffic which may be confidently expected to increase considerably, but by calculation of risk to a finer degree than is now common practice, it is possible to balance the greater cost of high-speed delivery by air against reduced inventory and warehousing requirements for materials and the components for production. This technique is already being employed by the motor industry. Application of these principles to new potential markets is of the very greatest importance to the United Kingdom. Where new fields of enterprise are opened up use of the trading aeroplane can reduce capital requirements for the erection of stores and depots.

In its application to the economics of production, air freighting can introduce a higher proportion of variable cost, and its most competitive position will be established where the fixed costs of distribution associated with surface means of transport must be covered by low or medium levels of output. Thus, in the newly developed territories such as the Canadian North West, South America and the Australian Northern Territory, the costs of air distribution will in many cases be less when the cost of new rail and road buildings are taken into account.

Detailed cost analysis provides a means whereby the industrialist can determine the point at which sales volume justifies the acquisition of warehouses and the lower costs of surface transportation. With output lower than this, air transport can be shown to pay off. The Harvard results can be written quite simply as the break-even equation:

$$a = x(c - b)$$

where a = Total fixed cost of stores and depots (including interest, insurance and taxes).

x = Break-even production volume.
c = Air freight variable unit excess cost.
b = Warehouse variable unit cost.

With gradual improvement in the level of air costs, the volume, x, for break-even will be correspondingly increased.

Fig. 5.3 shows a probable distribution of the sea, road, rail and air transport rates in relation to speed. This follows a method of presentation used by Hage in 1948. These curves indicate not only the general increase in rates due to costs during the last fifteen years, but the considerable widening of the speed spectrum which has been achieved since 1948. Such a range of transport rates for surface transportation is now on offer that there is little question that air transport services will often be highly competitive. It is clear that a very careful and detailed comparison of transportation and associated costs is called for if the industrialist is to arrive at a meaningful answer.

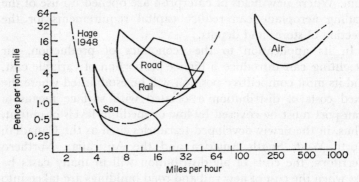

FIG 5.3. Direct Costs as a Function of Air and Surface Speed

If we could assume an empirical value for the average operating cost of surface transportation systems we could use a further analysis to show the indirect savings which need to be achieved through the use of air transport, if an overall economy is sought.

If then our total air operating costs may be written as C units per hour and V_b and P are respectively the block speed and payload, then the specific direct operating costs, say pence or cents per ton-mile

$$= \frac{C}{P \cdot V_b}$$

Now, in the general case, the comparable surface transport costs are less than this $= \dfrac{K \cdot C}{P \cdot V_b}$ where K is less than unity, so that disregarding the time differences or other indirect cost factors, the additional costs of air transport will be

$$(1 - K) \frac{C.R.}{V_b} \text{ per ton moved a distance } R$$

This, therefore, will be equal to the minimum saving in additional costs (i.e. non-transport costs) which it is up to the air transport agent to prove to be possible through use of the aeroplane. Fig. 5.4 shows one presentation of this result for the case where the surface transport vehicle costs are 5 pence per ton-mile. The radial lines show the additional costs of the air transport vehicle for the given stage lengths when aircraft type costs are those given on the curves. The Boeing 707 is the example taken for a long-haul freighter; for the short- and medium-haul conversions (passenger aircraft converted to use as freighters) the DC 3 and DC 7 were selected. The Argosy specialised medium-haul freighter is the heavy-line curve with a

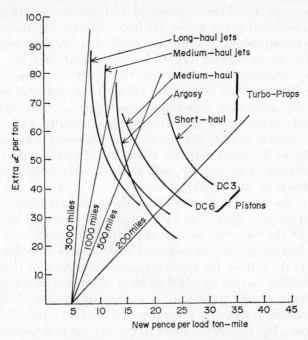

Fig. 5.4. The Higher Unit Cost of Air Cargo Transport

237

minimum direct operating cost of about 4p per capacity ton-mile. If we now assume a 100 per cent increment for indirect cost and a 50 per cent load factor, then the additional costs on a 200-mile flight for this aircraft (at 15p per load ton-mile) compared with 5p surface transport rate is about £30 per ton (or 3p per kilo). This should not often be difficult to equate with indirect savings due to reduced time, packing, insurance and possibly reduced inventory. What is of great interest here is that the additional costs per ton are considerably higher on the large jet air freighter on its design stage, the intercontinental route, than for the medium-size freighter on short or medium stages. With a given load factor it may be slightly better even on a 500-mile stage. Two important conclusions emerge. Firstly the main case for use of air cargo on long-haul routes such as the North Atlantic is likely to lie with better use of capital and simplified distribution methods rather than with lower term-inal costs, packaging etc. Secondly, if indirect savings with air freighting can be made as effectively on short and medium stages as on the long continental and transocean stages on which so much of the traffic has been built up, the short-haul cargo growth could be immense. Naturally, the time saved on the shorter routes will be far less important, but the com-modity provided by air on short-haul service between in-dustrial centres may be of equal value. It is a matter of history that the converted four-engine passenger aircraft became available early on for the Atlantic freight traffic and hence the traditional priority of long-range air transport re-appeared, but just as the great majority of the world's passengers travel on short routes so also the bulk of the world's freight always has moved on shorter stages.

Over 50 per cent of the existing short-haul air cargo is still carried as secondary load in the holds of passenger aircraft. Since on the passenger services the timings are often wrong for cargo and the oversize or awkward load becomes an embarrass-ment to the airline, the special requirement arises for freighter aircraft that can be operated to meet more exactly the traffic requirements and can readily be loaded and unloaded. Rapid load transfer is indeed a necessary facility of all forms of trans-portation, but clearly the more frequently the task needs to be performed, the greater the penalty incurred in any unnecessary delay which conflicts with the objective of high-speed service and wastes the potential revenue-earning airborne life of the aircraft. This feature of the short- or medium-haul aircraft suggests that passenger aircraft conversions cannot provide adequate economic solutions to the problem.

First thoughts on rapid loading

The rapid loading and unloading of the conventional aircraft with a low wing, high floor level and side doors is difficult to achieve. Plate 2 illustrates the problems. Profligate expenditure of time, manpower and equipment is required to achieve rates of loading in such a case in excess of 250 lb/min. The type of equipment which may be required to ease the problem is shown in Plates 4(a) and 5(a).

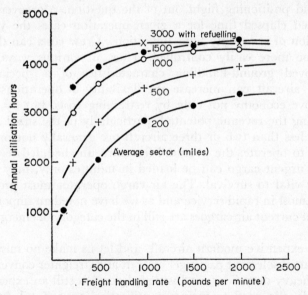

FIG. 5.5. The Freight-handling Rate and its Effect on Utilisation

Fig. 5.5 will illustrate these points further. Here we show the potential aircraft utilisation when various freight-handling rates are achieved with aircraft flying on various stage lengths. Note the advantage in achieving at least 500 lb/min particularly on the short stages. Larger aircraft will however demand higher loading rates.

Utilisation

There are many associated advantages of an increase in utilisation, not least of which is the more rapid development of component lives, particularly in the early years of service with a new aeroplane. High utilisation means fewer aircraft to meet a given traffic target, and with fewer aircraft we can ease the capital burden. But other considerations follow. With reduced ground time we can provide a greater margin for additional flights. A given charter operation can frequently be fitted in where formerly the lengthy handling operation made a tag-end positioning flight out of the question. Moreover, the reduced elapsed time for a given operation eases the vexed question of crew duty hour limitations. Crew costs can therefore be more easily controlled. Thus, in various ways, the improved ground-handling characteristics of a specialised cargo aircraft can increase the flexibility of operations and improve economy not only by restraining costs, but by augmenting the revenue potential, particularly in the small fleet. Since less than two or three aircraft are generally not practicable to operate, the potential for extra unscheduled services when urgent cargo can be loaded in minutes only, may be a factor vital to survival. The air cargo operator must provide the utmost in rapid service and as we have noted an important part of current air cargoes are still in the category of emergency loads.

On expensive modern aircraft, and let us make no mistake, even an obsolescent passenger aircraft after freighter conversion with heavy-duty floors and widened doors is still an expensive aircraft, the need to maintain utilisation on 500-mile stages above 2500 hours per annum is paramount. Fig. 5.5 points clearly to this problem on the shorter routes where the bulk of the world's air work still lies. It tempts us to think of the economic advantage of more sophisticated freight-handling systems which might achieve loading rates exceeding 2000 lb/min on extremely short shuttle operations.

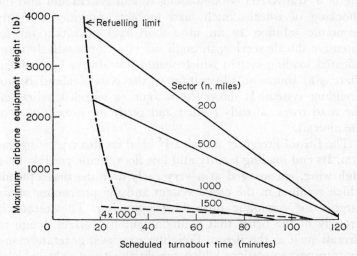

FIG. 5.6. The Justifiable Airborne Equipment Weight

We may take this thinking one stage further. In Fig. 5.6 we introduce the concept of the break-even between airborne weight of freight-handling equipment and the time-saving achieved by such equipment on various stages. These cases were based on realistic figures for time off-service for engineering checks and for practicable operating schedules. We assume, however, that the aircraft is at all times payload-limited by weight and that the time saved by freight-loading improvements is employed in revenue-earning service. These assumptions do not apply in all cases and are discussed further under the heading of cargo density.

For two examples of these principles we can look at the Bristol Freighter and the AW Argosy. A classic example of the rapid loading of the Bristol aircraft as a freighter are the New Zealand Straits Air Freight Express Operations* which link the rail systems of North and South Island. The capacity payload of 14,000 lb is there unloaded and loaded in an elapsed time of twelve minutes. This is a fact which has been observed and

* Now Safeair.

recorded by the author. The rate is well over 2500 lb/min. The time as measured included door opening and closing, positioning of a 'transverser' trolley along its rail system and also the chocking of wheels. Such load mobility provides a highly economic solution to an ultra-short-haul operation on an intensive shuttle service, through use of a comparatively complicated loading system which would not always be justified. Plate 4(a) shows an illustration of the New Zealand Bristol Freighter system. It shows the Cargon (a wheeled pallet) on the road truck, already loaded and ready for presentation to the aircraft.

The Bristol Freighter was clearly ideal for this type of operation. Its end-loading facility and low floor, made possible by a high wing, encouraged at a very early date the development which resulted in the cargo system and the preloading of air cargoes for economic ultra-short operation. The author is strongly of the belief that a fundamentally correct design of aircraft such as the Bristol Freighter can itself generate many air transport operations which simply await the right vehicles for their initiation.

The case for the converted passenger aircraft

The market price of the second-hand passenger aircraft which has been used extensively for all-cargo operations in recent years has fallen to a low level owing to the introduction in the late 1950s of the four-jet long-haul transport aircraft. This is true even of the later marks of the Douglas DC 6 and DC 7, and prop-turbines such as Vanguard and Viscount. It is important, however, not to exaggerate the low price level since a passenger-type aircraft, of which the DC 6 may be taken as an example, usually requires major modification to increase the floor strength and the door size before it can be effectively used for the carriage of cargo. These costs may be very considerable and frequently rise above £100,000 per aircraft, which may raise the book value of the aircraft ready for service with spares to well above £200,000. In the 1970s these figures must be expected to fall sharply.

Bearing in mind the relatively restricted life to be expected from such aircraft, it is to be questioned whether the cost incurred per useful year of operations is not considerably lower in the case of the specially designed aircraft than for the obsolescent type whose life has been prolonged for cargo use. The special aeroplane with its better geometry and layout for loading awkward cargoes, and its performance parameters keyed to the high power (or thrust), and low weight of long-life prop-turbines or jets, will have a life expectation which can be conservatively forecast as at least 10–12 years. This may not counter satisfactorily the argument that financial policy may not permit depreciation accounting to extend for so long a period, but to the operator who can look ahead, and who seeks the strongest competitive position in the air cargo field, the uncompromised design able to accept every load and compatible in all possible respects with modern ground-loading methods, may often be the most economic answer.

The question which needs to be answered is whether the specially designed aircraft is justifiable when second-hand aircraft, perhaps already operated by the same airline, with trained crews available and previous costly engineering experience on the type, can be operated at a cost comparable with the total operating cost per unit of load uplifted, of the new specialised type.

The all-cargo aeroplane has been with us for a long time and the Gloster Company, in 1923, evolved a design with a Rolls-Royce engine which incorporated the then novel feature of a swing tail. The swing tail and the swing nose are still much in vogue and assessments are still being made as to the economic advantage of direct access provided in this way compared with the simpler solution provided by the side door.

The manufacturer must assess for himself the possibilities of building and selling an adequate number of aircraft for any new design so as to spread the cost of development and control the cost of the unit product. Adequate and independent market research is a key factor at this stage and no novel tricks with unproven components can establish essential markets in the competitive situation existing today.

Design of the specialised cargo aircraft

While the dependence of the traffic volume on the freight tariff can be recognised as a basic factor which will determine the design of future freight aircraft and the potential market, it must be kept in mind that the depression of the specific direct

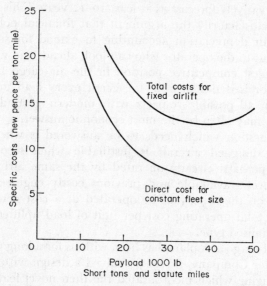

FIG. 5.7. The Influence of Aircraft Capacity on Specific Costs

operating costs may not be possible beyond certain limits. Once again we encounter problems within the province of both the designer and the operator of the aircraft. It can be established, however, that with increasing size a diminishing return in *direct* aircraft operating economy is encountered at gross weights exceeding 200,000 lb and a progressively decreasing advantage must be expected in the *overall* specific cost index, or break-even revenue rate, at gross weights above 100,000 lb. Fig. 5.7 shows the significance of these considerations for an actual case study where the full advantage of the lower unit direct costs of an aircraft exceeding 100,000 lb could not be taken, owing to the route density anticipated and the uncertain reaction on load factor of reduced frequency. This conclusion would not necessarily apply to all operators in all territories. However, the reduced back-load on all but the densest air cargo routes presents a great problem which may be met by such means as the introduction of mixed passenger-cargo services, by multilateral air cargo routes or by special rates for shippers willing to tailor their transport demands. The problem, however, militates against the oversize freight aircraft in the next decade and cautions the aircraft designer to consider the load factor as well as the specific direct operating cost in his overall assessment.

On certain high-intensity route systems such as the North Atlantic the large all-cargo aircraft will undoubtedly pay its way, but the transport aeroplane which can compete with rail and ship in the cheap movement of primary produce and the basic raw materials of industry is not yet within our grasp.

The influence of aircraft size on the operating economy and market potential has been studied by many authorities who have now clearly established the prime factors involved. These are of particular importance to us in this context since the demand for a freight aircraft must be the result of its efficiency in design, and its traffic-generating capability (i.e. load times speed) (Stoessel, 1956).

1. There is an optimum size and number of cargo aircraft to perform a given airlift duty in a given time so as to achieve the most profitable operation.

2. A smaller number of larger aircraft may achieve lower costs per capacity ton-mile because of the inherent advantage of size, but the overall load factor will be lower owing to the reduced frequency of service and lessened flexibility of operation.

3. A larger number of smaller aircraft will be less economic because of their higher specific direct operating costs in spite of the inherent advantages of high-frequency service. There is a minimum size of aircraft below which adequate cargo holds and doors of access are not feasible.

4. For the manufacturer, a compromise in size will often be an advantage since it will tend to maximise his production (lb of airframe and equipment per annum). It will also favour the wider application of his aircraft for allied purposes such as car ferry, mixed passenger/freight and military operators.

Our own study of current airline operations and possible

developments in air freighting during the next decade has suggested the probable breakdown of aircraft types into the four major groups given in the table below.

TABLE 5.6. *The Four Basic Freighter Types*

Long-range: large-capacity and high-performance type. Probable basic passenger aircraft design with jets. A specialised design for cargo handling facility not usually justified. Example: Boeing 707, DC 8. Exception: Lockheed 500 project and Boeing 747 F.

Long/Medium-range: large-capacity. Jet fan or turbo-prop power. Requirements strongly influenced by the military. Many conflicting specifications. Example: Canadair 44, Boeing 727, Vanguard.

Short/Medium-range: medium-capacity with turbo-props. Special freight-handling facility and high wing mandatory. Example: A.W. Argosy, Franco-German Transall. Exception: DC 9/BAC 111.

Short-range, general-purpose aircraft: turbo-prop or piston engines. Example: DH Canada Buffalo, HS 748, Short Skyvan, Pilatus Porter.

Details of aircraft specification

The most careful consideration needs to be given at an early stage in the design of a new project to the fine points of the specification, and to a long list of detailed questions exact answers must be provided. We have described in an earlier chapter how the specification for a new transport aircraft may be drawn up. Here we shall amplify only those points which present special problems in the case of a cargo aircraft.

The consideration of range, payload and performance (in all its aspects) must be a first priority. Clearly the design range for maximum payload is the first decision of all. This will be determined by the operational requirements and will take full account of the weight of cargo tie-down equipment and pallets, and restraint fittings which are likely to be carried. We consider later the hold volume in its relation to payload and the variable density of the payload envisaged. Certain key routes may define the essential stage length for maximum payload uplift and the principal types of cargo aircraft are to some extent circumscribed by the range for which they are designed. The comparative inflexibility of the transport aeroplane with regard to range and payload is a factor which limits the operating economy on many route systems. This is true as much for the cargo as for the passenger aircraft. The North Atlantic stage length, e.g. New York–London (3442 st.m.); Chicago–Los Angeles (1756 st.m.) and Rome–Beirut (1378 st.m.), may be cited as sector lengths which are critical in certain airline networks and may determine a specification without further discussion.

The choice of turbo-fan or prop-turbine power is rarely a simple question of the direct comparison of alternative designs and an assessment of their operating costs. There is quite often a series of factors which have a strong bearing on the choice of power plant and one or more of these may well determine the choice. For example, the development stage of the alternative engines and their status in other more advanced products may be a pertinent factor. Other key issues might be the time between overhauls (TBO) especially at the date of anticipated entry into service, and the provision of overhaul facilities throughout the world. The national investment in the engines considered and the likely programmes of further development which may prolong the life of the airframe-engine combination are points which could not be neglected in any thorough analysis of the economic viability of the project.

Detailed studies of the loading requirements and the access/ loadability features of a new freighter would be carried out today as a matter of course. We discuss in a later section the techniques which may be used to establish optimum features for given sector conditions. End loading and the provision of truck-bed-height floors for all-cargo aircraft require no measurable increase in direct operating cost. This was concluded by Lockheed and by Hawker Siddeley as a result of experience in their designs on Hercules and Argosy aircraft. NASA studies, moreover, have indicated negligible parasitic drag difference between the high- and low-wing configuration when associated with adequately designed fuselage-wing fairings. Moreover, the high-wing layout which is an essential feature of low-hold floor levels provides a better span loading distribution and hence a lower induced drag. The most recent work of Lockheed's seems to confirm this.

But further detailed questions must be answered. What is the required height of the hold floor? Should the sill level be fixed so that no vertical movement occurs during the loading and unloading operation? For what cabin loading should the floor be designed? Is pressurisation essential, and if it is required for the hold, is it also essential for the flight deck and crew quarters? How should the strong points for tie-down be arranged? Are they required on wall and roof? Is a crash barrier essential? Is a power supply for a winch required to facilitate the load transfer operation, or is a manual operation adequate?

The choice of speed will be determined in relation to the design range and the operational use to which the aircraft will be put. On short-haul flights clearly the block speed will be so much reduced below the cruising speed and the best cruising altitude will be so rarely attained, that the case for high subsonic speed in a cargo aircraft can rarely be sustained. On long-haul operations the position will be different and here the case can be made more readily for the jet or ducted fan engine as indicated in Table 5.6.

The designer's contribution to improved economy

It is our thesis that the specialised freight aeroplane can be established if the overall economy of operation can be brought above a critical level. It is certain that the currently operated conversions of passenger transport aircraft are well below that level both in Europe and America. In what way then can the designer hope to improve on these aircraft when he begins again today? It is certain that he is working to stricter levels of airworthiness both in performance and design requirements with their attendant weight penalties.

If we consider this carefully there seem to be two main factors which now provide us with the capability of building a more advanced freight aircraft in the long- and medium-haul category:

1. The availability of well-proven ducted-fan and propeller-turbine power plants of high thrust or power/weight ratio.

2. The data and experience on which the optimum fuselage can be based, taking account of payload, volume usability, accessibility, weight and aerodynamic drag.

In the final analysis many other factors, such as the ground manoeuvring criteria (tyre pressures, LCN, turning radius, wheel track, etc.), wing and tail loading, flight-handling characteristics, must be assessed but decisions here will be taken to meet the various operational and airworthiness design cases and will not necessarily offer us an economic advance on an earlier generation of aircraft. The following table sets out the important factors directly controlling the economy of operation which can be influenced strongly by the aircraft designer. The items of cost listed below may be considered in relation to the discussion on direct operating costs in Chapter 2.

The Designer's Contribution Towards the Reduction of the Operating Costs of Freight Aircraft

DIRECT OPERATING COSTS	
Depreciation and obsolescence of equipped airframe and spares	Low-cost simplified design with long fatigue-free life of major structures. Rapidly extending overhaul life of components with minimum spares. Low rate of type obsolescence, high-efficiency wing, high-utility fuselage for minimum weight penalty and drag. Strongly influenced by the product finding a wide market.
Insurance	Rapidly proven safety record. Good crash landing and ditching characteristics.
Depreciation and obsolescence of power plants and propellers	Cheap, simplified design of adequate power or thrust output in all flight regimes and through full ambient air temperature range.
Fuel and oil costs	Low cruise fuel consumption (over a wide altitude range), and fuel of low price desirable.
Crew costs	Design for simplified control where possible with two flight crew within limits set by Airworthiness Authorities and Air Navigation Regulations. Space provision for diverse crew requirements without a profligate waste of payload volume.

Airframe engineering costs	Simplified design especially of electrical and hydraulic systems and components. High standards of accessibility for component change and long overhaul life of timed items. Ease of inspection and interchangeability.
Engine overhaul costs	Low cost of replacement parts. Long and rapidly extendable overhaul life. Safety in operation and after engine failure.
Landing costs	Generally minimised by designs giving maximum payload per unit of gross weight. On long term, minimum airfield length and strength requirements.

INDIRECT OPERATING COSTS

Administration and general overheads	Not normally influenced directly by aircraft type design. Lower for all-frieght operations. Station costs are greatly reduced by intensive operations on compact route networks.
Ground handling costs	Reduced by simplified freight-handling systems; airborne and ground installations used in conjunction with an aircraft hold designed for freight carriage. High-utility fuselage structure; low-level and special freight doors with minimum weight and drag penalty for reduction of turnaround time and maximum utilisation.
Type introduction costs	Minimised by use of proven components, particularly power plants and other systems. Facilitated by minimum engineer and aircrew training needs, and on-schedule deliveries.

GENERAL FACTORS

Payload capacity	Maximised by strict control of equipped aircraft weight and by careful selection of equipment with payload penalties and economic criteria in mind. Plan fuel requirements to give adequate range flexibility. Foresee extension of maximum gross, landing and zero fuel weights in relation to overall design factors. Ensure potential stretch in aircraft type and design for ultimate development. Obtain adequate recommended cruise powers from engine manufacturers.

Block speed	Maximum values are advantageous to economy, but on short/medium stages a higher proportion of air time is lost through climb, descent and circuits. Careful optimisation of performance at useful altitudes.
Utilisation	This is assisted by effective cargo ground-handling equipment, particularly on short/medium sectors. High utilisation reduces hourly operating costs through reduction of standing charges *et alia*.
Aircraft size	Increased size reduces specific direct operating costs per ton-mile owing to the lessened effect of constant-cost items. A contrary influence tends to increase production costs and cost of spares as size increases.
	Low load factors may further damage the potential economy of large aircraft. Optimisation of size desirable to suit market requirements in detail since simplified direct operating cost assessment is not an adequate criterion for cargo aircraft.

The basis of economic analysis

In consideration of the economic studies that are now an essential tool of civil aircraft design, it may be of interest to note some of the parameters that have been considered valuable in providing effective criteria.

We have described in Chapter 2 the increasingly sophisticated criteria which have been proposed, starting from such simple formulae as ton-miles per gallon and payload times speed divided by gross weight. These factors gave useful guidance in design so long as their limitations are appreciated, but it was not until extensive operational experience became available that the fuller cost parameters were developed. When Mentzer and Nourse developed the operating cost formula for United Airlines in 1930 an important step forward was taken in the development of the economic parameters for transport aircraft. It must be remembered, however, that the economy of the vehicle is not the whole story so far as air cargo economics is concerned. In fact, as we have noted above, the cost of packing, picking up and transfer will on short-haul cargo operations be more significant than transport to the shipper, but the air carrier is naturally concerned primarily with the aircraft and its economic operation on the ground and in the air.

There have recently been many confusing thoughts on the true basis of economic analysis on cargo aircraft. Some tendency has existed for the protagonists of jet and turbo-prop to select favourable criteria for demonstrating the merits of their own respective types of aircraft. Our own conclusion has been that the fullest possible cost analysis should be undertaken using (when the operator can make them available) all the details of the indirect costs of operation. A fleet study on a route system is generally far more satisfactory than a study of an individual aircraft on a specific route. However, when time or the availability of data do not allow a full analysis the operating cost index such as pence per ton-mile can provide an adequate basis for general study. For the air operator it can be shown that this index takes account of the profit and loss element and in effect represents not only cost per ton-mile, but also profitability likely to be achieved per ton-mile.

This can be shown as follows:

If C_d = direct operating costs of the aircraft per hour
and C_i = indirect operating costs per hour,
then C_t = the total operating costs per capacity ton-mile may be written

$$C_t = \frac{(C_d + C_i)}{P \times V_b}$$

where P = Load capacity available, tons
and V_b = Block speed, mph
Now the total costs per annum per aircraft will be

$$U \times (C_d + C_i)$$

U being utilisation in hours per year per aircraft. And the total revenue per annum per aircraft will be

$$l.r.P.V_b.U$$

l being the average load factor
and r being revenue rate per ton-mile assumed.

Thus profit per annum per aircraft is seen to be

$$PV_bU(l.r - C_t)$$

and is dependent upon specific costs per ton-mile, C_t, and also on aircraft capacity P, speed V_b, and U the annual utilisation.

But profit likely to be achieved per ton-mile unit of traffic generated is now simply proportional to

$$r - C_{t/l}$$

which is at a maximum for minimal values of C_t when r and l remain constant.

This simple analysis emphasises the weakness of the direct-operating cost index as an economic criterion for cargo aircraft, for we can see at once that few of the factors discussed earlier are reflected in this analysis: one exception is the aircraft utilisation. Since this, however, will affect only the standing charges such as depreciation, insurance and interest in our equation, a serious defect in the criterion is apparent.

The reason for this shortcoming is that the direct operating cost is based on the unit ton-miles per flight, whereas the merit of the efficient cargo aircraft is that it can generate greater ton-miles in the long term at the expense (because of installed weight) of the ton-miles per flight. Hence the annual revenue side of the cargo operation is crucial where the maximum profitability is the aim with a traffic target not restricted in advance. From these considerations it is the maximum value of $PV_bU(l.r - C_t)$ or profit per aircraft per annum which should determine the optimum cargo aircraft configuration rather than the minimum value of C_t. If we introduce the prime cost of the aircraft, equipment and spares, it is only one short step to compute the return on investment for the aircraft designs under study. In the case of the cargo aircraft the predominance of utilisation times payload times block speed or ton-miles per year suggests the significance of ground loading facilities far beyond the direct effects of utilisation on the standing costs of operation. If then the profitability per ton-mile be taken as a constant, the well-known criterion ton-miles per annum arises as a broad measure of profitability. Nor should we forget the importance of the group behaviour of the aircraft. To assess the fleet of whatever size or the combination of aircraft which make up the fleet, on a network of routes is the only completely adequate approach. This is equally true in the establishment of a specification, in the selection of a new project or in making the best commercial use of aircraft which are in current service.

Thus, the case for the higher loading rate of cargo aircraft follows as much from its effect on the indirect costs of operation as from the influence on direct operating cost. With increased utilisation on the same routes, the administration costs, station costs and engineering base overheads will be spread over a correspondingly greater ton-mile capacity, and the ratio of total costs to direct costs will fall. A favourable result may be anticipated even with some considerable expansion of the route system. However, the most impressive results are to be expected from the intensive utilisation of aircraft on a restricted pattern of routes when even the uneconomic ultra-short sector will often justify close study.

Cargo density and its influence on aircraft design

It has been common practice to make general assumptions with regard to the mean density of cargo when considering the layout of cargo aircraft. The requirement that pallets be made to standard dimensions may to some extent determine the width of the hold and, in the case of an axial-loading layout, the minimum door width. Oversize military equipment, often motorised, has determined the minimum vertical clearance required, but the length of the hold has in the past been empirically established perhaps with the requirement of conversion to a trooping role in mind. A check on the mean density offered when carrying maximum payload on shorter than critical sectors cannot now be considered adequate. Studies conducted more recently have established that only 85–93 per cent of the total airlift capacity of an aircraft designed for mean density will become available in actual operations. The order of loss in payload is determined largely by the density distribution of the cargo which, in the course of the loading operations, is actually packed into the aircraft. Much will also depend upon the shape of the hold cross-section, the proportion of the floor which will be usable on account of the pallet or container system employed and, even more important, on the usable height of the aircraft hold and restrictions which may be caused by limitations in the dimensions of access to the hold. All these factors will influence the loadability of the hold, but the density distribution of the cargo will determine the use that can be made of the loadable volume (or net cargo space) to lift the maximum payload on the sector.

By the selection of loads and by the creation of stockpiles whereby an easing of the variation in load density can be achieved, it may be possible to approach close to average cargo density. Clearly, however, there are strict limits to the possibility of achieving this on civil or on military aircraft, bearing in mind the significance of high-speed delivery in the promotion of air service.

It has been shown (Bickner, 1957) that the capability of one aircraft operating on a route which provides a certain cargo distribution will be very dependent on the capability of other types of aircraft operating on the route. The above report cites the C 97 and the C 124 operating a route together whereby an overall high-payload ratio was achieved through the C 124 carrying the low-density cargoes and the C 97 carrying the higher-density cargoes more suitable for its high-density hold. Thus, two complementary types can in this way provide a more economic airlift capability than either type operating above. This arrangement appears to have little application to civil air operations.

It is the common civil and military experience that air cargo density can be assumed to be approximately constant only in very exceptional circumstances, and full account must be taken of its variability in any proper assessment of aircraft capability whether in the project stage or on actual operations. Statistical evidence of the variability of cargo density is, however, essential if we are to provide a measure of the volume required in a given aircraft to achieve adequate airlift capability and also if we are to optimise the vehicle available under given conditions. Studies completed in the USA, Canada and Europe are available. These indicate a remarkable consistency in the mean densities and variance (or standard deviation) of the consignments offered for air transport. Average values tend to be very much higher than some air operators assert, and it is clearly the small but inconvenient proportion of aircraft loads of especially low density which gives emphasis to the problem (and remain in people's minds).

The Rand Report which was referred to above was a study of the variation of cargo density encountered in military transport operations and its influence on the airlift capability of existing transports and on new aircraft projects. This indicated the scale of variation based on daily shipments airlifted to the Pacific Area and drew conclusions of the greatest significance. It concluded that the relative cost of shipment depends upon the densities of commodities uplifted and that realistic cost comparisons cannot be made on the basis of weight alone. Cost analysis must, it was shown, take into account the relative frequency with which flights may be space-limited as well as weight-limited. Cost factors may be established which can aid in establishing the true cost of transporting goods of various densities, and also in establishing the design characteristics of an aircraft hold capable of airlifting given commodities for the minimum cost.

A paper read in 1962 by the Vice-President of Seaboard World Airlines, Inc., on the Canadair Unitised Loading System gave figures for the density distribution of air cargo carried on flights terminating and originating at New York on the Atlantic route. An average density on westbound flights of 11·54 lb per cubic ft was recorded. For eastbound flights, a density of 11·06 lb per cubic ft was reported.

During three weeks in October 1962 a study was conducted jointly by Hawker Siddeley and BEA. In this case the loads carried on a random sample of Argosy flights out of and into London Airport were analysed. The routes and the density of each consignment of cargo, the density on the pallet and the aircraft payload density were recorded. The overall results are shown in Fig. 5.8 for all flights included in the study. A mean density of approximately 12 lb per cubic ft was associated with this. The inbound density and deviation was considerably lower than the outbound density and deviation. Table 5.7 summarises these figures.

Because of the variation in the average density of consignments offered for air transport, particular consideration must be given not only to the most effective loading methods used for

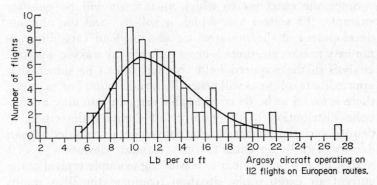

Fig. 5.8. European Air Cargo Density Distribution

the aircraft in current operation so that high-payload factors and high-volume utilisation is achieved, but also that the most economic hold design is provided in the project and development stage. Furthermore, some attempt must be made to estimate the penalty of not providing the optimum volume to suit the form of the density distribution and in respect to the operational pattern over which the aircraft is likely to spend its active life. Estimates of the cost of airlifting commodities of differing physical characteristics will also be of the greatest importance and this will in due course become essential to the derivation of more precise rate structures which are now widely thought to be necessary in the interest of the well-balanced and economic growth of air cargo traffic.

TABLE 5.7. *BEA Argosy Cargo Density*

	density lb/cu ft		
Route	Total number flights	Mean density per flight	Standard deviation of density per flight
Total all routes	112	12·23	3·95
To London	43	10·39	3·22
From London	69	13·30	3·86
			October 1962

Since the exact use to which an aircraft will be put (for example, the sectors over which it will fly) and the ultimate development of the performance and payload capability are not easy to forecast, there is great difficulty in making a precise analysis of the required hold volume. It can be shown that approximate solutions will generally be adequate. For example, there is found to be no considerable error in assuming a parabolic distribution of the number of flights with respect to density variation and it may be convenient to consider a mean density of 12 lb per cubic ft with a standard deviation (σ) of $\frac{1}{3}$ of this, or 4 lb per cubic ft as a working example typical of the current air cargo traffic situation (compare the BEA results given above). We should, however, bear in mind that there is a wide variation in the actual loading requirement through seasonal and directional factors, the backlog that may be available for load selection, the longitudinal trim situation which may sometimes arise, the variation in the stage length flown and the fuel reserves demanded. There will even be some variation in space lost in tying down or stacking the load, with or without pallets, on similar types of aircraft. The summation of the variances arising from all these factors may, in some airlines, create a density variation widely different from that suggested above.

In an aircraft designed for an average density of cargo, with due allowance for unusable space, tie-down volume, gangways, etc., on 50 per cent of flights the aircraft would be expected to be volume limited; in other words, it would on those occasions be unable to lift the maximum payload. Clearly, extra volume is required, but volume requires additional structure whether in length of hold or greater cross-section with a concomitant increase in weight and cost, and with a small-order increase in wing area and power with the inevitable malevolent spiral which ensues involving again higher drag, weight, power and cost. The compromise situation will be sought by the designer, with the general tendency to determine fuselage volume on the minimum side so long as no specific conflict with an operational requirement is seen to arise.

If the usable hold volume were increased by 1 per cent then overall an increase of approximately half of one per cent in payload uplift should be achieved. In this hypothetical case, where the mean density and the variance in density (σ) are respectively taken as 12 lb/cu ft and 4 lb/cu ft, it can be shown that for a normal distribution the result will be that on about 15 per cent of occasions a density as low as 8 lb/cu ft (12–4) will still be inadequate to accommodate the loads offered. Any requirement for density lower than this will carry with it large associated diseconomies for the reasons given above.

In an unpublished study which sought to establish the economic penalty arising from variations in the density factor, the following results were obtained. A range of hypothetical cargo aircraft designs were projected to meet a 2500 nautical miles design range with 70,000 lb payload and using prop-turbine power. An uncompromised all-cargo hold design was adopted which allowed fuselage stretch to vary the effective hold density. Density variation was assumed to vary symmetrically in accordance with the results indicated above for European operations.

1. The design density for minimum direct operating cost was approximately 22 per cent below the mean density for the route system considered and with the density variations assumed.

2. When designed for the average cargo density the direct operating costs per ton-mile of cargo uplifted were increased by $4\frac{1}{2}$ per cent compared with the optimum design of lower overall density.

These results do not greatly differ from those published earlier in the Rand Study.

In the life of an aircraft it may be difficult to judge the variation in density which will arise on different routes and services. However, it is essential for the aircraft designer to make the most realistic estimates possible from data obtained from the potential operators so as to give full significance to the economic value of the cargo-hold volume.

The cost of providing air cargo transport

One major reason for a sound understanding of the cost of air cargo service is the need to establish a proper basis for the establishment of air cargo rates. Instead of approaching this problem from the point of view of the aircraft design and the

259

estimated direct and indirect cost of operation, many parts of which are not amenable to accurate assessment and take little account of the route pattern, the utilisation expected, and the anticipated traffic, an alternative method based on historical cost data could be used. The movement of cargo has been closely related to the cost of the service, and a deeper insight into the build-up of the cost in recent operations might give considerable guidance if adjustments called for by improvements in technique or by use of new equipment are made.

A close understanding of the cost elements in current air cargo operations is difficult to achieve for many reasons. Firstly, no adequate record of the costs of this side of the business have been kept. In the USA the CAB Form 41 reports do not separately record the essential independent cargo data. No item in the accounts is purely for cargo; for example, no record of the number of consignments is made. The records of the British Air Corporations are also far less well documented for cargo than is the case with passengers and the results published in the reports and accounts make little contribution to the study of air cargo costs. Other British aviation statistics are unfortunately of very little assistance in such air transport investigations whether for passenger or cargo operations.

SARC study for the CAB

In 1962 a study was prepared by the Systems Analysis and Research Corporation for the Civil Aeronautics Board which aimed primarily at deriving the origins of US domestic air cargo cost behaviour within the limits of available information. It sought to provide also a yardstick by means of formulae for the measurement of the principal cost elements of air cargo transportation. These formulae were designed to provide measures of cost elements such that the changes in cost resulting from changes in the scale of operation or volume of traffic, or in its composition, might be estimated with reasonable accuracy. Direct reading of the original source material (*The Cost of Air Cargo Service*, 1962) is to be recommended, but the principal method and conclusions of this work are of such significance as to justify a summary here.

With the above objectives in mind, it was thought to be inadequate to approach the problem by means of engineering studies (i.e. the study of direct operating costs) or time and motion study (i.e. stop-watch field work at the air freight base), still less by the analysis of average CAB recorded costs, and a technique based on the methods of a controlled experiment was adopted. While not possible to carry out in a fully rigorous manner the concept was utilised so as to form the framework of an analysis of the partially recorded costs of cargo service in selected trunk carriers and all-cargo operators in the United States over a range of operating scale and traffic volume and with some variation in the passenger/cargo composition.

Such studies are extremely difficult to effect because of the limitations of information using past records and the lack of significantly large samples of traffic and cost at both ends of the scale of volume selected. The international carriers, for example, have levels of cost higher than that of the domestic trunk combination operators, and the local service and all-cargo airlines operate on a relatively small scale which introduces high specific or unit costs due to the lower level of investment in specialised equipment and operational intensity usually associated with smaller companies. Additional problems arise due to the combined operations (passenger, mail and cargo) promoted by most carriers (even by the so-called all-cargo operators who provide extensive passenger charter services). Associated problems arose when differentiating fixed and variable cost elements, common and joint costs and the special groups of cost such as discretionary costs and terminal costs which require judgment and familiarity with the day-to-day working of the industry.

In the outcome the method of analysis proposed by SARC enables a reasonable degree of accuracy to be achieved when estimating the cargo service cost of the medium-sized combination carrier (i.e. the carrier uplifting cargo on passenger flights), especially the long-term marginal costs of the efficient operator. This must be accepted as being the most meaningful basis of which rate determination can be established even though considerable adjustment might need to be made by the licensing authority. Clearly the rates at which air cargo will move will depend upon the value which industry sets upon the utility of time, this being the premium commodity which the aeroplane has for sale. The demand will be that schedule of prices which will be paid for the whole range of advantages in time and place.

The total costs of air cargo service

Studies completed on the behaviour of marginal costs in air operating companies with varying scales of output have shown that beyond some minimum output the total operating costs increase proportionately with the increase in the transport product. We may then draw up a relationship between total costs and the output or product as shown in Fig. 5.9. The marginal cost, or increase in cost per unit increase in output, is the slope of the cost curve and will be at a minimum for the medium-to-large-size transport organisations which have generated enough traffic to have reached out beyond the threshold level of efficient scale and equipment developments, but have not reached the situation of excessive size which may as yet be affecting only three or four of the largest European airlines. We note that the minimum overall cost per unit of capacity is to the right of the linear portion of Fig. 5.9.

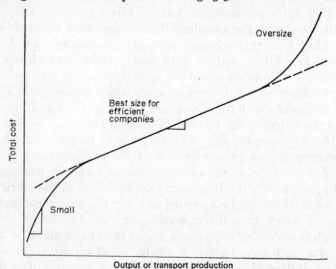

FIG. 5.9. The Effect of Scale on Operating Economy

The SARC study in 1962 has developed this theme as the principal framework for the establishment of a sound costing and rate structure in the USA. We suggest that this concept can be applied quite fairly to the development of a new transport system such as an all-cargo service between the UK and Northern Ireland. Although BEA, taking all operations into account, are probably within the linear range of the total cost curve, the other airlines providing service on the routes to Northern Ireland are likely to be on the steep lower section of the curve. BEA within its all-cargo operating activity, however, is still working on a very limited scale, with a relatively low level of aircraft utilisation, high crew costs and a still minimal investment in ground-handling equipment and cargo operations training. Moreover, the overhead costs of the Corporation reflect the high promotional charges associated with extensive international passenger services. It is therefore probable that a steadily improving level of marginal costs is to be anticipated through the 1970s, on extended Vanguard operations which should enable the costs of well planned air-cargo transport to become progressively more competitive. One would not in any way wish to disparage the fine operating record of BEA. with the Argosy fleet since it came into operation in December 1961, but a comparison of the Corporation's direct-cost figures for the Viscount 806 and the AW 650 shows up the economy of scale and type experience which the more highly intensive operations of the former were able to achieve. The above proposition has been very well substantiated in the recent history of air transport, and air cargo traffic of which the growth rate has been considerable over many years, holds out every expectation of a similar pattern of advance.

A study by E. Wiegenfeld for the Department of Management Studies at the London Polytechnic (May 1964) took account of the above and drew attention to the need for a flexible method of cargo rate fixing. He was concerned with the manifold characteristics of commodities which affect the marginal cost of transport. The desired level for any commodity rate will be that at which the commodity volume which is attracted makes its maximum contribution to the fixed costs of the operation. The marginal long-term costs would be used for assessing the minimum contribution which a commodity should make if it were readily calculable. The difficulty here is an administrative one, and this difficulty explains perhaps the usual recourse to average rather than marginal costs but it is thought that more effort could be expended on rational cargo rate development which takes more account of the cost of air transport and the limitations of the vehicle itself. We put forward, therefore, the following recommendations from the above studies on cargo aircraft and the ensuing discussion on rates.

1. That the rate structure should be flexible and, if necessary, experimental and not linked to the requirements of any special interest, but developed for the long-term advantage of an expanding and economically viable industry. Some rates might rise though more should fall.

2. That rates should reflect the actual costs of providing service and take account of the particular nature of the commodity. Its density, shape, weight, vulnerability, unit value and environmental requirements should be taken into account.

3. Carriers should be required to provide separate cargo transport statistics in parallel with passenger statistics with regard to operations and finance. The provision of small controlled samples of operating and load particulars for use in airline development and by industry planning staffs would be of special value. It seems particularly desirable that scheduled air service operators should be required to provide just such essential records for basic research on routes and rates as here proposed. Air cargo transport is today in such active development that all possible information is essential for the adequate planning of future projects.

BIBLIOGRAPHY

The Future for Air Cargo, I – Europe, II – North America, Whitworth Gloster Aircraft Limited, 1962

E. D. KEEN, 'Freighters – A General Survey', *Jnl. Roy. Aero. Soc.*, April 1959

SIR RALPH COCHRANE, 'Development of Air Transport during the War', *Jnl. Roy. Aero. Soc.*, 1947

H. ASHTON, *The Time Element in Transportation*, The American Economic Review, 1947

R. F. STOESSEL, 'Air Freighter Suitability', *SAE Journal*, April 1956

R. E. BICKNER, *Cargo Density and Airlift*, Research Memorandum, Rand Corporation, Jan. 1957

J. T. FARRAH, *Operational Experience with the Canadair Unitized Loading System*, SAE First International Air Cargo Forum, Nov. 1962
The Cost of Air Cargo Service, Systems Analysis and Research Corporation, June 1962

McCONACHIE and BAJWA, *Cargo Density as it Affects Aircraft Design*, SAE Second International Air Cargo Forum, May 1964

A. H. STRATFORD, *Economic Basis for Design of a Freight Aircraft*, Lecture to New Zealand Division, Roy. Aero. Soc., Dec. 1957

I. H. GRABOWSKY, *Northern Australia. The Contribution of Air Transport*, Australian Institute of Political Science, 1955

A. H. STRATFORD, *The Growth Rate of Air Cargo*, Financial Times Aerospace Review, June 1963

W. J. BAUMOL, *Economic Theory and Operations Analysis*, Prentice-Hall, 1965

G. BESSE, *Comparative Examination of Some Air Freight Forecasts*, ITA Study, 1963

Report on Survey of Potential Air Freight Market, PD. GEN/14, Short Brothers and Harland

BREWER, KAST and ROSENZWEIG, *The Europe-Asia Market for Air Freight*, University of Washington, Seattle

BREWER and DE COSTER, *The Nature of Air Cargo Costs*, University of Washington, 1967

ROBERT HORNBURG, *The Air Cargo Container and its Impact on Aircraft Requirements*, International Air Cargo Forum, Frankfurt, 1970

Year's Report on Air Cargo, Aviation Week, 26 Oct. 1970, 1971

SIR ANTHONY MILWARD, 'The Development and Future of Air Cargo, 24th British Commonwealth Lecture, *Jnl. Roy. Aero. Soc.*, Nov. 1968

Conference Papers, SAE Fifth International Forum for Air Cargo, Frankfurt, June 1970

6 Mechanical Load Transfer Systems

Introduction

Ground handling, whether by mechanical/electrical means or by hand labour, is in its essence the transport of loads over very short distances. It can be considered as ultra short-haul transport and has become an industry today in its own right with a technology and an armoury of tools which have an application in industries of the most diverse kind in every part of the world. In its application to air transport, mechanical handling as a load transfer technique differs in few particulars from its more general form in a medium-size industrial plant where loads of up to ten tons are moved on conveyors or vertical-lift trucks. The essential need is to transfer cargo from road or rail to the warehouse floor or ramp and from there to truck or other vehicle for transport to the aircraft. The reverse process is obviously equally necessary and it may be possible at one or at both ends of the load-transfer process to introduce a powered or hand conveyor system, thereby cutting out the vehicle and the costs associated with its individual control.

In the early days of air freight, the only real advantages which operators could press on potential shippers were the speed of delivery and security in transit. These advantages are reflected in the existing structure of the air freight industry, the basic characteristics of which are the high-premium charges for speed and the consequent dominance of high-value, low-weight consignments and emergency shipments. Most of this traffic has been carried in the holds of passenger aircraft.

This era is closing. We described in the last chapter the attraction of major economies in packing, distribution networks, warehousing. These advantages are creating a demand for the routine delivery by air of a much wider range of goods and manufactures. The rapid growth of the business has established the need not only for specialised types of freight aircraft and for increased attention to cargo handling and loading methods, but for the application of advanced methods of materials movement throughout the airport terminal area.

Roller conveyors are commonly used to provide easy mobility at low cost in unitised cargo loading systems. Consignments are generally consolidated on pallets, and tied down to the pallet with a nylon rope net or other similar means. Each pallet, loaded to a maximum weight of several tons, may be moved about the freight area and into and within the aircraft hold by two or three men, using roller conveyor. To make such systems flexible light detachable lengths of conveyor are sometimes used. For larger pallets power assistance may be required. Standard conveyor track has many further applications in solving transport and handling problems. These may include the side loading of converted passenger aircraft, the loading of rail and road vehicles and the movement and storage of goods generally in freight sheds, factories and warehouses.

We have noted in Chapter 5 that a key factor in the economics of freight aircraft operation, particularly on the short to medium stages, is the cargo-handling system. The economic contribution to be made by an efficient system lies in the reduction of cargo handling costs, in allowing greater scope for high aircraft utilisation, in increasing the revenue-earning potential and in reducing aircraft operating costs. It is apparent at once from a most cursory investigation of the handling of air cargo by means of the mobile truck that this is a costly mode of load transfer. The first cost, maintenance expense and operation of individual flat bed or lift trucks is extremely high when considered in relation to the duplication of the units required to cover the overlap in aircraft arrival and departure, unserviceability, working hours and overtime. Moreover, a service must be provided at all points likely to be covered in an airline network. In a study undertaken to assess the requirement for five-ton flat-bed trucks to serve three aircraft of twelve-ton payload when scheduled on an intensive European network, it was computed that 78 vehicles were required! Since a high utilisation of these trucks could not be achieved for this one operational system alone, without further local work being provided (which would jeopardise unacceptably their availability), the overall first cost of the truck service at the overseas stations was a major item approaching that of one-third the price of one aircraft. When the other capital costs of mechanical handling systems are also taken into account we may well be prepared to start again and study alternative means of load transfer.

Countless studies have been made and reference is given below to a number of the most significant ones. Stoessel has pointed out that the road haulier has brought costs to a level close to $10 per ton (£3·6 per ton), and he sought to locate the principal means for bringing down the US air operators' costs to a more realistic level.

In a paper presented to the Air Cargo Forum at Montreal, Stoessel (1964) identified the effects due to aircraft type, the size and weight of the shipment, the use of containers and the methods of allocating indirect operating costs as principal factors in determining the level of cargo aircraft ground-handling costs. He found that the use of squared instead of contoured pallets will decrease the air cargo terminal labour element by 15 per cent. This saving, although amounting to only 5 per cent of the combined origin and destination terminal costs, is equivalent to 0·1 cent per revenue ton-mile for a 1200-mile sector. In this study the air carrier's terminal costs per ton were decreased by more than 75 per cent when one single-piece 2000-lb shipment was handled instead of five individual pieces of equivalent weight. As in other studies of this kind, documentation and load control was identified as the largest single item of cost affected by the unitised load. Consolidation by the shipper is likely to lead to considerable economies in load preparation, packaging and management. It is also universally rewarded with a bulk rebate from the air carrier, but shipper, carrier and customer ideally must share in the overall reduction in cost.

Pallets

To find optimum solutions to the design of equipment for low-cost load transfer the right balance and reaction between matter, money and men must always be sought. In this context we mean goods for transport, the capital investment in the equipment, both airborne and on the ground, and the handling labour available.

From practical experience the airborne pallet has been found to be the universal solution. Following wide use in industry, special development for the military user, and modified to meet the conditions set by the commercial air carriers, the pallet has now developed into a limited number of forms which we should identify.

1. The *Flexible Pallet*, as designed by Douglas for the DC 7 F is light in weight and low in cost. Special care in lifting is required and a transfer pallet may be used. American Airlines have tested a flexible five-ply pallet of this type designed by the American Machine and Foundry Co.

2. The *Rigid Pallet*, such as used on the BEA Argosy freighters and designed by Whitworth Gloster. Also used by Eastern Airlines in the L 1049 H Flying Freighters and designed by the Eastern Rotorcraft Corporation of Pennsylvania. Both these types use a light alloy construction and operate on rollers within guide rails. Locking devices are provided. This type gives longer life and has the advantage of being a fully stressed structure allowing direct transfer to surface vehicles and/or fork-lift trucks. The much publicised USA Military Air Transport Service standard '463L' pallet is based on this principle, but is of added strength to allow hoisting from the four corners.

3. The *Slide Pallet*, as utilised on the Canadair CL 44, is of a flexible design and is used directly on the aircraft floor. A special material known as 'Nylatron' consisting of nylon impregnated with molybdenum-disulphide, was developed to meet the need for low friction consistent with good mechanical life.

In the various aircraft applications differences in design of detail arise. Aircraft such as the CL 44 require mechanical propulsion for the slide pallet in spite of the low inherent weight of the airborne system. The heavier and more complex MATS system requires power and the provision of special load transfer vehicles. The Rolamat system of the Argosy requires neither power nor special vehicles, since the light-alloy pallet when loaded can be moved by hand (usually by two men) in or out of the front or rear door directly over a bridge ramp on to a standard load truck at the same 4-ft level above the ground (see Plate 5b).

There is a striking lack of uniformity in the design solutions indicated here, but it must be remembered that we are providing for a range of aircraft from converted DC 7 and British and Canadian prop-turbine aircraft to the long-range jets of the most advanced conception. When we consider the other and more vital aspects of standardisation, the non-uniformity becomes yet more apparent.

Great progress is at present being made in the programmes of standardisation, both in the United States and in Europe. It is true that among the pallets referred to above we can find a variation in width varying from 80 in to 125 in. The standards adopted by the USAF for pallet dimensions, however, now seems likely to be accepted internationally. These are 88 in wide by 54 in or 108 in. The American Standards Association, the British Standards Institution and European counterparts have now agreed in principle that such a standard can be accepted in due course for pallets for use on air and surface transport vehicles. These dimensions provide the essential advantage of compatability with road and rail transport. Maximum permissible road dimensions dictate a limit of less than 8 ft in one direction and the need for the closest collaboration between air and road does not need to be reiterated. Nevertheless the most economic use of the available cube in Boeing 707 and DC 8 jet freighters has encouraged recent moves towards an 88 in × 125 in standard. This is supported by TWA, PAA, American Airlines and United Airlines. The development of even larger jet freighters makes standardisation in all particulars most difficult to achieve.

With fully effective aircraft-truck load transfer systems, thirty-minute turn-round times become readily feasible with medium payload aircraft such as the Argosy. The DC 7 and L 1049 conversions require more time, because of sill height and side doors, unless rather costly special arrangements are made. On the long-haul jets such a load transfer time is less essential and certainly the need to introduce highly sophisticated loading systems is not likely to pay off until aircraft size has increased beyond the 85,000/90,000 lb payloads of current types. On the Boeing 707–320 C jet transport (convertible to all-cargo use in less than two hours) thirteen standard pallets can be loaded by nine men with the special high-lift loading truck in one hour. The

Douglas DC 8 F jet trader has a similar capability. Studies of North Atlantic air cargo growth have suggested the need in the mid-1970s for all-cargo transports of very much greater size. The freight hold capacity of the Boeing 747 is already providing an immense increase in capability, but the all-freight version of this aircraft, the Boeing 747 F, is planned to commence Atlantic operations with Lufthansa in 1974. This is related to the expectation of increasingly competitive total distribution costs by air on the key North Atlantic routes, and the penetration of air competition into a widening market of lower-value goods. The need for specialised automatic handling equipment to deal with this situation is not by any means remote in time. Large payloads will require more rapid unit loading rates if the high-cost flight equipment is to be well utilised. Remember, too, that at higher flight speeds the rapidity of the turn-round assumes added significance. Study of these problems in detail so as to establish the right balance of priorities for the development both of short-haul and long-haul flight and ground equipment for air cargo transport is an essential task for the various industries concerned over the next few years.

On the airport side far too few investigations have been made of the economics of the handling of cargo. There is an urgent need for close study of the use of towed trucks, standard chassis vehicles, fork-lift trucks and labour. The training of labour and the grades of labour to be trained is of the greatest significance in decision-taking on mechanical equipment of all kinds. We discuss further in a later section the use of computers in the control of air cargo in the terminal.

Advantages and disadvantages of containers

Containers give great advantage in protection to the shipper as well as to the carrier. They guard against weather, adverse temperature, damage and theft. By unitising the load they reduce handling labour and cost, thereby increasing the speed of throughput, minimising management, labour and paper-work, but there are adverse factors which must be clearly recognised. Containers of adequate specification for air and and surface transport are expensive to manufacture. They must be maintained in good condition and must be subject to operational control like other transport equipment. The movement control of containers is an added cost which it is easy to forget. Empty containers must be returned to the point of origin.

The container has the major disadvantage of weight and loss of volume which inevitably results in a reduced potential payload per flight and can be corrected only by an increased utilisation of the aircraft. This will involve not only an increase in the number of flights until an equal payload has been uplifted, but ideally that number of flights which will ensure that the revenue less cost (or the total profitability) of the operation is at least as great as it was without the use of containers. The assessment of this situation will require that the most exact figures that are available should be fed into the computations.

Some air carriers have reported that the weight of unitising containers can be more than offset by the indirect cost savings effected. When developed in smaller sizes, or modules, it is possible for efficient loading and stacking to be achieved with least volume lost on the pallet. The Lockheed Aircraft Company have reported on this. The use of containers may be greatly encouraged by the greater efficiency and economy in handling larger units of cargo. It may then be acceptable to load the container (which is by its enclosed design far heavier than a pallet, but with a higher loading efficiency) on to medium and large sizes of transport aircraft. Unfortunately, the weight limited payload efficiency of a container decreases considerably with small sizes and at least an 8 ft × 8 ft × 20 ft container is required to provide an efficiency approaching 80 per cent. Efficiency here is defined as the load disposable with the container minus the container tare weight as a ratio of the weight of payload displaced. Results of the American analysis indicate that the economically acceptable tare weight for a container, because it is displacing potential cargo, is greater for lower rates of revenue return, and for lower load factors.

It is clear that we have reached the stage of full acceptance of the pallet for the load transfer of air-transportable products, but the case for the container is less easy to make. Its greater weight and loss of volume in the transport vehicle, whatever its type, needs to be justified. Handling costs may be reduced and loss and/or damage by theft, mishandling or weather can be important factors, but in air transport the weight penalty can be over-riding. Increasing use of the container will, however, be made without doubt to meet special cases, and may provide a special advantage to individual industries and their products. New materials must be expected to open up new uses in the future. Standard dimensions and systems of loading and location on the aircraft will be as essential with containers as with pallets. More-over, as in the case of pallets, the justification for the weight of containers is easier to prove on the shorter stages, such as within Europe, than on the longer transocean sectors. This is because time saved in loading will arise more frequently and thus offers a greater total gain in revenue potential.

The road truck operator who is becoming increasingly linked with railway flat-bed operators, especially in the USA and in other countries where long-distance transportation is a high-cost factor, is now developing a keen interest in standardisation. On the roads this means enclosed containers. The long-term influence of this on air transport will be immense. Every air journey has two road journeys to complete the total transport function and large fleets of road vehicles will be required to support the larger air cargo vehicles which are likely to appear in each succeeding generation.

The use of containers on the railways and on the shorter-stage shipping routes is now developing rapidly, but while some loss of cube utility arises there also, the penalty is easier to bear. Full investigation of the many factors must be made and air carriers have been actively investigating the economics of the rate of exchange between weight and cost of pallets and containers versus the time-saving and potential revenue-earning advan-tages. Nor should the labour and cost of handling the smaller items without consolidation be thought of only in the small loading operation. The costs of sorting, labelling and tracing the package has become an immense burden to the airlines, vital though this business is to their survival. The scale of air cargo growth has made the pallet the first essential stage of a modernisation programme which will develop throughout the whole complex of air cargo distribution management and must eventually encompass the container also.

Cargo comprises mail as well as freight, but freight, by present scale and rate of growth, presents the central problem. It varies widely in size of consignment and in overall weight and density. It varies in value, in fragility, in its need for a special environment, and in the urgency of shipment. But the uneven flow of cargo in the two directions on a route is a more frequently quoted disadvantage than its advantageous passivity. In this it surely possesses the greatest possible advantage over passenger traffic. Cargo can't walk upstairs, but it can be processed and moved along the most efficient path determined for it. It is in this area of the controlled movement of freight between carriers and between the various modes of transport, including the load transfer and the customs inspection processes, that the major advance in operating economy can now be expected.

Containerisation on ships

The problems confronting the shipping industry are only in certain details different from those of the air transport industry. The loss of volume is clearly of far less significance than the weight loss on a transport aircraft. However, the case for the container has not been easily won even in this industry except on shorter runs. It is possible to reduce the turnaround of a vessel on the coastal trade if converted to full container service, from fifteen days to less than two days. In this case a gain of thirteen days' steaming service is exchanged for a loss of perhaps 30 per cent of its measurement tons. It may be possible to operate a service on short coastal runs with a considerably reduced fleet, but when the voyage distance becomes greater (exceeding 5000 nm) it is less easy to make the case for the container service. The British Railway handling costs at Heysham, where container handling has been standardised now for several years, are in the order of 10 per cent of conventional handling costs. The stage lengths operated by British shipping companies are in general longer than 3000 miles. Even the New York–Liverpool run was for a long time a boundary case. The introduction of deep-sea long-haul container services such as those of Overseas Container Lines between the UK and Australia indicates a gradual change in the economic situation due largely to the increase in the cost of labour at the docks. These services however have yet to prove themselves profitable since they are developing in a period of low growth in the UK-Australia trade, and difficult labour reaction. Use of the container is at present no more attractive to the air transport operator on inter-continental flights. Study has shown that the case for the container cannot yet be made on the North Atlantic sectors with subsonic jet cargo transports.

Functional and economic analyses carried out by the National Research Council of the National Academy of Sciences in the United States sought to break down the handling of shipborne cargo into its principal cost segments. These studies included all operations from the breaking down of bulk upon receipt at the terminal to the positioning inside the cargo hold and securing for sea. Although not necessarily applicable to all cargo situations, it was apparent that the major contributions to improved economy were the increase of cargo unit size, which should be maintained as nearly as possible to standard dimensions, and the cutting out of bulk-breaking and reloading. These objectives are readily achieved by use of containers.

The loading costs with a conventional ship are comparable to those quoted earlier in this chapter for US road haulier costs, and should at least be matched by small-pallet loading on current transport aircraft.

Many research studies have been carried out in the US and in Europe into the design of containers and of ships for containers. It is estimated that in many areas 75 per cent of the cargo carried is suitable for containers, but seldom will pure containerisation be justified without provision for other cargo. Many of the lessons being learnt in the shipping industry may be absorbed with advantage by the air carrier and manufacturing industries at this formative period.

It is concluded that in many situations a feasibility study into the case for conversion to containerisation will be well justified, especially when high labour rates apply and when the route length is no greater than 3000 miles. There may then be a good expectation that the high cost of containers and ship redesign or conversion will be economically justifiable. Comparable methods may be used for Air Transport. The principal transport, shipping and manufacturing organisations are represented on the technical committees of the International Container Bureau which has developed recommendations for standards with regard to dimensions and materials of construction. Special studies have been made both at the request of outside organisations and on their own initiative. Also, the International Standards Organisation at Geneva has made recommendations on the subject of containers. Standard van containers 8 ft × 10 ft × 10 ft and 20 ft are gradually coming into use. The weight of these containers will, however, in most cases, rule them out for use in the air.

The IATA Container Board

The International Air Transport Association introduced its container programme in September 1963 so as to encourage industry and the general shipping public to use the facilities provided by pallet and container services. The shipper is encouraged to rent containers from the air carrier or to use his own if of approved design and construction. In the latter case, he is offered reduced transportation rates. An International Container Board has been set up. Its principal function is to develop the worldwide use of containers and pallets by approving suitable types which will encourage the extensive practice of unitising for low-cost handling within the airlines themselves, and on other forms of transport vehicle. Inter-modal compatibility of pallet sizes and means of pallet restraint and locking has for many years been expressed as a desirable aim by operators, manufacturers and shippers. The IATA Container Board is now actively putting these objectives into practice. Registration of containers is required to be followed by permanent marking of tare weight, the maximum allowable net weight of goods that may be contained and the external volume on each registered unit. These steps indicate the determination of the air carrier industry to achieve further economy through standardisation of loading units and methods of load transfer. Until loading units have achieved a high degree of standardisation it is difficult, if not impossible, for mechanical or automated systems of load transfer to be widely introduced. Further, standardized aircraft hold dimensions cannot be considered seriously until thinking on unitising techniques and modules has reached a considerable degree of maturity.

Air cargo terminal layout

We have considered the need for efficient means of loading and unloading cargo aircraft and have provided some examples of recent studies into the alternative methods of solving the technical problems on the air side. We have also illustrated how some of the difficulties on the land side can be reduced by means of mechanical systems of rapid load transfer.

It is necessary now to consider some of the basic problems arising within the air cargo terminal itself, where the principal transfer operation takes place, but where a number of additional processes must be carried out between the arrival and unloading of the individual item of cargo and its onward movement as part of a consignment ready for loading on to the aircraft. The function of the air cargo terminal, in short, is to identify the significant characteristics of an air cargo consignment and to direct it to or from the aircraft through the correct processing channel.

Cargo handling studies can be seriously commenced only when full investigations as to the pattern of the expected air cargo growth in the particular airport have been carried out. The commodity breakdown is an essential part of this study as well as the accurate assessment of the broad characteristics of cargo business expectations over at least one decade. Under consideration will be Air Mail, Air Freight with a separate assessment for deferred air freight if thought to be significant, and unaccompanied passenger baggage.

The routing of the cargo will be of importance, whether on domestic or international air services, whether for onward transport by surface operators (inter-modal) or on interline or intraline routings. The special characteristics of the cargo will also be assessed. In particular, the need to take precautions for certain commodities will be studied. Valuable cargoes, live animals, perishable goods and human remains will require special facilities and the scale of the cargo loads likely to be handled will need to be known. One of the key factors in successful air cargo terminal design has been the need to provide a layout which is flexible enough to allow for expansion plans within a year or two of its initial use. The overall costs of operation of an air terminal include considerable development costs which are a constant source of expenditure. The basic layout must allow for continuous expansion and for the gradual introduction of more sophisticated means of handling as the traffic grows and as experience is gained with the initial arrangements. It is almost always undesirable to commence using complicated means for handling cargo until some years after the initial operations at a particular air terminal. The warning is particularly valid at the present interim period of air cargo development when all-cargo aircraft of several types are still under critical assessment, and when a decision on a particular terminal ground system might in a short time offer conflict with the need of an individual specialised cargo aircraft layout.

At this time there has been little evidence of a marked interest by the air carriers in co-ordinated handling facilities at airports so as to share the development cost, spread wider the work load on facilities and join in the learning process of the current airport handling revolution. This is to be greatly deplored since there would seem to be little in favour of airline competition in this area. Joint study of the pattern of growth of air cargo in various world regions might also be well justified, and some beginnings here are noted in Chapter 3, where the techniques of Aviation Market Research are discussed in some detail.

A thorough knowledge of the various types of transport aircraft which are in service today, and are likely to be in service during the next decade, is required by the air cargo terminal designer. The basic data in regard to their cargo payload capacity and maximum range with the maximum payload are readily provided by manufacturers. Information as to the dimension of the doors of access, the width, height and length of the hold and the height of the sill of the principal hold door is essential. No less important to the terminal designer is a detailed knowledge of the characteristics of the road trucks and vehicles which will load and unload on the land side of the air terminal. Some of these may be used for interconnexion between the terminal and the aircraft themselves.

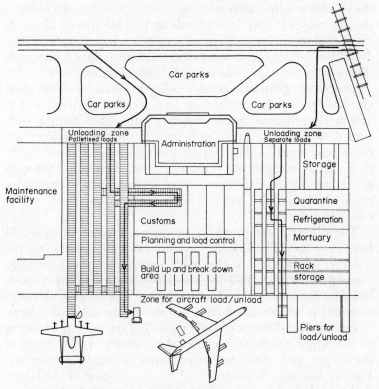

Fig. 6.1. A Projected Air Cargo Base for a Regional Terminal

Functions of the terminal

The principal operations undertaken in the terminal itself are:

Unloading and breaking down
Identification
Weighing
Labelling and documentation
Customs inspection (when applicable)
Loading (pallets or containers)

Space provision for all the above processes needs to be made with the many additional special requirements of each stage in the sequence. Alternative routings need to be supplied. On high-density routes it may be desirable to provide special channels for high-flow volumes. On some sectors a seasonal factor arises. Provision for storage to meet emergency situations is required. There is a need to provide separate unloading/loading areas for shippers and agents delivering or collecting their own individual consignments. Adequate private car access is required and is still rarely provided on an adequate scale. The situation with regard to rail connections will depend on the individual air cargo base situation. Propinquity to a rail siding is undoubtedly of the greatest value, but it must be remembered that the very great majority of air shipments have been and will be sent on by road. Dock facilities may, in certain cases, also need special consideration.

The different requirements of various aircraft designs still have to be met. The fork-lift truck, for example, is still in use for a larger proportion of the loads carried on predominantly passenger aircraft. With the small pallet the fork-lift truck is indeed a convenient load-transfer device. The modern air cargo terminal must provide facility for the deployment of a large number of fork-lift trucks while providing space for the loading of the larger pallets which meet the capacity requirements of the larger and more advanced types of transport aircraft. Facility has now to be provided for the loading of the larger pallet in the holds of the all-cargo aircraft, and the loading of the pallet itself, or the container as the case may be, is a skill which requires training and adequate space for all-round working. Container loading may require the provision of vertical movement for the loaders. The ultimate efficiency of the cargo operator, especially in modern high-performance aircraft, depends on high stacking proficiency. To achieve this an increasingly high standard of training is demanded.

The path of the cargo consignment through the base has been the subject of a considerable number of studies in recent years. In the specialised literature will be found reference to investigations which have deplored the vertical movements of cargo as it makes its way from the land to the air side and back. In effect, a loss of energy is involved in such a path, but with aircraft of widely varying hold levels it seems difficult to maintain one fixed level without provision for vertical lift. A level ramp and truck operation can be maintained throughout with aircraft such as the Argosy and Lockheed 300, but even in these cases much of the loading work must be hand operated at 4–10 feet above ground level and power assistance can profitably be provided. Depression of the ground level for truck loading is feasible, but larger modern aircraft types make this no longer possible on the air side.

Automation in the air cargo terminal

The stage has now been reached when a high degree of automation can be seriously considered as an economic factor in the design of an Air Cargo Terminal. Already this has been introduced in Railway and Post Office Terminal sorting in the USA and Europe, and the scale of air cargo in the major terminals is now adequate to justify detailed study of the concept.

It is characteristic of the ideas behind automation that, concomitant with the necessary scale of throughput which itself justifies the capital outlay, there is an inevitable inflexibility which makes it mandatory that a high degree of finalisation is reached in the sequenced processes concerned. Very rarely even then will a completely automatic programme be economically sound. It is for consideration, then, whether the air cargo movement centred upon a certain region has yet reached the maturity which would allow sound process design decisions to be taken. Together with this is the essential need to determine the objectives of the project. It is a widely held view that the most vital developments in the reduction of cost of air cargo movement lie not in the hands of the aircraft manufacturing groups, but in the area of cargo handling and terminal services which vary from airline to airline, which are competitive, costly and unco-ordinated, and which might well be planned as a co-operative service on a larger and more economic scale for the benefit of the shipper. This approach would not require the abandonment of the individual airline image over a wide area, and would justify the more rapid installation of the automated terminal. Other objectives relate to the overall airport plan, perhaps in respect to other national airports and to the position of the terminal in the air route and surface transport complex of the region. The physical limitations of the site may set the most crucial boundary condition and the objectives set for the project.

The next essential need is the establishment of facts on which the principal design criteria can be based. Data on air cargo has been very sparse in the formative period of the air cargo industry. However, an increasing number of studies are now being made of the characteristics of the packed commodities which are being shipped by air. Weight, size and density patterns of the goods, together with their value (a readily available statistic) and the trends of change as determined by the growth of business in the most favourable areas of low air distribution cost, are the principal elements of commodity data which will be required. Secondary data such as perishability, noxious qualities or the need for special environmental treatment, are no less indispensable for an accurate assessment of the problem.

Operational data are also required. These may include the traffic growth expectation as well as the seasonal and periodic variation in the loads delivered. The effects of the surface communication links and the timings of truck deliveries will be significant elements here. No less essential will be assessments of the aircraft capacity, both combination passenger/cargo and all-cargo aircraft in the period ahead with the likely scheduling in each season. Other information on the existing methods, the process time required, the space available and the labour employed will be required. In particular, data on the following are needed:

1. Loading and unloading rates for road trucks, aircraft.
2. Documentation procedures and sequences. Existing and those liable to change.
3. Methods of building up and breaking down load.
4. The times for pallet and container loading and unloading.
5. Mail procedures. Times and sequences.
6. Existing facilities for handling animals, perishables, noxious commodities.
7. Refrigeration facilities. As available and those required.
8. Load and trim control.

From such data the principal operational concept may be formulated and the physical framework can be tentatively projected within the recommendations of the operators themselves, IATA's recommended practices and the existing communication system and topography. Advanced problems in statistical analysis and operational research are posed at this stage and competent handling of the material acquired is essential.

In the development of an economic and effective automated system of cargo movement within the terminal, speed of throughput is not the only objective nor indeed the principal source of overall economy. It is in the essence of the concept that data processing should be an integral part of the system. Herein lies a principal factor in the overall economy of manpower in the project. As we have encountered in other problems where highly productive capital equipment has been under consideration, the commercial objective will most readily be obtained when a high throughput can be achieved. For a given volume of production, however, we may be able to achieve comparable costs by utilising a varying degree of balance between investment in equipment and the employment of labour. No sharply peaked optimum solution may be presented and a solution tending towards flexibility in the light of subsequent changes in traffic requirements or vehicle design and technology may be favoured by the promoting authority. Maximum use of available equipment and knowhow will be tempting in view of the lower development cost, but strong arguments will be put forward by the designers of an automated system in favour of minimum compromise with the most effective scheme to achieve the set objectives.

There will be little doubt that a major problem in the operation of the automated terminal will be that of management. Less manual labour will be required and the higher grades of technician and supervisor will need training and refresher courses in the equipment, its routine maintenance and its control to maximise the exploitation of the investment.

Computer control of air cargo

At the present time a number of factors restrict air cargo development and make less justifiable the heavy investment required in cargo handling equipment. In an era of rising labour costs, the increase in aircraft size and in the cargo unit is an important factor in restraining overall costs increases.

However, without a wider application of data-processing a very large part of the costs will continue to rise. Airline rates and traffic are highly complex, credit and accounting systems are archaic and slow, and Customs procedures are cumbersome. But by proper storage and processing of information using modern computer techniques it becomes possible to introduce considerable economies in many air cargo organisations. The right computer, with no more and no less capacity to meet the immediate future needs of the airline, is required. The need for co-ordinated action, however, is very real. Airlines, forwarding agents, finance houses and Customs are in need of processed data at various stages. Thus a fully integrated computer-based system is essential. Systems now under development will in the 1970s allow industry to integrate its control of stock, and its pricing, invoicing and sales organisation with the air transport systems of the world. Already a beginning is being made and airlines are impatient to see effective results from the use of computer-controlled air cargo as in the inland container transport field.

The London Airport cargo EDP scheme

The National Data Processing Service of the UK Post Office now operates the world's first on-line real-time computer system at Heathrow used in the first instance to control the movement and documentation of imported air cargo. Its prime purpose is to speed-up clerical work in the control of goods and in the collection of revenue. The computer is fed information extracted from air waybills, by the airlines and in due course from overseas points of origin. Each consignment is then recorded and declared to customs. On acceptance the duty and purchase tax is calculated and displayed at the appropriate terminal screen. In addition to the great reduction in staff work offered by this L.A.C.E.S. system, an immense advantage to the user will be the 24-hour facility to check the consignment situation.

One US example

American Airlines, who in 1970 operated in the USA a nationwide computer system (SABRE) linking 2,000 stations employed this to print out waybills and after formal acceptance for flight, to notify destination station and freight agent of the status and progress of the shipment. Thus an instant tracing capability is provided. Even more significant this system provides the basis for a data bank for management and product control. However, it is essential to recognise that this superb equipment and its output is useful only in so far as it can be put to effective use by management for the more economic control of the production and transport process.

Loading studies for airport terminals

As the amount of freight handled at a particular airport increases the importance of quick turnround becomes progressively greater and the associated handling problems become more difficult to overcome by conventional methods. The twin problems of reducing turnround time and simplifying handling arrangements can most easily be solved by using mechanical handling techniques. The degree of mechanisation which can be justified for a particular airport depends on the individual characteristics of that airport and on the likely future growth of freight traffic through it. It is probable that at some stage in the future fully mechanised systems employing computer control will be a necessity for the larger freight airports. Mechanical handling on the ground implies a mechanical handling system in the aircraft, therefore the smaller airports will be forced to use mechanised handling arrangements although on a less complex scale. The time at which automatic handling will become a necessity is still a matter for argument, but in the interim period there is a need for simple partly mechanised systems which can be applied to all airports so that airborne equipment can be matched to ground equipment installed at the majority of points of call. It is not only essential in the interests of immediate efficiency that the main parts of the system adopted should be standard for all airports used by aircraft carrying freight, it is also desirable that most of the installations should be capable of conversion to more advanced methods of mechanical handling when the need arises.

The variables influencing the selection of the best method of providing pallet mobility now need to be identified. These are:

1. Height of the aircraft sill.
2. Distance of the aircraft position from the cargo base ramp.
3. Scale of the operation.
4. Variation of the types and size of aircraft likely to use the terminal.
5. Location and arrangement of outside surface transport connections.

There is no question that truck bed sill height is a highly desirable characteristic for a specialised all-cargo aircraft. In Chapter 5 we set out the principal points arising and showed it can be established that for medium- and short-haul aircraft the time and cost saving through obviating the need for special high-lift equipment justifies the low-level hold. On long-haul sectors such as the North Atlantic the high-lift device may be easier to justify since the frequency of loading is less and the advantage of a standard passenger airframe configuration may determine the issue at this early stage of air cargo development. However, some degree of mobility must be provided for the pallet or container and the height of the aircraft sill will determine very largely whether this is provided by standard flat-bed trucks or by higher-cost specialised vehicles with the built-in capability of vertical lift, or perhaps by less flexible systems incorporating conveyor principles.

The factor of distance between the aircraft and the cargo base ramp was studied recently as a preliminary exercise when planning the ground system requirements for a European Airline. The principal steps in the analysis are given in the following table as an example of the kind of approach necessary to provide guidance in such a problem. The aircraft used in this study was the Argosy which was the first specialised all-cargo aircraft to the modern formula providing a level hold at truck-bed height and end-wise loading. The basic particulars of this aircraft were given in *Jane's All the World's Aircraft* (1965). Note that the overall length of the hold is 46 ft 10 in.

Various arrangements for pallet mobility on the airside apron were considered as practicable alternatives for the airline concerned. These arrangements utilised varying numbers of either 16-ft trucks, 25-ft trailers and prime movers, or 45-ft special vehicles. The turnround times achievable with each arrangement were calculated firstly at stations where the distance between the aircraft and the loading bays is half a mile, and then at stations where this distance is two miles. A direct-loading scheme with an automated system of loading by conveyor belt from the ramp to the aircraft sill was studied, but with the scale of operations envisaged the cost of this installation was at once seen to be unjustified.

Results of the time analysis

Using a required maximum turnround time of 45 minutes as a criterion and assuming a half-mile airport distance at all terminals, the arrangements which would be acceptable are two or three 16-ft trucks or two 25-ft trailers with one or two tractors, or two 45-ft trucks.

Only the two 45-ft trucks could achieve a 45-minute turnround in operations over two miles. Three 16-ft trucks over this distance were a marginal case (47·3 min).

The result of this study suggested that a simple holding platform at truck-bed height located as close to the aircraft as possible, would be a means of overcoming the serious effects of distance between aircraft and loading/unloading bays. By the use of such a platform, at any given distance between aircraft and loading bays, the choice of arrangements was widened.

Results of airline cargo handling experience

In confirmation of the type of operational study presented overleaf, some notes on the experience of operation in the preliminary period of introduction of turbine-engined cargo transport aircraft may be significant. From the range of experience which has been reported, that of Air Canada and British European Airways, who were early operators of the new equipment on the North Atlantic and on European routes, is of special interest.

Load transfer by pallet, roller track and truck		
Data used in time analysis		
	Min	Sec
Engines off to door fully open, and door closed to engines on, same for all systems	—	45*
Posititioning of 16-ft and 25-ft vehicles to aircraft to loading bays	1	0*
Unloading and loading of 16-ft and 25-ft vehicles both at aircraft and at loading bays	1	15*
Positioning of 45-ft vehicles to aircraft and to loading bays	2	0
Unloading and loading of 45-ft vehicles at aircraft and loading bay	3	20
Securing of palletised load on all vehicles	1	0*
Time taken for all vehicles to move – $\frac{1}{2}$ mile	3	0
– 2 miles	12	0
Movement of all vehicles from incoming or to outgoing aircraft	—	40
Overall delay factor on total elapsed time	20%	

Aircraft studied: Armstrong Whitworth Argosy

Times indicated thus * are measured times.

The long-haul operator of jet freighters

The technical press has covered very fully the development of the apron equipment for handling baggage and cargo on the 747 and later wide-body jets. Early recognition was given to the need for automated support equipment. Difficulties have not yet been fully resolved, costs have soared and basic faults have been cured only slowly. Transporter vehicles and 'scissor-action' lift trucks with flexible sill arrangements to cope with a 10-ft vertical threshold movement during loading and refuelling are the basic system requirement.

Air Canada was faced with the problem of pallet transportation on the airfield in an acute form since the distance between warehouse and aircraft was very variable and adverse climatic conditions made movement difficult; moreover, since it was desirable to introduce a flexible system which could be used also inside the freight sheds, it was decided that the large fork-lift truck of 20,000 lb capacity combined with single- and double-deck transporter units and with fixed roller conveyor track capable of carrying two or four pallets was the best solution. The double-deck transporter is capable of handling a total weight of 28,000 lb. Within the warehouse a four-wheeled trolley of a size capable of taking one pallet is used. This airline initiated its cargo jet operations with flexible pallets secured in the aircraft by means of side and end restraint brackets and made mobile on the aircraft floor by means of ball transfer conveyors in the door area, and roller assemblies in the main fore and aft hold areas. The flexible pallet was believed to be more economic in use than the rigid type since it was cheaper, lighter and less bulky. A standard 108 in × 88 in pallet was employed.

In a paper presented to the International Air Cargo Forum in Montreal, J. L. McLellan (1964) of TCA stated that it was the intention of the airline to determine the economic and practical desirability of utilising a direct bridging system between the cargo terminal and the freighter aircraft parked adjacent to the ramp. He emphasised the need for flexibility in the design so that it could be used within the warehouse to provide faster breakdown and build-up of load and speedier distribution to the terminating points. Plate 4b shows container loading on a Boeing 747 of Pan American Airways.

The medium-haul operator of prop-turbine freighters

The experience of BEA when planning the introduction of the Argosy was in many respects similar to that of TCA. None of the airports to be served in Europe could provide a direct link between warehouse and aircraft without provision of the intermediary transport link which varied considerably in length. In this case the truck-bed height of the Argosy door sills at either end of the fuselage made the use of a standard truck very attractive. However, the type of vehicle available varied considerably and subsequent investigations revealed that the number of self-propelled trucks of suitable size was strictly limited. The need for flexibility was predominant in the early stages of the operation and at stations with high-frequency service with the freighter, the self-propelled road truck was introduced and at other points single-pallet trailers and fork-lift trucks were used. A light form of conveyor, known as Rolamat, was used on the road trucks, on the aircraft floor and on the short bridge ramps between truck and aircraft in order to offer maximum mobility. Standard pallets can normally be moved along this by two men. Initially, a pallet of 80-in width was used, but in the later mark of Argosy which is now in service with other airlines, a standard 108-in × 88-in pallet is in use. This provides higher aircraft uplift capability and a compatibility with the long-haul jet cargo aircraft which are in many cases now using this pallet size.

To facilitate handling pallets in the warehouse at the major European terminals, loading piers have been introduced. These provide a working platform at the truck-bed height (4 ft) over which the pallets may be pushed directly on or off the vehicle for transit between the warehouse and the aircraft. The pier at London Airport is located at the despatch end of the Export Warehouse and is used for direct loading of cargo on to the aircraft pallets. A powered conveyor can also be used for loading directly on to conventional vehicles. It is sometimes necessary to re-arrange the pallets to suit the requirements of the aircraft trim. The pier was introduced so as to provide rapid transfer to and from the loading vehicles. Roller conveyor track and pallet guides are used throughout. Where loading piers at the warehouse are not available, time can be saved by positioning the pallets as close to the arriving aircraft as possible, preferably on trucks or trailers. Once the doors of the aircraft are opened empty vehicles are moved into position and unloading proceeds. In the case of the road truck capable of taking three pallets, only three separate positions are required to clear the aircraft.

The breakdown of the off-loading and on-loading time was quoted as follows in a paper presented by Mr D. L. Dobson and the author at the Air Cargo Forum in Atlanta, Georgia (November 1962). These results and the mobile equipment used may be compared with the operational study described earlier in this chapter.

Off-Load

Time to position one vehicle at each end of aircraft and attach bridge ramps	2 min
Time to position third vehicle and attach bridge ramps	2 min
Average time to position eight pallets on vehicles (1 min each)	8 min

On-Load

Time to position one vehicle at each end of aircraft with new load	2 min
Time to position third vehicle	2 min
Average time to position and lock eight pallets in aircraft (2·25 min each)	10 min
Contingency time	4 min
Total	30 min

A turnround time of 15 min has been achieved on several occasions.

The application of mechanical handling in other industries

The best possible air cargo handling system is likely to be one adaptable to other forms of transport. In this way the advantages of the 'through-unit concept' may be more fully realised, permitting the movement of a palletised load from the factory or warehouse of the shipper by the most suitable modes of transport until it reaches the consignee as an undisturbed unit.

The significance of this concept lies in the following factors. It is the pallet which is loaded and unloaded and not the vehicle. Pallet loading and unloading may therefore be fitted into a production schedule at the factory or warehouse, rather than being concentrated when and where transport is available. The conditions of loading on the tarmac are still a major contributory factor in the high cost of load transfer in the case of converted aircraft without mechanical loading means. Working conditions are generally very unfavourable, the work load is variable and labour performance is at a low level. The peak demands which arise from a desire to achieve quick turnround determine the labour force available. The flow of work is therefore not continuous and productivity is low. When the unit transported becomes a palletised load it allows considerable simplification of documentation, particularly in the international trade. One single document could cover hundreds of items through all stages of transportation. Some transshipments might well be avoided altogether. Trans-shipping direct from truck to aircraft, for example, could effect a large reduction in the airfield warehousing area and in labour and handling equipment costs.

J. F. R. Brown studied the application of mechanical-handling systems in a number of industrial applications with a view to determining whether common applications existed for a roller conveyor system designed initially for use in cargo aircraft. It was found that a wide application with many common economic features existed in industry quite remote from aviation and only indirectly concerned with transport. One example may be selected since this indicates the pattern of advantage which can often be recognised in this work. The organisation concerned were manufacturers of animal foodstuffs and utilised a fleet of twelve eight-ton trucks, delivering within a radius of eighty miles from a county town in the English Midlands. The requirement existed for a more economic turnround of their transport in a restricted loading area with the future expectation of continuing business expansion, which might demand the acquisition of additional transport loading premises.

The most effective system identified was one using pre-loaded demountable truck bodies running on roller-conveyor track for endwise positioning on to the waiting truck chassis. The system proposed was estimated to increase the turnround speed to the point where the trucks could make an average of two journeys per day instead of an average of $1\frac{1}{2}$. It became possible to recommend to the company that with the initial scale of business the transport fleet could be reduced by one truck and the night loading shift could be discontinued. With the retention of the fleet at its existing size it was estimated that an increase in delivery capacity of 4500 tons per year was possible, together with a 30 per cent reduction in the cost per delivery ton.

BIBLIOGRAPHY

R. MAURER, *Modern Cargo Loading Systems*, ITA, March 1962

Terminals for Air Cargo, Hackney Airlift and Boeing Transport Division, 1961

D. A. ARGYRIADIS, *Cargo Container Ships*, Institute of Naval Architects, March 1959

D. L. DOBSON and A. H. STRATFORD, *Unitized Loading with the Argosy in B.E.A.*, First International Forum for Air Cargo, Atlanta, Nov. 1962

M. L. MCKENNA, *An Automated Air Cargo Terminal*, Second International Forum for Air Cargo, Montreal, May 1964

P. HUNTER, *Containerisation and Land Bridge Concepts*, Fifth International Air Cargo Forum, 1970

R. B. ULVESTAD and B. H. SMITH, *Future Trends in Terminal Concepts*, Second International Forum for Air Cargo, Montreal, May 1964

R. F. STOESSEL, *Economics of Air Cargo Ground Handling and Control*, Second International Forum for Air Cargo, Montreal, May 1964

SMYKAY, BOWERSOX and MOSSMAN, *Physical Distribution Management*, Macmillan, 1961

J. L. MCLELLAN, Second International Forum for Air Cargo, May 1964

Planning Study for Air Cargo Development at Los Angeles International Airport, Leigh Fisher Associates, 1960

Airport Buildings and Aprons, 3rd Edition, IATA, Montreal 1962

JOHN L. EYSE, 'Containers, Pallets and Standardization in Air Cargo', Air Logistics Conference, *Jnl. Inst. Aero. Sci.*, Oct. 1960

Mechanical Load Transfer Systems, Sky Trader International, June 1963

Flat Pallets for use in Aircraft, British Standards Institution, M.28, 1964

Jane's All the World's Aircraft, Annual, Sampson Low, Marston & Co. Ltd

E. DREYFOUS, *Computer Aspects of Air Cargo in the next decade*, Fifth International Air Cargo Forum, Frankfurt, 1970

A. F. DEVENISH, *Cargo Terminals*, Frankfurt, 1970

I. R. MACNEIL and A. D. TOWNEND, *Ground Handling of Cargo*, World Airports Conference, ICE, Sept. 1969

7 Research in Air Cargo Development

Air freight and physical distribution

The subject of air cargo cannot be adequately treated without giving some consideration to the research studies in this field. A large number of these have been published in the last five years and the more significant ones will be noted with their most important conclusions. Much of the study work initiated over this period had been prompted by the slow development of air cargo which had caused disappointment in the air carrier and manufacturing industries. Investigations were often put in hand with the object of gaining a deeper insight into the economics of cargo transportation and the mechanism of the marketing of goods moved by air.

It will be recognised that this research work has been in no way parallel to the activity in the passenger field. We have already discussed differences in the requirements for transport aircraft in the passenger and cargo roles. The facile prognostications of the late 1940s gave way to a mood of serious enquiry. Work published by Harvard University (1956) was the first to draw attention to this subject, at a time when serious effort was being expended by the aircraft industry on the design characteristics of new all-cargo aircraft. This work, entitled *The Role of Air Freight in Physical Distribution*, by H. T. Lewis and J. W. Culliton, was an extension of previous aviation research in a number of different areas at Harvard. It drew attention to the characteristics of air movement which were already in evidence in the older forms of transport, for its greater speed and its higher cost were still in the tradition of earlier modes of more advanced transportation. There was now offered, however, in a unique form, a new 'transport package' which included reliability, flexibility of service, potential savings in inventory, warehousing management, packaging and handling and new possibilities of economy in overall distribution management. These were subjected at Harvard to new lines of disciplined enquiry.

It is well known that the freight agent now has advantages to offer the exporter by surface transport of larger consignments, due to the higher break points in the rate structure. It is a recommendation of the report that attention should be paid by the airlines to consignments over 500 kgs where the packing advantage is greatest. Any new rate structure might take into account the fall-off in the use of air freight over distances greater than 500 miles in Europe. This would help to encourage the export traffic to Scandinavia and the Mediterranean from the UK. These conclusions could well be further studied in relation to the economics of containers which was discussed in the last chapter.

The analysis of distribution costs

The second part of the survey was an investigation of the comparative distribution costs of UK exports to Europe by surface and by air freight. Other aspects studied included the time spent in distribution. Here once again distribution was considered in a wider sense than is understood by the word transport. However, not all aspects of the distribution process could be fully covered.

The following items were included and the interviews as well as the supporting questionnaire were aimed to obtain the fullest information concerning them:

> Transport and incidental transport
> Inventories
> Warehousing
> Packing, including labour, materials and space required.

Because of the lack of precise and readily available information in industry the later analysis largely omitted the warehousing and the inventory problem, and the conclusions drawn are, as a result, conservative from the point of view of air cargo.

A sample of 100 firms was decided upon as being large

enough to include both large- and medium-size exporters, but not so large as to be unmanageable by the investigators. The personal-interview system was used in conjunction with a comprehensive questionnaire, the completion of which often required a return visit and a meeting with more than one executive or staff member of the exporter concerned. The greatest co-operation was received. The effort was finally concentrated on the machinery group whose significance is indicated by the following table summarising a sample air waybill analysis of the air exports to Europe in 1958. A comparable study in 1963 by this author showed that machinery, vehicles and instruments represented a slightly decreased proportion of air exports from the United Kingdom to Europe.

	% of trade
Machinery, including vehicles and instruments	45·8
Metals and manufactures	8·4
Textiles and clothing	4·8
Chemicals and drugs	3·6

As was anticipated, total distribution costs were found to be a better yardstick than freight transport costs alone. Most of the firms interviewed knew this, but frequently there were difficulties in assessing the total distribution costs.

More often than not it was found that the manufacturer did not (perhaps could not) break down his packing and other costs, or he might include them in production rather than distribution. The authors of this report felt that the manufacturing and shipping executive should be given encouragement to analyse their distribution network in relation to the process of production and distribution within the company as a whole. Later studies have strongly confirmed this recommendation.

The forwarding agent was found to play an important role since the majority of shippers export through him and he offers specialised services. He will, of course, consolidate shipments to gain lower rates for bulk and larger shipments. New rate structures offering higher breakpoints should be encouraged in everybody's interest. Even at current rates it was felt that a good deal can be done by the re-orientation of the structure to give agents more scope for bulk consolidation and to encourage air freight over the longer European routes. However, the level of freight rates is the key to air freight growth. The total level of freight is rising and there is no reason why the air freight share should not rise with it; by rate reduction air freight could achieve a larger share of the total market.

An important conclusion of the report was that there is a favourable elasticity in the air freight rate-traffic relationship which could well be exploited by the air carrier. A study of the effects of straight rate reduction suggested that a 20 per cent decrease would mean a 33 per cent increase in present air freight traffic. This is equivalent to an elasticity of 1·7.

An interesting concept which was explored in some detail by the London School of Economics was that a rate reduction extends the geographical area over which air freight may compete effectively. Fig. 7.1 reproduces one series of these results. This is for the weight group 46–100 kg. Here the competitive market area for machinery exports is plotted in a series of contours assuming various rate reductions below the current

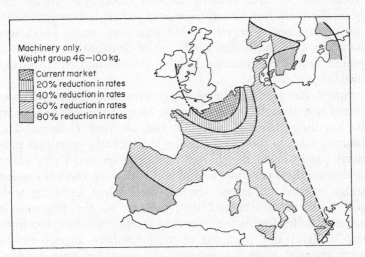

Machinery only.
Weight group 46–100 kg.

- Current market
- 20% reduction in rates
- 40% reduction in rates
- 60% reduction in rates
- 80% reduction in rates

FIG. 7.1. UK Exports by Air and the Influence of the Freight Rate

commodity rate. In the study of the export consignments from the UK, transport costs averaged 1·7 per cent and total distribution costs 4·5 per cent of the export value. For air exports the incidental surface transport costs often rose to 10–15 per cent of total distribution costs, usually when firms in the Midlands and North sent shipments through London airports. Over 500 miles, air transport costs rose to 60–90 per cent of total distribution costs (Sealy and Herdson, 1961).

Air rates are certainly higher than those for rail or sea, but this study showed effectively that comparisons based on rates alone can be misleading, since differential savings on other costs may be omitted. Of the 151 types of consignment studied in the machinery group there were only five cases where air rates were favourable, but twenty-three cases where distribution costs were favourable to air. It is the large proportional increase that is so important and not the numerical values themselves which related primarily to consignments which are naturally favourable to air transport. These may nevertheless be conservative estimates since, as already noted, full allowance could not be made for warehousing and inventory charges which would often follow a major decision to swing to air transport throughout a large organisation. It was found that where total air distribution costs were favourable, the air was generally used. Surprisingly, some 12 per cent of consignments were found not to travel by that transport means which was found to give the lowest total cost of distribution. Here is a potent field for education by the airlines and by transport distribution analysts!

Speed was found to be of the greatest importance and was recognised as such by the exporter. Much passive time is spent in handling, loading, packing and clearing customs. The journey time to the airport is also significantly large and proportionately so on the shorter European sectors. Every effort to shorten these processes is vital and with the growth of regular traffic carried on larger aircraft mechanical handling with pallets or containers and systems such as the Rolamat is urgently called for. As traffic grows an extension of services from the Midlands and from one or more northern airports would seem essential, since the necessity at present for some consignments to use a London airport inhibits the use of air freight.

The future of the specialised air freighter

Sealy and Herdson showed that there is an actual and potential loss to air freight because of consignments which are too large to fit into the holds of some freight aircraft. These are still too often converted passenger aircraft or short-haul jets with unsuitable access which are not readily modified to suit higher flow methods of palletising and freight handling. A serious difficulty in the immediate development of air freight is that operators of these aircraft will find it impossible to take advantage of the higher traffic potential which lower freight rates would generate because of their lower productive capacity and their higher unit operating costs.

The final part of this report was a study of the economic prospects for freighter operations using the data on traffic growth and rate reductions which were suggested by Dr Sealy and his associates.

Four primary air freight routes were considered. These covered short, long and average stage lengths for Europe, such as London to Paris, Copenhagen, Dusseldorf and Rome. Based on the most realistic operating data to which the authors had access, it was computed that the overall direct-operating cost per capacity ton-mile can be reduced from 18·3 pence for converted passenger aircraft of 16 tons capacity to 10·1 pence for similar capacity aircraft of specialised design. Such potential reductions when viewed in relation to load factors and frequency of service at the critical traffic times hold high hopes for providing much of the potential economy which the associated economic study had thought possible. Until recently, the specialised all-cargo aircraft has not been an essential item in the re-equipment plans of the world's airlines.

The growth of European air cargo traffic

Using the methods developed by the London School of Economics, a new approach was made by the Transport and Economics Department of the ATS Company (a subsidiary at the time of the Hawker Siddeley Group) in 1962 to the assessment of the growth in demand for air cargo services in Europe. The analysis was carried further so as to include items of cost previously omitted, and the computations were orientated so as to establish the competitive position of air transport in relation to surface transport. It is intended to give a detailed account of this work with the permission of the Centro per lo Sviluppo dei Trasporti Aerei before which it was first introduced by the author in 1962. My former colleagues, M. E. L. Spanyol and P. J. Detmold, were responsible for much of the economic analysis involved.

Against the existing air cargo situation in Europe the object was first of all to study the movement of trade especially in the industries which are most amenable to the advances of the air carrier and his agents. The total cost of the distribution of these goods was investigated. By the cost of distribution we meant those costs which arise between the issue of the inspector's stamp in the workshop to the delivery of goods at the consumer's door.

For each of forty key commodities and on seventeen important routes the air freight rate was computed at which goods could in the future be distributed more economically by air than by surface modes of transport. In this way we were able to establish a relationship between the air freight rate and the air cargo traffic which would be generated if the merchant or his agent were to base his choice of transport entirely on cost. Now there is a very important bonus which the air carrier has to offer and this is well enough defined even on the short-haul routes within Europe; it was therefore possible to take some account of it. We studied a number of commodities on selected routes in Europe and concluded that no less than 10 or 15 per cent by weight of the goods travelling by air do so although the total cost of distribution is lower by surface transport.

We have called the above technique cargo substitution analysis, since in its essence it evaluates the probable penetration success of air transport in moving representative goods as a substitution for surface modes of transport. The concept stems from the growing part of distribution management which aims at establishing economic control in areas of manufacture normally excluded from departments of design, production or marketing. No study of this kind can be totally without assumption but the principle hypotheses upon which we built up the main analysis are briefly stated:

1. European industry will choose that mode of transport which lowers the total distribution costs.

2. The growth of the total trade in Europe as shown by the last five years' demand for transport of key commodities will continue during the next decade, subject to modifying factors of which the most important is the development of surface transportation systems, such as the English Channel tunnel.

3. All-cargo aircraft of modern design will be available and would be used to take over the primary cargo transport role.

To explore the reaction of cargo traffic volume following a rate reduction we chose the commodities which form the existing and potential market for air freight. We may note that they fall naturally into seven groups according to the Standard International Trade Classification, viz:

0. Foods, including coffee and tea.
1. Beverages and tobacco.
2. Inedible crude materials, excluding fuels.
5. Chemicals and pharmaceuticals.
6. Manufactured goods including leather, pottery and textiles.
7. Machinery, office and industrial equipment.
8. Miscellaneous manufactured articles, including scientific instruments, footwear, watches and books.

We found that the ratio of the value to weight for any commodity is one significant indication of its suitability for air freight. For convenience, therefore, we used this parameter in studying commodities and we will be referring to it as a criterion for the effectiveness of the penetration of air transport into the total market. It should be emphasised, however, that this is not by any means the only measure of air cargo penetration power.

The movement of these goods was studied on the following seventeen routes or trade streams. Clearly, since we are considering the total flow of goods we are not only concerned with city terminating traffic which is usually the case in air transport. Our seventeen routes or trade streams were:

United Kingdom – to and from	Eire
	France
	Switzerland
	Belgium
	Netherlands
	Denmark
	Sweden
	Norway
West Germany – to and from	Denmark
	Norway
	Sweden
	France
	Switzerland
	UK
Italy – to and from	UK
	West Germany
	France

We chose these because they experience heavy traffic in the forty chosen commodities, and they include both long and short routes with and without geographical obstacles.

It will be noticed that the majority of these are routes to and from the United Kingdom, Italy and West Germany. This is because these countries are predominant in European trade in current and future air-transportable commodities, especially where physical barriers exists.

Transport costs and substitution

It was now necessary to estimate the transport costs that would be incurred by air, sea, road and rail for a representative sample of shipments in the forty key commodities. Allowance was made for collection and delivery to or from airports, stations and ports, and for all handling costs not included in the freight charges. We then estimated for each combination of transport media, on each route, the additional cost of carrying inventory, or warehousing, packaging, insurance and of documentation, finally obtaining the total distribution costs by air and surface.

The Total Cost of Distribution
Transportation
Packaging
Insurance, Loss and Damage
Inventory (Interest, Obsolescence and Warehousing)
Commissions, Sales Promotion and Advertising
Taxes and Duties

We then computed for any alteration in air freight rates, the tonnage of consignments for which it would be possible to reduce total distribution costs by substituting air for surface transport. We constructed a set of substitution curves showing the reduction of the air rate against the air share of the market for each group of routes.

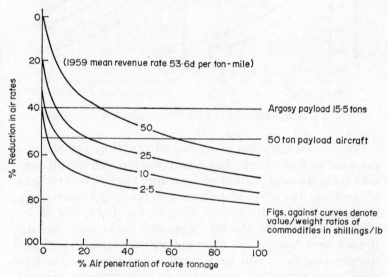

FIG. 7.2. Rate Reduction and Air Penetration, West Germany and Italy

In the first Route Substitution diagram (Fig. 7.2) we show how the route between West Germany and Italy might be expected to react to such rate reductions. It will be seen that decreases in air rates of up to 40 per cent have little effect on low-value goods (say less than 50p per lb) though a quarter of the total cargo valued at £2·50p per lb would then fly. It is probable that the majority of current all-cargo aircraft could do little to encroach on the surface traffic on this route and even the specialised cargo aircraft would not penetrate the market very deeply. Moreover, cheap and efficient surface transport between West Germany and Italy, in spite of the barrier of the Alps, now exists and is being actively developed. In the second Route Substitution diagram (Fig. 7.3), however, we show by contrast the highly rate-elastic overwater London–Paris route, on which any reduction in rates would yield a substantial gain in traffic.

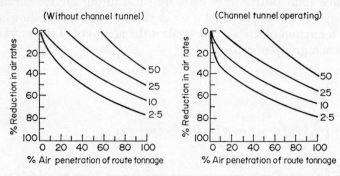

FIG. 7.3. Rate Reduction and Air Penetration, UK and France

We assessed the effect of a Channel tunnel by recalculating the total surface distribution costs using reduced transit times with their favourable effect on inventory charges and the costs of handling. The effect of the tunnel on the longer cargo stages, for example from the United Kingdom to Italy, will be less marked than for the shorter stages such as London to Paris, Brussels and Amsterdam, since the surface transport and load transfer economies will be a smaller proportion of the total distribution cost which then includes a large transport element. Without the tunnel a 24 per cent rate reduction which might be achieved by 1970 with 50-ton-payload aircraft would lead to market penetrations varying from 12 per cent for goods valued at 12·5p per lb up to over 80 per cent penetration for goods at £2·50p per lb. In the same figure is shown how the introduction of the Channel tunnel would reduce the reaction of this route to rate decreases. After the Channel bridge or tunnel is built the market penetration would now be only 5 per cent for goods valued at 12·5p per lb. Higher-value goods are affected less but the penetration for goods at £2·50p per lb would be considerably reduced.

It is evident that reactions to rate reduction vary widely between different routes. The characteristics of commodities and the pattern of air and surface rates and costs on each route are highly important factors in determining the future of air cargo and it would be folly to contemplate air cargo transport prospects without considering them all carefully. We have seen the effect of the air rate reduction on the penetration by air transport into the total cargo market. This emphasises the importance of assessing accurately the rate reduction which is possible for each type and each succeeding generation of cargo aircraft. We do not expect that surface transport organisations will stand idly by as the airlines invade their traditional markets. They will certainly retaliate. It was for this reason that we carried out the parallel study of surface vehicles, rates and costs which is described below. We reached the broad conclusion, however, that the slenderness of current surface transport profit margins would limit severely their ability to retaliate by reducing the rates for cargo transport. Improvements in the efficiency of handling by means of mechanical aids would offer big rewards in the reduction of surface transport costs, especially on the railways. However, European railway losses are likely to remain heavy during the time scale we have considered so that in general surface rates will tend to rise, perhaps rather less rapidly than over the last ten years.

Transportation can be accomplished by a variety of media, all having different prices and characteristics. Rapid development of air cushion craft in the next decade may well lead to large-scale Hovercraft services across the English Channel. These could provide low-cost rail and road links with more flexibility and requiring far less capital investment than the Channel tunnel.

The nature of the transport media chosen and the number and type of trans-shipments en route, together with the nature of the goods themselves, determine the packaging methods. The criteria governing packaging also govern the expenditure on insurance, loss and damage. The cost of maintaining inventory is usually one of the largest items of distribution cost. The size of the necessary inventory is strongly dependent on transportation time.

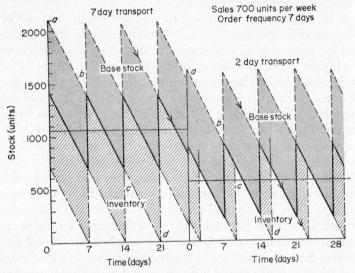

FIG. 7.4. The Inventory Cycle

In the illustrative example (Fig. 7.4) the uniform sale of 700 units per week of an industrial product with a seven-day order cycle was studied to show the effect on inventory of a reduction of transit time from seven days for surface transport to two days for air transport. The goods are considered as inventory, the moment they leave the base stock. In this example air transport gives a 43 per cent reduction in inventory without causing any increase in base stock.

The order cycle also has a strong effect on inventory, but it should be noted that to a certain extent the savings in inventory resulting from more frequent ordering are offset by the higher transportation costs associated with smaller consignments. For large traffic flow, the adoption of satellite assembly plants may yield further inventory savings through the holding of inventory in the form of less valuable unprocessed goods (Stratford, 1963). In many export markets taxes and duties may be avoided by remote assembly. It should be borne in mind that the payment of commission to agents, wholesalers and retailers is very largely a payment to cover the costs of inventory. Often these commissions could be cut substantially if central distribution direction were to be adopted.

It may be concluded that the best method of transportation for goods cannot be selected without recourse to a full analysis of the pattern and costs of the whole distribution system. At this moment, only a very small proportion of business concerns has given its distribution organisation the type of searching analysis briefly outlined here: when this practice becomes more widespread not only may transportation patterns show startling changes, but the whole pattern of marketing and even trade flows may be radically altered.

In assessing the air and surface distribution costs, the costs of packaging, insurance, documentation and customs, collection and delivery, warehousing and inventory must be considered in addition to the freight rates for each commodity on each route. Fig. 7.5 shows a typical example for a 200 lb consignment of

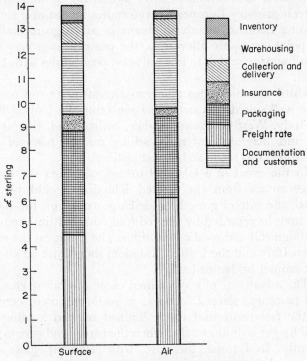

FIG. 7.5. Surface and Air Distribution Costs

office machinery shipped from London to Paris. This is the type of consignment study that is now becoming essential in the export department of any manufacturer alert to the need for finding ways and means of reducing cost. In this illustration the cost difference is negligible, but the many other factors which cannot be given numerical analysis are wholly favourable to a user of the most rapid means of transport.

Conclusions of the air cargo market study

The map in Fig. 7.6 presents the principal quantitative results from this work, and a number of individual results can be evaluated from it. Some conclusions of general interest, however, may be drawn.

1. The growth pattern which emerges from this study of the total costs of distribution of forty significant commodities on seventeen primary European cargo routes is that of a steadily increasing demand for air shipment in all-cargo aircraft. At some point, probably after 1970, the prospect of a very steep demand may arise due to low unit-cost possibilities with larger aircraft.

2. Until the mid-1970s all-cargo aircraft of 15-ton payload will be well suited to a network connecting the United Kingdom, Italy, West Germany, France, Switzerland, the Netherlands and Belgium. Intensive selling on the basis of total distribution costs seems to be most justified.

3. In the event of a Channel tunnel, although the longer-distance routes from the United Kingdom would be little affected, the rate of growth of air cargo traffic on the shorter stages may be retarded by the reduced cost and time required for through rail and road connections. The traffic on the routes between Italy and the United Kingdom should not be affected by a Channel bridge or tunnel.

4. The advantage of a specialised cargo aircraft over a converted passenger aircraft increases as sector distance decreases, since the fast turnround time obtained by end loading and low sill height is of most value when the turnround occurs most frequently. In Europe, therefore, with relatively short stage lengths, and the traffic concentrated on a small number of key

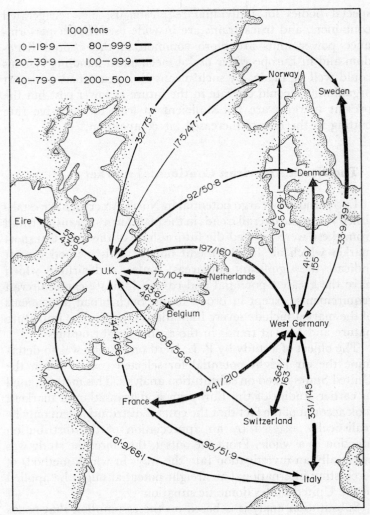

Fig. 7.6. An Estimate of Trade in 40 Commodities Suited to Air Transport, Early 1970s

routes, the importance of efficient ground handling and aircraft turnround is self-evident.

In general, European road transport on the trunk routes is alert and employs up-to-date equipment. Full use of the great flexibility of the road vehicle is made. Multiple containers,

309

special bodies for individual requirements, e.g. refrigerated containers, and truck trains are in wide use. Higher-performance power units are more common in the United Kingdom and in Europe wider use of mechanical handling systems could well be made. By such means European road transport organisations could operate in the future at lower cost but the present margins are not sufficient to lead to extensive rate cutting in the face of increased air competition.

The North American Continental market

Early studies of cargo potential in North America have established the broad overall trends in the main forms of transport, and from these were assessed the future share of the total transport market which air freight might obtain. This method cannot indicate the significant sub-areas, routes, and airlines which have the greatest potential and cannot indicate cargo aircraft requirements, except in broad terms. Such broad assessments of the market include severe limitations owing to the immature nature and present trends in the airline freight business.

The object of a study by P. L. Herdson in 1963 was to determine the air freight potential for selected routes within the United States based on substitution analysis. This method, used in earlier studies of the European and transatlantic markets, took account of the fact that the costs of distribution can only be realistically assessed by an appreciation of the distribution function as a whole. From the outset, therefore, the study was essentially an investigation into the ways in which methods of forecasting international air freight potential might be applied to the United States domestic situation.

Substitution analysis is based on the assumption that goods will be shipped by air when their total cost of distribution is as cheap or cheaper by air than by surface modes. Air cargo is forecast by estimating the total traffic which may be expected to travel and then by assessing, for each commodity, the level of air rate at which total distribution costs become equal by air and by surface transport. Summation of the total weight of goods for which, at each level of air rates, air distribution costs are the lower, indicates the total tonnage available to air cargo.

There are two basic inputs required. Firstly, the total volume of freight moving, by commodity, between any two selected points must be determined. Secondly, the costs of physical distribution when using the various alternative transport methods must be assessed. In the case of the United States both requirements present unique problems because of the structure of the domestic market. The investigations, therefore, were concentrated essentially into two stages; (i) the attempt to establish a model of the American internal commodity flow structure and, (ii) the estimation of cost differentials between air and surface distribution methods.

It was hoped that, in themselves, both stages of investigation would present valuable insight into the air-freight market situation. In the final analysis both stages were brought together to provide an estimate of the air cargo tonnage potential at selected levels of the air rate. Statistics relating to the volume and structure of US inter-state movement of goods, however, were at that time not available. International trade movement statistics are provided as a customs requirement and are published by national and international agencies in sufficient detail for our purpose. It was necessary, however, to attempt to establish the United States domestic trade by indirect means.

The method of determining inter-regional trade flows was first of all to establish points of origin of the commodities which were regarded as potential air-freight and then to estimate the volume of shipments out of each of these areas. Next, the regional demand for the selected commodities was investigated. The final stage was the matching of the supply with the demand for the goods in question. The significance of this investigation lay in the development of a technique for applying the distribution cost or substitution analysis to a domestic market. Unfortunately the work was not carried on to its ultimate conclusion during the study described. However, it has been developed further in a UK regional survey undertaken by the author in 1964.

A study sponsored by the Douglas Aircraft Company and four US air carriers has carried the assessment of the US domestic air cargo situation and its future requirements considerably further. The airlines concerned were American Airlines, Flying Tiger Line, Pan American World Airlines and

United Air Lines. The sponsors formed a working group with the Douglas Aircraft Company nominated as co-ordinator. It appears that the Massachusetts Institute of Technology, having a continuing interest in the development of aviation and being a non-profit-making organisation, was selected as consultant and contractor who was thereby in a position to seek the assistance of the US Bureau of Census in collecting the required statistical information. The objectives of the study were to investigate the most likely approaches for determining quantitatively the US domestic air cargo potential. Guide lines to sales action on the part of manufacturers of aircraft and air operators were also sought.

A very extensive range of information was obtained from this survey which essentially was set up to obtain a record of the existing situation. To obtain a wide view of the position a postal questionnaire was used. Two hundred and thirty-five commodities were selected on the basis of their potential for air transport. It was reported that over 90 per cent of the 7000 industrial groups receiving these mailed questionnaires returned satisfactorily completed forms. As a follow-up on this initial coverage, the Bureau of Census surveyed 35,000 Bills of Lading which were photographed on business premises dealing with selected commodities exported from Southern California. A computer programme was instigated to process the value per pound data and relate these to shipments recorded which are in money value.

The principal information sought in this survey was reported by the Douglas Aircraft Division to be:

> Value of shipments
> Value per pound
> Length of haul
> Mode of transport
> Volume flow by origin and destination
> Weight of shipment
> Comparative rates

Some of the detailed results have been made available by the Douglas Company. These have been summarised and are presented below with acknowledgment to the sponsors of the survey. Total US domestic freight movements of commodities selected for the analysis totalled 106,000 million ton-miles of which 86,000 million (or 81 per cent) were carried on stages less than 500 miles. The 235 commodities included in the survey represent 46 per cent of the annual value of the domestic shipment of manufactured products. Of the selected commodities 54,000 million ton-miles (or 51 per cent) were of a value greater than $1 per lb and 12,000 million ton-miles (or 11 per cent) were of a value greater than $4 per lb. However, our most recent investigations warn us to be very cautious over using the value per lb as a sole criterion for the potential penetration of air cargo transport.

This particular study seems to have found likewise a lack of correlation between value per pound and the percentage of the commodity which is at the present time moving by air. Three examples may be taken of pairs of commodity groups with closely comparable mean values per pound, but which are found in this survey to return a widely different percentage penetration by the air transport industry.

		Mean value per pound	Air penetration
Group A	Motors and generators	$4	10%
	Carpets and rugs		4%
Group B	Men's suits	$8	12%
	Pharmaceuticals		1%
Group C	Optical instruments	$22/18	13%
	Musical instruments		5%

We have emphasised the significance of the competitive tariff of the surface transport operators in the European studies which have been reviewed above. Douglas analysed the competitive rates of selected commodities between sixteen major US cities. A result of special significance was the close comparison of rates between surface and air operators on the shorter stages. One result cited by Douglas indicated that for drugs and pharmaceuticals on stages below 200 miles, the 100 lb rate was closely identical between Air, REA* and Motor Truck.

The Douglas studies were of the greatest importance in the formative stage of air cargo. The accumulation of facts and their interrelation must precede the formulation of a sophisticated theory of air cargo growth. The US manufacturing

* Rail Express Agency.

industry are wisely testing by observation the speculation which some starry-eyed optimists in many parts of the world have confused with more scientific methods of forecasting.

The industrial use of air freight

In 1962 a major research project sponsored by Emery Air Freight set out to determine the principal factors which determine the policy of industrial organisations as to whether or not to use air transport. A research team of the Stanford Institute of South California completed the work which covered investigations in 21 states and involved 165 interviews. The final report by James Gorham classified industrial use of air freight into 3 general categories, and 13 more specific ones which were formulated into 28 commercial situations in which an economic case for air freight was likely to justify close consideration. (Compare also Gorham, Sealy and Stratford, 1964.)

The classification evolved by Mr Gorham was based on the general and specific reasons for use and by type of situation. The three classes of general use are:

Use of speed to reduce time in transit.

Use of speed to reduce cost of holding goods in inventory while maintaining or improving service.

Use of air freight because of superior conditions of carriage.

A further breakdown within each of these classes was established and we may illustrate this most usefully by taking Group A, which covers the most wide-ranging concepts for potential economy through use of the aeroplane. This covers the possibility of increased sales of improved service to the customer in situations which are in any way limited in time. This may arise through style-dating or seasonal factors, or through perishability being minimised by extending markets in time or in space. This group covers also the increase or extension of production and/or procurement facilities, the speed-up of turnover and more rapid achievement of the distribution of output.

When a company finds that it has the combined characteristics required to make the use of air a significant possibility in the interests of lower total distribution costs or greater and wider marketing potential, then a full cost study is indicated. One major conclusion of the Stanford Report was that it is 'the individual Company situation, as defined by particular combinations of company characteristics, that affects the choice of transportation media and not the commodity or industry characteristics alone'. We have noted above that the commodity value per unit of weight was often a misleading criterion for the choice of transport media. The Stanford study suggests that no simple combination of parameters can by itself give guidance to the air cargo salesman. Unfortunately the conclusions of the Stanford Report suggest that no quantitative method can have any high chance of success as a means of air cargo traffic forecasting. We have previous commented that without a numerical approach it is not easy to make a case for the use of air transport. It is believed that although the precise analysis of the cost situation, case by case, category by category, would indeed have made the Stanford research project far more difficult, it would have made the results considerably more vulnerable (Gorham, Sealy and Stratford, 1964).

Future air cargo growth will result primarily from the selective use of air freight in those circumstances on which the cost differential of air transport can be rationally justified. This requires that quantitative data should be acquired and this should be a prime objective of all research in this field. This was the principal achievement of the Douglas Survey of Domestic US Cargo. The fact that some elements in the situation may be difficult to quantify should not divert us from this objective. The studies completed so far suggest the lines on which the mechanism of transport growth can be drawn. If we are to develop the subject further, we shall need far more data and must aim in the long term at a general theory based on quantitative experiments and research.

North Atlantic cargo operations

Utilising the methods developed by Dr Sealy and the ATS Company for assessing the competitive penetrating capability of air cargo transport on the basis of total distribution cost, an approach was made to North Atlantic operations. On these routes the growth rate has been maintained at a very high level for many years and the influence of the freight rate and its structure as determined through IATA can be shown to be of the very greatest significance.

The North Atlantic differs from the European routes in various important respects. On routes of this length, less importance should be attached to the economy of loading and unloading which occurs less frequently and therefore has a reduced influence on annual utilisation. On the other hand, the smaller variation between the stage lengths of sectors involving a North Atlantic crossing enables us to consider the requirements for future aircraft in great detail. On most European routes there are two principal carriers of air cargo who are able to influence the structure of specific commodity rates to suit their particular operation. On the North Atlantic there is less freedom of individual operation and the outcome of the various longstanding controversies regarding rate levels and tariff structures may be expected to have a very important bearing on future traffic and on the requirements for cargo aircraft. The economic analysis which has been developed enables us to compute the effect upon traffic of various rating policies; the accurate assessment of future rating policy is equally essential to the attainment of valid conclusions. In the European studies the assessment of future rating policy with all-cargo fleets was based on aircraft operating costs alone. On the North Atlantic, various other commercial influences on rating policy should also be considered.

It is possible to identify the factors which will determine the optimum size and type of future North Atlantic transport aircraft. The probable fleet requirements of representative airlines can be established. The need to achieve an adequate margin of improvement over the operating economy of the aircraft it is intended to replace imposes a lower limit on the size of aircraft. The margin should be sufficient to allow for the effect of inflation during the development period. An upper limit on size is imposed by the need for the aircraft to be the most profitable available over a broad range of routes and tariffs. The rate structure and the size and operating economy of a new generation of cargo aircraft are clearly most intimately connected. Many of the larger airlines have, for several years, offset losses made on all-cargo operations against the profit from carrying cargo in passenger aircraft. The greater growth of cargo than passenger traffic has created for them a special problem as the proportion of unprofitable all-cargo operation has grown, aggravating the effect of the lower revenue yield.

The imbalance between trade and transport in the east- and west-bound directions on the North Atlantic has also imposed operational and commercial problems. The rate structure should overcome the imbalance of air cargo by attracting a broad variety of goods to travel in each direction. A more effective balance in Eastbound and Westbound Cargo has now been achieved on the North Atlantic. In 1969 and 1970 the loads carried were as follows:

	Eastbound		Westbound	
Scheduled	1969	1970	1969	1970
All-cargo	122,681·3	115,257·5	133,596·9	126,287·8
Passenger A/c	75,602·3	77,982·5	84,865·0	85,640·2
Charters	6,209·8	3,198·3	6,045·5	2,594·6
Total (Tonnes)	204,493·4	196,438·3	224,507·4	214,522·6
% of Total Cargo	47·6	47·7	52·4	52·3

All-cargo aircraft in the 1970s

It is necessary now to consider how the present development in the rate structure will influence the design and the introduction of the next generation of all-cargo transport. What will be the most suitable payload size for the generation of cargo aircraft to succeed the Boeing 707 and DC 8 F on the North Atlantic? We should consider how such an aircraft would fit into the networks of the prominent airlines, and the prospects of its profitable operation with the traffic forecasts at the most likely level of the revenue rate.

A project of this kind would face two particular hazards to its commercial success. The first of these is that though sufficient traffic to ensure its profitable operation might be available at a rate structure specially adapted to its needs, the proposals for

317

such a tariff by its protagonists might be successfully resisted by those opposed to the project. The first condition for such a project is, therefore, that it should be able to operate at greater potential profit than the Boeing 707–320 C and DC 8 F's it would replace, even at rate levels designed to suit the latter's operation. The Boeing 747 F is the first aircraft offered for this market.

The second hazard is that during continuing inflation the early 1970s would escalate the price of the new project which would be contrasted with that of second-hand 40-ton payload aircraft. These older aircraft would have avoided a large part of this escalation by virtue of their earlier development. Should no supersonic transport be in service or about to enter service by the early 1970s then, undoubtedly, third-generation jets will be in production for both passenger and cargo use but the second-hand prices of current jets would be expected to remain high. Even if supersonic aircraft are used for premium services in small numbers, the effect on second-hand prices might not be very great.

In considering a new project it is wise therefore to assess the effect of the most pessimistic circumstances which could reasonably be foreseen. However, traffic estimates have indicated that 75–100-ton payload aircraft on the key North Atlantic routes should be in the right size bracket by the mid 1970s. It has been estimated that if the capital element in Boeing 707 operating costs were to be reduced to 30 per cent of those of a new aircraft and if, at the same time, the effects of inflation were to raise the new price of the 75-ton-payload aircraft by £500,000 then the advantage of the latter aircraft in operating cost per capacity ton-mile would be expected to be reduced by 0·5 pence.

On a realistic assessment, Boeing 707 direct-operating costs on North Atlantic cargo service are in the region of 2·0 pence per ctm, so that a newly projected 75-ton-payload aircraft would need to have direct operating costs no higher than 1·5 pence per ctm to obviate these risks for all practical purposes. This is not to say that it is necessarily unwise to proceed at a somewhat higher direct cost, but the element of risk would need to be borne in mind. Studies recently completed suggest, however, that this cost level could be achieved in the present 'state of the art'. The so-called C5A technology will now allow such cost levels to be achieved with all-cargo aircraft gross weights below 500,000 lb. Such aircraft will always be considered of course in the light of the detailed requirements of the major airlines concerned.

Other conclusions

The strong recent growth of North Atlantic air cargo is likely to continue through the 1970s.

The introduction of supersonic aircraft may be expected to have a dual effect on air cargo, increasing the tonnage carried in the holds of wide-body passenger aircraft and displacing older subsonic jet aircraft which might be suitable for conversion into cargo aircraft. Whether such displaced aircraft could offer air cargo transport at the highly competitive rates which will be undoubtedly called for in the next decade is open to question. In the mid-1970s an important market is most likely to appear for large specialised all-cargo aircraft, perhaps initially in small numbers, but eventually proving a major airline purchasing requirement. This aircraft is likely to require a capacity of 100 tons on the principal North Atlantic routes. Through the early 1970s Boeing 747 passenger aircraft are able to offer a large cargo capacity at minimum cost.

It has been suggested that by the late 1970s the North Atlantic air carriers will derive more revenue from cargo than from passenger operation. This may bring about a change in emphasis throughout the airlines reaching to the heart of boardroom policy. The strongly commercial atmosphere of cargo carriage might then change quite radically the pattern of business, now geared primarily to the needs and desires of the passenger.

BIBLIOGRAPHY

Air Freight Trends and Developments, ICAO. Doc. 8235
Avenement de L'ere de l'avion civil, ITA, Oct. 1953

The Place of Air Freight in Physical Distribution, Harvard University, Division of Research, 1956

SMYKAY, BOWERSOX and MOSSMAN, *Physical Distribution Management*, Macmillan, 1961

K. R. SEALY and P. G. L. HERDSON, *Air Freight and Anglo-European Trade*, London School of Economics, and Hawker Siddeley Aviation, 1961

A. H. STRATFORD, *Prospects for the Growth of Intra-European Air Cargo*, Centro per lo Sviluppo dei Trasporti Aerei, Rome, June 1962

A. H. STRATFORD, *Transport Studies for Industry*, Review of the Federation of British Industries, Jan. 1963

Survey of U.S. Domestic Freight Movement, 1960–1, Douglas Aircraft Division

M. E. L. SPANYOL and P. J. DETMOLD, *The Future of Air Cargo on the North Atlantic*. Private report (1962)

How to Identify Potential Company Uses of Air Freight, Stanford Research Institute, 1963

J. GORHAM, K. R. SEALY and A. H. STRATFORD, *Why Companies Use Air Freight*, International Forum for Air Cargo, Montreal, May 1964

S. H. BREWER, *Rhochrematics*, Bureau of Business Research, University of Washington, Seattle

P. JACKSON and W. BRACKENRIDGE, *Air Cargo Distribution*, Gower Press, 1971

8 V/STOL. New Vehicles and Economic Prospects

V/STOL

The new technology of V/STOL is directed towards two distinct and important objectives in the field of aviation. These are (1) the easement of the environmental conflict between aviation activity and other land use, and (2) the establishment of air transport in the ultra short-haul field where to date the aeroplane has been unable to compete with surface transport. Such aspects of V/STOL as contribute to noise alleviation will be considered in Chapter 10. We discuss there also the pressing question of congestion at the major airports, which arises largely through the intensive movement of short- and medium-haul air services which could be operated with great effect by several of the V/STOL aircraft now in the project stage. To alleviate noise and congestion by their less demanding airfield requirements and less extensive noise contour areas, while offering a potential for air transport growth in market areas so far outside the capability of the conventional aircraft: these are the principal promises which give V/STOL its significance. It is appropriate to define the designation given to the new developments in short-haul air transport as follows:

CTOL: Aircraft with conventional requirements for airfield specification in the period 1970–5. For transport aircraft this generally demands a runway of 4000 ft or above.

RTOL: Reduced take-off and landing aircraft (field length 4000–2500 ft). Included within this range are certain existing turbo-props, new conventional turbofan aircraft and 'boosted' versions of existing conventional types.

STOL: Short take-off and landing aircraft (field length 2500–1500 ft) which include existing and developed turbo-props and new 'aerodynamic' and direct lift turbofan types, in the last of which the total lift is augmented either by silenced lift jets or advanced low-noise lift fan engines (RB 202).

VTOL: Fundamentally vertical take-off and landing aircraft with the ability to operate at higher weights from ultra-short runways (field length from 1500 ft downwards). Aircraft of this type use low noise lift fans and steep-gradient flight paths.

Many studies have been in train in the period 1967–72 to assess the relative merits of VTOL and STOL projects. Of particular interest have been the aircraft industry and independent research studies which have sought to assess the total costs and profitability of air systems operation in precisely defined operational areas with a presumed 'state of the art' at a given future time. In some design groups, early studies seem to have led to technical solutions which have proved to be inflexible in the changing pattern of experience and demand.

Most research teams have been led in the 1970–2 period to conclude that STOL solutions may be a little inferior to VTOL in theoretical economic terms, but offer immense advantages in time scale, R and D funding and in pragmatic matters like airline acceptability and ease of introduction into service.

We will at the outset consider the characteristics of short-haul transport which is initially likely to be the principal field of application of short take-off and landing and also of vertical-flight vehicles. Clearly it is in their ability to achieve flight with minimum time lost in ground manoeuvre to the take-off point and in climb to and descent from the cruising altitude, that the various vertical-take-off and landing aircraft, from the helicopter onwards, have their greatest economic potential. High movement rates offer to such aircraft their greatest competitive opportunity. Thus, the development of short-haul operations may be given a considerable impetus by the introduction of effective low-cost V/STOL aircraft. This will necessitate consideration of the greatly increased movement at airports and the handling problems which will arise. Let us consider in the first instance the significance of short-haul traffic.

Short-haul traffic demand

Many aspects of short-haul air traffic demand have now been studied and it is generally agreed that a very large increase could be expected if economic and practicable vehicles and facilities were available. Typical studies are indicated by Rowe (1964) and the results of MIT, SARC, Hawker Siddeley, Boeing and the British Aircraft Corporation. Results have shown that the peak in passenger-miles, now at 250–300 miles, would be developed at much shorter stages if low-cost high-frequency services were provided. There is in effect a gradual falling off in the demand for transport of all kinds as the length of the journey increases. This probably arises through the greater cost of the longer journey in money and in time, and because the number of mutual personal and business interests are likely to diminish with increased distance. Thus an

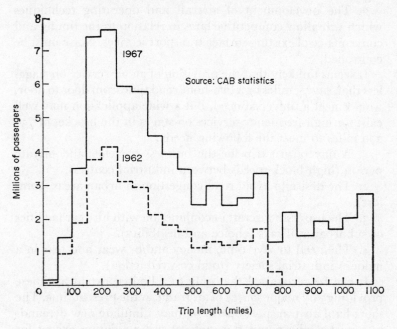

Fig. 8.1. Distribution of US Domestic Passenger Flights. Trunk and Local Service Operators, 1962, 1967. *Source*: CAB

increased demand for transport on short distances may be presumed and the limits set today by air facilities and surface competition, particularly from the motor car, cannot be expected to persist under all conditions. R. E. G. Davies has shown in his *History of the World's Airlines* that in 1960 the largest percentage block of passenger-miles was generated in the 200–400 miles bracket on regional routes. Figure 8.1 shows the number of passengers uplifted for various lengths of air journey in the US domestic trunk and local service operations in 1962 and 1967. The need exists for the aeroplane to penetrate into the shorter-haul category, 0–200 miles, and to achieve this aim it is clear that a considerable increase in the competitive power of air transport is required in this domain.

The increased contribution of the scheduled airline will depend upon:

1. The provision of high-frequency service between selected terminals giving convenient travel facilities with safety and regularity.

2. The development of aircraft and operating techniques which will allow competitive fares in relation to the timing and convenience of existing surface transport services. Norse must be controlled.

It seems unlikely that the provision of an air service on stages less than say 75 miles or a two-hour road time from door to door, would meet a universal need, but a wide application may well exist for high-frequency services on stages in the bracket of 75–200 miles to meet the following needs:

1. A day return trip for the business traveller and private person (high block speeds between industrial centres).

2. The desire to avoid road congestion in urban areas (comfort).

3. The use of an aircraft in conjunction with hire car facilities or suburban railways (choice and flexibility).

4. The need to save time, money and/or wear and tear in a modern industrial society (total cost reduction).

It can be recognised that only to a limited extent are these providing any major source of air traffic at the present time. The short-haul air transport operation may stimulate new demands in a part of the population not yet using aviation except for tourism.

324

Most estimates of air transport growth have forecast a larger proportional growth in passenger traffic on short as compared to long-haul routes. If these estimates are correct, an increasing demand for aircraft movements will arise since a characteristic of the short-haul operation is the high utilisation of terminal facilities which is incurred. Already an immense pressure upon existing airports is being exerted in the regions surrounding the capital cities. High-frequency services of a kind likely to meet the demand potential which we have been discussing may need to be supported by newly developed airports and ATC systems closely integrated to the existing pattern, but not directly superimposed upon it. Certainly experience with vertical-take-off aircraft (helicopters) has shown that the true potentiality of these vehicles in a high-density urban environment can be met only by segregation from the fixed-wing operational pattern of ATC to the greatest extent possible (Fitzek, 1962 and Dickie 1970).

Airport requirements with special consideration to short-haul operations

Already the airport authorities in New York, London and Paris are seeking locations for third and fourth airports to deal with traffic in the mid-1970s. The rates of traffic growth upon which these requirements are based are related to medium- and long-haul operations of a type which is existing today. The potential for capacity increase due to the lesser number of movements with larger aircraft, the increased capability of more advanced ATC and tighter control on the approach pattern and on the ground, may however delay for some years the need to open up new airports. We must recognise first of all that the annual growth of aircraft movements does not necessarily bear any relationship to the growth of movements in the peak hours or, to use the jargon, 'the busy hour rate'. Indeed, the natural tendency to spread the times of operation by voluntary airline action (or by such means as discriminatory airport charges to discourage peak-hour use) could considerably modify the situation. Bearing in mind the high concentration of holiday travellers in the peak summer hours, it does not seem impossible to contemplate a means of inducement to spread the travel times broadly about the peaks. The natural continuation of the present trend to operate aircraft of increasing size is also a factor of such importance in this connection that it might even stabilise the peak movements if airline management recognises the problem. A steep increase in short-haul traffic demand will however accentuate the aircraft movements as a whole and at the morning and evening peak times.

There is also the possible increased use of runways, and the potential for closer spacing of aircraft, especially when the approach paths' speed variations are small and consistent, seems to offer some considerable advantage. The slicker handling of aircraft on the runway – with smarter get-away, quicker turn-off and faster taxi speeds – offers even greater scope. Improved radar, means of locating vortex turbulence, and the development of navigational aids to minimise delay in positioning up to the final approach are key factors in development. US practice already allows eighty movements per hour on parallel runways at Kennedy and O'Hare (Chicago) during peak hours.

Of special significance at the present time is the impact of a new major London Airport site on the industrial concentration in the south-east of the UK. Airports attract industry. The site of a new airport will become the centre, in ten to fifteen years, of an industrial area which will resemble West Middlesex and the Heathrow environs. The overall cost to the nation of a new air industrial complex, with road, rail and air connections – together with the sterilisation of agricultural land, the cost to the air carrier industry of staff and service duplication, interconnections and delay is incalculable. The cost of road or rail links will have to be paid for.

A heavy investment in research and development in the operational and technical fields most likely to yield greater airport capacity, without deterioration of the safety standards, may well be justified. Vertical-flight aircraft will need to be considered in this context because of their long-term influence upon short-haul airport movements and air traffic volumes. There is a strong possibility that STOL transports will be in an advanced stage of development by 1980. This is less than ten years away. Technological development is rapid and it is highly desirable that major airfield developments should be planned to take account of the probable trends of at least two decades.

Finally, there is the development of regional air services which are now at last beginning to make a serious impression on the UK traveller. A strong case has been made for the concentration of air transport development on key airports with their greater facilities for passenger handling, their wider provision of schedules in time and destination, and their more diverse fare opportunities. The overruling factor now, however, is the predominant influence of London and its increasing demand for air services at a cost which is becoming a heavy burden to the nation. London needs air transport – not long journeys to the airport. Local and regional airport sites are now being considered as nodal points in regional transport plans in the United Kingdom. Feeder services to the capital cities are the first essential and subsequently there should be direct services from major provincial or regional airports to overseas centres of business and tourism. However, the incidence of a higher concentration of ultra-short-haul routes would exacerbate the situation, and it would seem inevitable that a ring of suburban or satellite airports will be required to provide close access to the capital city for short-haul domestic (perhaps some international) services. Availability for executive and general aviation purposes must also be considered.

Clearly, many important and some conflicting factors will arise when considering the location of an airport to suit particular requirements, and some studies (Stratford, 1963) have investigated areas of population and industrial concentration in a given territory so as to establish whether a regional airport to cover a wider area, or a larger number of small airfields to meet the supposed local and municipal requirements, would provide the best economic solution. It is necessary to bear in mind the transport requirements in passengers and cargo, the destination and route pattern most likely to develop in the future and, not least important, the current situation with regard to the national and local airports which are at present providing air transport facilities. It would be entirely unrealistic and unjustly damaging to the various interests who had sponsored and supported the risks inherent in a local airport development if a regional airport could be superimposed upon the air transport pattern without the fullest study and assessment of the local and the national interests.

Heliport requirements

Nor should our thoughts be confined only to the development of fixed-wing aviation. The introduction of multi-engined helicopter services in the mid-sixties has provided operating experience upon which improved heliport design and location could be based. The need to consider key factors such as traffic sources, the availability of surface transport links, Air Traffic Control, noise, and the operating vehicle's flight path in emergency conditions, have been recognised from the earliest days. These subjects have been debated in IATA and ICAO meetings, and American and European helicopter experience is widely reported (Cummings, 1960; Slocombe, 1964 and Hafner, 1954 and 1970).

Intensive operations have now demanded further consideration of passenger handling and terminal design but even in 1963 BEA at the Penzance heliport were content to specify an apron area capable of taking one (Sikorsky) S 61 without obstructing the landing and take-off path, although capable of expansion to two or three stands (Slocombe, 1964). Terminal buildings to handle fifty passengers and parking for 200 cars was required. Air traffic control on the Penzance–Scillies route was undertaken by specialist Ministry personnel and communication was maintained between air and ground by BEA traffic staff. This heliport, which comprised a 2-in pad of asphalt on quarry fill, 100 ft × 100 ft, constructed on a strip of land 900 ft × 150 ft wide, limited passenger facilities and a maintenance hangar for one helicopter, was estimated to cost £73,000 excluding the price of land. These modest requirements were determined by the needs of a seasonal and primarily tourist service and would not reflect major city centre operations at the present time.

In contrast, the Port of New York Authority invested $500,000 capital in the 30th Street heliport in addition to which a very substantial rental has been paid. The support given by far-sighted national and city authorities, so as to encourage the development of commercially viable helicopter services, has provided heliport facilities in the USA and in Europe at less than cost. The level of investment may be compared with that required for municipal and local airports.

The commercial viability of helicopter services

Because of the large potential in the ultra short-haul transport business which could be open to air transport if suitable vehicles and facilities were available, and because of the high cost of providing conventional airports for the high frequency of service which will eventually be required, it is necessary to consider the only VTOL aircraft currently available – the Helicopter.

The use of multi-engined helicopters of the Sikorsky S 61 and Boeing Vertol 107 types has already improved the economic possibilities of the situation as anticipated. In 1960 the intensive use of the Vertol 107 was planned to wipe out the deficit of New York Airways by 1966, although in the previous year a subsidy of $4·9 million had been received. In 1964 the subsidy had been cut to $1·9 million by the use of three of these aircraft.

As the President of New York Airways Inc. said, 'Turbine multi-engined helicopters mark the most important step taken thus far in the transition from development to business for that segment of the transportation industry, which utilises the capability for vertical flight' (Cummings, 1960). Even so, the fare level is extremely high and the view may well be expressed that a yield of 37 cents per passenger-mile is too high to stimulate within a reasonable time scale a business even with so large a potential market. If the basic requirement for the development of ultra-short-haul transport is the capability for vertical take-off and landing, we must consider whether the helicopter in its most developed form will provide the best prospects for the long-term competitive operating economy which is required. Many areas of special development have been explored. One example is the Rigid Rotor Helicopter which has been under flight development by the Lockheed Aircraft Corporation. This design has concentrated on the low first cost and maintenance advantages of an inherently simple rotor system. A capability for high-speed cruise provides an improved operating economy for the helicopter whose inherent disadvantage has been the limit set upon forward speed by the compressibility effect on the advancing blade and the local stalling of the retreating blade when exceeding 200–250 mph. Other forms of vertical-flight

329

aircraft have considerably better capability for horizontal speed and on medium- and long-haul operation are superior to the helicopter. Can the development potential which is inherent within the helicopter, taking into account the many lines of current development, be directed to short-haul civil airline operations with expectation of commercial success?

Some basic considerations

Although the helicopter may suffer in its limited cruising speed in certain important respects, its capability for hovering and vertical flight is without equal. This is largely due to the efficiency of the large-diameter rotor when moving at a low vertical speed, and the low power requirement. The low airflow velocity in the downwash ensures a moderate noise level. This high efficiency is inherent in a low disc loading not exceeding about 5–6 lb/sq ft for large transport helicopters as compared to the intensive loadings (over 1000 lb/sq ft) and high-velocity gas efflux of aircraft achieving vertical flight by means of jet lift.

A disadvantage of the helicopter for short-haul operations lies in the high drag of most configurations and the high cost of maintenance and servicing. The cyclic variation in the loads on the rotor systems, and especially the stalling effects on the retreating blades, set up vibrations which are a principal source of maintenance trouble requiring sophisticated design solutions, expensive engineering and up till now short-life components. In multi-engined helicopters automatic equipment is required to make corrections to available engine power distribution after power unit failure. In the achievement of greater simplicity and lower first cost and maintenance, the current developments such as the rigid rotor may improve the situation.

Studies reported by Raoul Hafner (1954) on the optimum configurations for four-engined helicopters, showed that maximum payload was achieved, for a design of 40,000 lb gross weight, using a total power of about 5000 hp. This was a 'high-speed' tandem rotor helicopter of compound design, that is, one in which a substantial aerodynamic lift was to be obtained from fixed wings in addition to the rotor. The disc loading was 5 lb/sq ft with a disposable load of about 14,000 lb with fuel allowances for take-off, landing and stand-off. A minimum direct-operating cost of 1·7 pence per seat-mile was deduced using the standard method of estimating helicopter operating costs developed by BEA. Even allowing for some improvement in these figures, and taking account of the limited size of air-craft considered, it is apparent that a high premium is being paid for the privilege of vertical flight and the lower cost of terminal facilities.

F. H. Robertson, the Chief Project Designer of Short Brothers & Harland, said 'No amount of weighting of such factors as utilization, prime cost or maintenance cost is ever going to bring the pure helicopter or the compound helicopter into the picture economically. . . . The simple facts of the matter are that they are too heavy and too slow and in the case of the compound, too complicated' (Robertson, 1955). His estimate for the direct operating costs of a compound helicopter (sixty passengers on a 300 nm stage) was rather higher than those of Hafner. The latter, in a more recent paper, confirmed his own cost estimates for the compound helicopter which he said was not competitive on stages above 300 miles (1961). Many inde-pendent investigations into the prospects for airline use of helicopters have confirmed this conclusion.

Helicopter research and development

The programme of research and flight test development carried out by the Bell Helicopter Co. of Texas, has opened up a wide range of possibilities for the technical and economic solution of the problems associated with the use of rotors for high-performance VTO transport aircraft. The inherent advantage of low disc loading to achieve, at low cost in power, weight and noise, a given hovering performance, has stimulated development in a field which lies between the pure helicopter and the tilt-wing prop-turbine aircraft. An incentive to seek solutions in this area is provided by the overall economy of installing a well-balanced power supply which meets the needs of high-speed cruising and take-off thrust with adequate reserves. Because the economic operation of the VTO aircraft as a transport vehicle necessitates the provision of a high cruising speed the most intensive efforts to raise speeds to 350–400 mph are being made.

Methods of approach include:

1. The rigid blade or stiff hinge rotor which confers high control power and manoeuvre damping for compound helicopters.

2. The rotor-propeller which, by rotation through 90°, can give good propulsive efficiency without an unbalance of power required for cruise and take-off.

3. The stopping rotor which can be designed for low drag in high-speed conditions such as with jet engines.

4. The trailing rotor which folds in flight and trails in a low drag configuration for high-speed cruising.

5. The variable span or telescopic rotor.

The tiltwing and deflected slipstream

These two principles for achieving vertical flight have one thing in common; they employ propellers to provide thrust for both horizontal and vertical flight. In the case of the tiltwing aircraft the propeller axis is rotated from the vertical to the near-horizontal position either with the whole engine-wing system (such as the Vought-Hiller-Ryan XC 142A and Canadair CL 84) or with engines only tilting (such as the Curtiss-Wright X 19A) and the Bell X 22A (in which airscrews are located in tilting ducts). It is found that the tilting designs in general suffer from a number of limitations, due to the conflicting requirements of hover and cruise, which may restrict the payload ratio and limit cruising speeds to about 350 mph (Cheeseman, 1963 and Stepniewski, 1957). It is estimated that the installed power requirement for a four-engined aircraft would be nearly twice that required for cruising flight so that excess power is likely to be available at altitude. Engine failure during vertical flight and the need to provide faultless interconnection between the power units requires at least a four-engine installation and some complication and weight penalty.

The Canadair CL 84, a twin-engine tiltwing project, completed development flying in 1967. This aircraft is controlled conventionally apart from the rear rotor, use being made of the strong inter-action between the free stream and the propeller slipstream which acts over the full span of the low-aspect ratio rectangular wings. In spite of the apparent complexity of the tiltwing mechanism, the engineering design and maintenance problems are likely to arise rather in the multi-engine shafting necessary to achieve balance due to power variation and engine failure. Of the greatest commercial importance is the flexibility available to the operator who can use the aircraft as a STOL performer when runway length is available. In the design of the Canadair CL 84 this should allow an increase of take-off weight of at least 20 per cent thereby achieving payloads, with short runways, which are twice that available for VTO.

Important research at Langley field has related to the evaluation of flaps on tiltwing aircraft to improve control and transition between conventional and vertical flight. This research will also influence the deflected slipstream transport exemplified by the Breguet 94 family of aircraft (Ziegler, 1961). In these designs an 'integral' wing entirely within the slipstream of four propellers is fitted with slats and slotted flaps which steeply deflect the total airflow, thus achieving a very high lift coefficient and a very short field requirement. High approach drag in the powered landing configuration is achieved by setting the two outer propellers at zero pitch thereby increasing slipstream on the centre wing and generating an effective reduction in the Aspect Ratio, with augmented induced drag (Chapter 2). An early deflected slipstream aircraft was the Ryan VZ 3RY Vertiplane, a small experimental aircraft with one Lycoming T 53 gas turbine engine driving two propellers.

The overall advantage of any one type of the V/STOL aircraft which we have considered has not yet been proven in scheduled operations. Certainly the multi-engined helicopter has up to the time of writing been able to maintain a tenuous hold on many special ultra-short-haul 'direct' operations, nor has a serious challenge yet been made to its position. The economics of the helicopter, however, are still not good enough to encourage a large-scale expansion of local services. No tiltwing, convertible or deflected slipstream aircraft has yet been successfully marketed. The major developments in this field are still in the hands of defence authorities to whom only recently has the true value of VTO been apparent. Nor does the clear advantage of the lower cost of heliports yet provide adequate incentive to the inauguration of short-haul air services with helicopters. If airports are available or if governments and local authorities will provide them and reasonable facilities at acceptable landing fees, there is some reason for leaving with the passenger the long down-town journey from distance airports.

The commercial application of the Skycrane

One specialised application of the use of rotors for direct lift is being given keen attention by the US Army and the Federal German Government. This is typified by the Sikorsky S 64A Skycrane. In this vehicle, designed for a useful load of 20,670 lb and normal take-off weight 38,000 lb, a full fuselage structure is not provided, but provision is made to hoist interchangeable pods required for various military transport duties. Larger cranes based on this principle have been planned, as well as projects based on hot-rotor propulsion, thereby dispensing with the need for a rear rotor and offering further potential weight saving. The vehicle has a remarkably high disposable load in relation to the basic equipped weight and it therefore has a high lifting capacity in terms of first cost. As with all vehicles, this has a powerful influence on the operating economy especially when the vehicle is not being highly utilised, and it therefore offers opportunity for use in a wide variety of roles. The maintenance costs of such vehicles will be moderate in comparison with the classical designs of helicopter and even when compared with fixed-wing aircraft, so that the variable costs of operation will be largely fuel and crew costs which can be more easily controlled and which, incidentally, can be more accurately forecast in the planning stage.

The high payloads which are possible with such a vehicle are not contained within a limiting fuselage shape, so that heavy loads and loads of very low density can be effectively uplifted by means of hoists, nets, or special containers. We have, therefore, the first transport vehicle in which there is no practical limit to the volume of the load which can be carried and it is here that a new concept of the transport vehicle emerges. It is for consideration whether there is a commercial requirement for this type of aircraft and, if so, whether the market would justify the development of a civil product.

Commercial characteristics of the Crane

The direct operating costs have been computed by the SBAC formula for a 21,000 payload vehicle of this type. With a utilisation of 2000 hours per annum and adjusted to take suitable account of the greater simplicity of the design characteristics of the Crane, these have shown that the direct operating costs could be reduced below 4 pence per capacity short-ton nautical mile on stages between 50 and 150 nautical miles. This is a relatively small aircraft: the economic advantage of scale will apply here again. This vehicle is not highly sensitive to the utilisation that might be achieved on a scheduled operation and on 1000 hours per annum the direct costs would increase by approximately 25 per cent. However, very intensive operation of a Crane on scheduled services would provide even more attractive economics, and operations of this kind would be essential if an adequate market for this vehicle were to be assured. The characteristic capability of the Crane to pick up and let down its load pre-packed and ready for the connecting operation could be exploited to achieve a remarkably short turnround time. This could suggest a shuttle operation transporting those goods which are of such weight, size and/or density that they could not be transported by other forms of transport, or goods of more conventional characteristics which could be more cheaply carried in this vehicle. These low transport costs can only be achieved where the two-way traffic flow is considerable, in which case the load factors could be maintained at a high level. We could consider such products as breakfast cereals as an ideal cargo for this type of aircraft, and a town of less than half a million inhabitants might require a weekly delivery flight for this product alone to satisfy its requirements, with minimum ground storage and deletion of truck road transport. The overall requirement throughout the United Kingdom might be very high since a number of other products of low density can be visualised which might provide scheduled delivery flights with economic two-way loads.

An important low-density cargo which is likely to warrant specialised scheduled services by a vehicle such as the Crane is motor car bodies. The loading of these on specially designed quick-lift containers could be a continuous operation with the aircraft turnround brought to a minimum and a very undesirable traffic would be taken off the road.

Preliminary estimates show that a Crane is able to move building contractors' equipment such as tower cranes and concrete mixing plant from site to site in urban areas considerably more cheaply than by conventional means of surface transport when full account is taken of the time-consuming operations associated with dismantling and manhandling for road haulage. A detailed study made of the operation of a Crane when used in the London area showed that with conservative estimates of the flight time required for each contracting operation and the distance required to be flown to the site from the central operating point, only 270 separate air lifting operations were required in a year to give economic operation with the Crane at a cost less than that required by conventional methods using road haulage. Further applications may be envisaged such as the transport of large indivisible prefabricated units for shipbuilding and construction work which are now too bulky for land transport facilities.

STOL

After the above consideration of conventional modes for the provision of V/STOL services including helicopters, we should now consider how the STOL aeroplane can provide new solutions to the current requirements. STOL aircraft are of course with us now and a number of types of aircraft such as the BN Islander, Beech 99, Short Skyvan, and DH Canada Twin Otter can be so categorised. These are, however, small aircraft and meet a generally local demand and a third level operating pattern of service. For reasons already discussed an emerging demand is apparent for larger aircraft with the characteristics of STOL or at least RTOL performance. The overall objectives in the operation of such aircraft have been well defined by BAC (J. H. Quick, 1971), but are somewhat rephrased for this text.

1. To reduce passenger access time by moving the airport closer to the demand areas.

2. To reduce congestion – in the airspace, on the airport surface and on the access routes between passenger origin/destination and aircraft.

3. To improve convenience (Higher frequency with smaller aircraft).

4. To increase the possibility of delaying or off-setting the cost of additional CTOL airports.

5. To increase the potential capacity of existing CTOL airports by the addition of STOL runway(s).

6. To reduce dramatically the noise-affected areas.

Thus the objectives are somewhat complex but are in the end simply twofold (a) to reduce congestion and nuisance and (b) to augment traffic. These two current essential aims require two important addenda. The prospects of improvement in the specific direct operating costs are not good within the short time scale, when compared with CTOL; and the application of STOL and also of VTOL to long-haul operations is unlikely to be significant until after short-haul services have become fully established in the late 1970s or early 1980s. To the protagonist of the STOL development programme, moreover, the key factors favourable to STOL as compared to VTOL are essentially:

1. Cost. Less complex engine installation and control, with zero speed flight control and profile guidance.

2. Time Scale. Very much less than required for advanced technology fan lift and high thrust propulsion engines.

3. Choice of location of sites to exploit the vehicle. More favourable for STOL since peripheral city sites and sites adjacent to airports are easier to locate and cheaper to develop than city centre sites. Many sites already are in use.

It would be premature to give detailed results of the many STOL project studies which have been published during the last two or three years when so much work is still being carried out. BAC and HSA in the UK, Boeing, McDonnell-Douglas and Lockheed in the USA and Dornier, Aerospatiale, Dassault and Aeritalia in Europe as well as Japanese, Canadian and

Australian firms have made active strides in this field stretching from conventional STOL designs to advanced applications of direct-lift fan power. A summary of the status of key European project studies may, however, be given.

The work of BAC and of Aerospatiale is based on the 14,000–15,000 lb thrust Snecma-Rolls Royce engine, M45 S 20, an advanced high by-pass ratio (10:1) development of the M45 installed in the VFW 614. This engine incorporates a geared fan with 25 variable pitch blades which is now under development by Dowty-Rotol. The A 904 of Aerospatiale is schemed as a 130-seat advanced STOL aircraft with a balanced airfield requirement of 1900 ft in ISA plus 15° C conditions. This design is part of a French Government $36 million STOL development programme which encompasses aircraft design studies also by Dassault and airport/air operations network studies for second generation (i.e. longer term) solutions to world market needs. BAC have taken similar steps in the project design programme, only hesitatingly encouraged by the British Government, but with a wider background of successful aircraft development than any other manufacturer in Europe. The BAC design studies are at this time under assessment by the Government, who are financially constrained by Concorde and Rolls Royce RB 211 recovery expenditures. Thus political and national economic issues, not for the first item, are distorting the potential for STOL development more especially in the United Kingdom.

Italian–US STOL Projects

The Boeing-Aeritalia STOL project has been based on an urban transport concept setting STOL performance and low noise level as the key criteria. Sized initially at 100–150 seats with both conventional (CTOL) and STOL capability the aircraft is powered by 4 high-bypass-ratio turbo-fans in the 20,000 lb thrust category. Various wing designs have been compared in the feasibility stage including externally blown flaps, internally blown flaps, and also direct lift. A field performance better than 2500 ft is the aim with a range of over 500 nm at a cruise speed of about Mach 0·8. As in other projects of the 1971–2 period, high bypass ratio (up to 15) variable pitch fan engines have been considered. Wing volume for STOL designs allow over-loading with fuel for longer range operations. Thus arises the possibility of longer range CTOL variants which should add considerable versatility to this type of aircraft which in many applications will operate from airfields in the 3000–5000 ft length categroies. The Aeritalia Group was founded in 1969 by the consolidation of the aviation and avionics division of Fiat and members of the Finmeccanica Group.

European Jet Lift

Dornier work has been directed towards a V/STOL system based on the DO 231 which evolved from the experience gained in the design and test programme of the Do 31E experimental aircraft. A comparison with the Hawker Siddeley HS 141 project is inevitable. The German design employs two RB 220 engines for cruise, and four RB 202 lift engines are fitted in a pod in each outer wing section, with another two each in the nose and at the rear of the fuselage. Basic requirements seem to have been related to Lufthansa route sectors. The DO 231 was ranked first technically and operationally by the West German Commission under Dr Karl Thalan who made in 1970/71 a comprehensive evaluation of the industry's V/STOL proposals.

A Flight International report (February 1971) describes the HS 141 V/STOL in the following terms:

'This design study . . . is of conventional low-wing layout, with a moderately swept wing and a T-tail. It would be propelled by two Rolls-Royce RB 220 turbofans of 27,000 lb thrust and lifted by 16 RB 202 25 lift-fans of 10,900 lb thrust in "blisters" along the fuselage sides. Five-abreast seating for 102 to 119 passengers would be available, but the fuselage could be lengthened to take 150 passengers. In this form, with only four lift engines, it would take its capacity payload out of a 2000 ft, 610 m strip for a 650 nm, 1200 km range. With 20 lift engines, the stretched version would again have a VTOL performance. The Hawker-Siddeley philosophy has been revised from "pure" VTOL to embrace STOL with a modified version of the same aircraft in order to meet possible political and commercial shifts of interest.'

The HS 141 incorporating the RB 202 fan lift engine introduces a new generation of low noise VTOL aircraft which when fully developed in the early 1980s could provide true city centre services. The noise footprint from this aircraft for a given payload capacity is estimated by Hawker Siddeley to cover no more than one-fifth the area of STOL projects available in the late 1970s and one-hundredth of that of CTOL aircraft to noise certification standards of the mid-1970s. The noise footprint would be defined as the area enclosed by a ground contour at a given PNdB (noise) level say 90.

The study of operating costs

Before making a fuller study of the cost effectiveness of a V/STOL transport it may be of value to establish some of the principal points of difference which are likely to arise when comparing aircraft of this type with a conventional long-take-off transport. It must be expected, for example, that the installed take-off power will be considerably greater for the VTOL aircraft. In spite of the remarkably low installed weight of the new generation of fan-lift engines, the overall weight of the installed power may be greater by a factor exceeding two. Certainly the first cost of the power units with their associated equipment, fuel systems and accessories will be higher. The fuel consumption must clearly be higher. A more elaborate engine control system plus fan or ejector systems, and almost certainly a sophisticated means of providing stability and control in hovering flight will be required by most types of VTOL aircraft. If two types of power plant are required, this must increase total overhaul costs and complicate maintenance schedules. Though it is difficult as yet to estimate accurate values, these broad facts must be accepted as self-evident but a number of important counterbalancing factors need to be evaluated. There is a marked difference in the block speed between VTOL and conventional take-off aircraft arising from the take-off, initial climb and landing path trajectory which is wholly favourable to the

VTOL. This factor will affect all direct costs which are generated on an hourly basis. This also augments the profitability of operations by increasing the miles flown per annum.

There is a reduced risk of catastrophic accident in the low fuel case, since the VTOL aircraft has a far wider range of diversion opportunity which must lead to less stringent demands for fuel reserves, especially when combined with automatic take-off and landing, the full development of which with conventional aircraft should precede extensive civil V/STOL operations.

The VTOL aircraft is a more flexible operating vehicle which will suffer a much smaller loss in economy than normal jet aircraft when operating on the shortest stages. Greater traffic potential therefore exists for both VTOL and STOL operations.

The VTOL aircraft has, of course, the inherent ability to operate as a short-take-off (STOL) aircraft operating at higher weights to increase payload or at reduced engine settings, without weight increase, such as in high-altitude conditions, or in order to control the noise level. The aircraft therefore provides a marked degree of economic and operational freedom. Making reasonable assumptions as to the proportion of payload available in a given increase of take-off weight, for a multi-jet VTOL design of 50,000 lb gross weight it was computed that the direct-operating cost could be reduced by 28 per cent if the VTOL aircraft was permitted a 500-ft take-off run. A payload increase of nearly 50 per cent was achieved. Fuselage redesign to allow greater capacity to stow the higher payload in the STOL case would reduce the direct-operating cost saving by 6–8 per cent.

Perhaps in the flexible operation of a V/STOL transport aircraft we shall find a new potential for air transport economy on the short-haul routes which still need to be opened up even in well-developed countries and where small fields or industrial sites may be turned to a profitable use by aviation.

Study of US short-haul transportation with V/STOL

In 1968 Boeing and NASA published a report entitled 'A Study of Aircraft in Short-Haul Transportation Systems'.

This study analysed VTOL, STOL and CTOL design concepts for the period around 1985, presuming a considerable degree of maturity in the short-haul system by that date and for each mode a marked technological advance. Chosen study regions included the North-East Corridor. Basing their work on a traffic forecasting model which built in factors such as GNP, aircraft seat-mile cost, air travel price, overall price levels, air travel quality and service, the study predicted an 8·7-fold increase in revenue passenger miles for the US domestic scheduled air carriers between 1965 and 1985. At that stage in project development Boeing, wisely perhaps, made no major pronouncements on the relative merits of VTOL or STOL aircraft, but by introduction of total surface access costs – the traveller implicitly valuing his own time – and with V/STOL fares set at the CTOL level, the advantages of the new technology were demonstrated.

The Boeing Study showed average total access costs to be

To and from CTOL port	$6.00
,, Suburban V/STOL port	$4.33
,, Downtown VTOL site	$4.00

For the year 1985 the basic CTOL fare estimated for New York–Boston is $7. Using Return-on-Sales as a profitability criterion, the Boeing Study showed considerable advantage on all flight stages (100–400 st miles) for V/STOL projects. Comparative profitability on 200-mile stages was 12 per cent for CTOL developments (200 seats), and 17 per cent on certain V/STOL projects of equal capacity. On 400-mile stages profitability fell, but in comparison with conventional aircraft results achieved were estimated as:

CTOL 13%   STOL 15%   VTOL 14%

For smaller capacity aircraft the advantage of V/STOL remained.

The market for VTOL

The VTO aircraft may find a large part of its potential market in the very short stage lengths for which most of today's traffic uses the railway or the private car. It might therefore be misleading to base any market study on the assumption that an existing aircraft market could be captured and evaluate the future size of this market as a guide to VTO sales potential; it would be equally invalid if we computed payload size from the extrapolation of recent air traffic statistics. A new approach to the study of air transport demand has therefore been called for. For these reasons we have made an attempt to compute the proportions of business travellers who would use a VTO service in place of a private car or train. It has been necessary in the space available to confine the discussion to one route, and we took London–Manchester as being the most suitable because of information available. The approach here described was originally developed by the author in association with P. J. Detmold for Hawker Siddeley.

On a UK domestic route we face a difficult problem. The 1000 or so passengers who on a typical week-day might at present travel by BEA between London and Manchester form an insignificant proportion of the potential VTO traffic on this route. The crucial question is how many of the business people who might drive from and to the general area of London would transfer to a VTO service? How many would be retained and/or won by British Railways? There is no established technique of traffic analysis which would enable an answer to these questions to be computed and we must therefore devise a new and rational technique. It may be of interest to the economist to consider a parallel approach described by C. D. Foster and M. E. Beesley (1963) who estimated the social benefit from constructing the Victoria Underground Line in London. The recent work published by the Roskill Commission on the Third London Report is also essential reading (Chapter 10).

An analysis of the value of time

If one particular form of transport is both faster and cheaper than its alternatives, then the passenger may be expected to accept it unless he is exposed to a deterrent such as an unreasonable degree of danger or discomfort. Equally, he will only take a means of transport that is both slower and more expensive than another if some other special advantage is offered. We may

343

therefore assume that where the VTO service offers an advantage in speed at no additional cost it would meet these requirements when compared with conventional domestic air services. We are now, however, primarily concerned with assessing the choice of travellers whose journey would be faster but more expensive by VTO aircraft. The VTO service would be more expensive per passenger journey than a private car driven by its sole occupant and much more expensive than a car shared by two or more. The time saved would depend on the speed of access to the VTO station and the proximity of origin and destination points to a motorway system. Clearly no businessman in his senses wishing to travel from Watford to Salford (see Figs. 8.2 and 8.3) would drive in a peak traffic period from Watford to Battersea Heliport for a flight to Ringway, and then rent a car for the final stage of his journey. We may therefore evaluate the relative increased cost and time-saving when using the VTO service as an alternative to a car journey from a large number of points in south-east England to various destinations in the Midlands and the North West.

We can, then, determine the equilibrium distance from the VTO station at which the time saved would be just considered worth while by the business and private traveller. The assumptions upon which the basic equations can be set up depend upon the cost and time factors in road and VTOL transport modes. For this study we assumed that short-haul VTOL aircraft could be designed to achieve operating costs equivalent to the current subsonic jets of equal seating capacity. If not yet quite valid there is every reason to expect this to be a reasonable assumption by 1980.

How can we estimate the value of time-saving? The financial circumstances of the individual must influence the choice of transport and those paying for their own ticket may be more parsimonious than those travelling at their employer's expense. There may or may not be an incentive for employees to use their cars on business journeys quite irrespective of the time lost when compared with an air service. The choice of transport may be influenced by many other factors such as the time of day and the weather. A practical approach to the matter is to establish how much is paid today for the saving of time. We have therefore compared the cost and time-saving of air and first-class rail on

344

sample routes and on others comparable, not limiting ourselves to the Manchester–London route where special conditions may apply. We also compared the cost and time-saving between second-class rail and motor coach as a guide to the behaviour of the less affluent. Figures of approximately £1 per hour in the former and 37·5p in the latter were obtained. These figures are not necessarily the mean of the values placed upon their time by all passengers using the service; each represents no more than a figure at which some travellers will choose each form of transport, but they do provide a general guide. We also considered the matter from the standpoint of the company sending its employees on business journeys; we evaluated the cost of a man's time at various salary levels. It seemed probable that a firm would pay £1 for each hour saved by a man earning £1500 per annum. The authors of the study on the Victoria Line (Foster and Beesley, 1963) seem to have used rather lower values such as 25p per hour for the 97 per cent of Londoners travelling in their own time, but the higher proportion of travellers making daily journeys on the London rail system might lead one to suppose that a lower value would be set upon time in that case. Studies in 1970/71 have shown considerably higher figures than those employed in the above studies thus reflecting inflation in wages and the increase in value of time in a changing society.

Using the above figures we found that the time-saving of the VTO over the railway would cost more than 37½p an hour for second-class passengers at the estimated operating cost of a jet-lift VTO in an overwhelming proportion of cases. The private motorist who considered transferring to VTO transport would also find that the potential time-saving cost considerably more than this figure even when he was travelling alone. This suggested that VTO transport was unlikely to appeal to the private traveller in large numbers at the fares envisaged and at the assumed values of time. This meant that we require a very considerable reduction in the total operating cost of VTOL aircraft if they are to break into the mass market. Unfortunately, the business traveller may have other reasons than economy for preferring his car to any form of public transport. The need to carry samples and the ease with which he may widen his itinerary at short notice are obvious factors which might

345

influence his choice in favour of the private car even though his time is worth no less than we suppose.

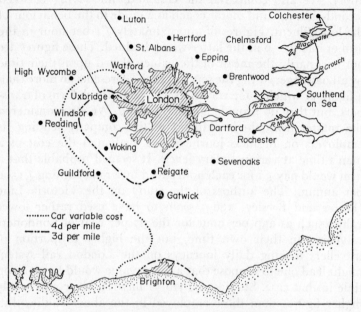

FIG. 8.2. London–Manchester VTOL Service.
The Car Traffic Catchment Areas

Discounting these factors, the basic equations have been used to calculate traffic catchment areas for VTO services between the city centre terminals at Nine Elms and near-central Manchester. These are presented in Figs. 8.2 and 8.3. A traveller starting his journey from a borderline London point and travelling to a borderline point around Manchester would be indifferent in his choice between road and VTO transport. Though it may be unrealistic to imagine such hard-and-fast areas, one assumes tacitly that for each traveller choosing VTO, though his journey were between points lying outside the catchment areas, there would be one preferring his car though his journey lay within the boundaries. The computation of these areas is based upon the assumption that the VTOL aircraft could operate profitably at current fare levels. Our computation would not be invalidated by further inflation of costs provided that these affected other forms of transport in equal proportion, but any substantial increase in operating costs for other reasons would reduce the size of these catchment areas and invalidate our conclusions regarding the size of the market and the optimum seating capacity of the aircraft. In recent years the inflation in surface transport costs has in fact greatly exceeded that in air transport. This trend seems likely to continue. Moreover the trend already mentioned towards a higher evaluation of time inevitably favours the VTOL transport system.

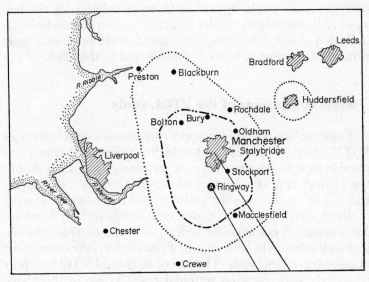

FIG. 8.3. Manchester–London VTOL Service.
The Car Traffic Catchment Areas

Our analysis produced an estimate of the capacity required, but in the assessment of the size of aircraft required the desired frequency of service is a determinant of equal importance which could only be assessed in a somewhat arbitrary manner. It should be borne in mind that service frequency may itself influence the volume of traffic since a high-frequency service is particularly attractive to businessmen. Traffic volume and aircraft size are therefore interdependent variables, and we only considered the former as a determinant, ignoring the 'feed-back'

347

effect. The record of the BEA traffic growth on the London–
Manchester route as frequency was increased is an eloquent
example of this. It would not seem reasonable to provide less
than 18 services a day including those calling at Heathrow and
Ringway. A recent check showed the number of direct express
trains on a weekday to be 16. Probably a frequency of 24 services
a day is the most reasonable estimate, calling for an aircraft with
120 seats under the conditions forecast above. When it is borne
in mind that the vehicle size should be suited to the traffic level
after two or three years of service, a rather larger aircraft with
over 200 seats would appear to be more suitable for the late
1970s. All such studies require constant revision and updating as
indicated above. Wide ranging studies evolved on similar basic
principles are now in hand in Europe and in the USA.

Some conclusions of the VTOL study

A comparison of total transport costs shows that a typical jet
VTOL aircraft will need seat-mile direct-operating costs comparable to and not more than 10 per cent greater than that of
the Boeing 727, HS Trident and Sud Caravelle if business
traffic is to be drawn to the air from road and rail to new types
of direct service on key UK domestic routes such as London–
Manchester. A considerable reduction in the current subsonic
jet cost levels would be necessary if private travellers were to be
attracted on a large scale. The cost of short-haul VTO transport
is strongly dependent on terminal costs. While in the above
comparisons landing fees were based on scales now existing for
UK airports, a full project study into the cost of building and
operating VTO stations is required before a reliable estimate of
comparative economics is possible. Noise is the other major
obstacle to VTOL operations and may for a generation exclude
regular services from near-central sites (Chapter 10).

From a broad examination of predominantly business traffic
on the one high-density route London–Manchester, it appears
that the optimum aircraft size for the late 1960s lies within the
range of 120–140 seats and at least 250 seats in the 1980s. A
larger aircraft would be expected to offer lower direct operating
costs and this line of approach may be tempting to the aircraft

designer if international markets justify the higher development costs. If on the other hand, a 20 per cent increase in fares might be expected this might lead to a reduction in traffic to between 30 and 45 per cent of the level estimated previously. A larger increase in fares would be expected to lead to traffic reduction of such magnitude that operation of jet VTO domestic services would in most cases become impracticable. The advantage of this method is that the sensitivity of the traffic to the various input parameters can be gauged.

These results, computed as they are from an estimate of the behaviour of limited classes of traffic on one route, can give no more than an indication in the broadest terms of the competitive significance of the VTOL transport at the various possible levels of operating cost. The need for a considerable reduction in the operating cost is apparent, so also are the consequences of a serious underestimation of the true costs.

VTOL Transport for business purposes

Already air transport has acquired in all parts of the world a major part of overseas business travel, especially when a sea crossing is entailed. There are six main reasons for this notable success.

(a) Time savings are often such as to justify the additional fares.

(b) Additional costs on the longer surface transport journeys (e.g. meals, sometimes hotels), may significantly offset their lower basic fares.

(c) Only middle to senior staff grades are sent on more expensive overseas journeys, which generally involve senior representation.

(d) Greater simplicity of arrangements for bookings; journeys require less interchange.

(e) Personal satisfaction in a more rapid return home (often same day).

(f) Status aspect; glamour of air travel.

On domestic journeys the reasons for the selection of a mode of transport are likely to be more complex. For one thing the motor car is a major contender and with improved roads and wider acquisition of the car this may become more serious. The economics of competition from the car are closely tied to the number in the party, which will effect tourism more than business travel. The improvement in rail services in the UK will be a further factor and this must be expected to challenge air transport growth in this country unless it can be shown to future governments that VTOL, or any other mode of transport, could offer a worthwhile alternative with a better return on investment and a higher overall benefit/cost ratio at present values. The capital investment in British Rail and London Transport has averaged £127 million per annum over the period 1965–8. (*Vide* National Plan.)

Time savings on domestic journeys are less, and with conventional aircraft offer very small gains on sectors shorter than 200 miles. Moreover, as London Airport's congestion increases, and future London Airport capacity is provided farther from the centre, the mounting advantage of rail communication is plain to see. VTOL services could modify this considerably. Items (c) to (f) apply with far less emphasis on domestic journeys but being unamenable to any form of analysis, we are left with items (a) and (b) as the principal factors offering a potential advantage to VTOL transport if it can be realised in practice.

Tourism

In the consideration of tourist services with VTOL aircraft we shall need to consider other criteria. The saving of a few hours is clearly less important to the traveller in this case, and price (especially for family groups), convenience and simplicity, is of crucial significance. Tourist travel is becoming organised on an increasing scale on the Inclusive Tour (IT) basis, and the travel cost element is not always easy to separate from the total tour cost. Essentially, however, the unit cost of providing the air transport is cut to approximately one half of scheduled passenger operation by group booking which allows load factors of over 85 per cent (as compared to 55–60 per cent). The cost of sales and passenger handling is also considerably reduced (see Chapter 4). To what extent can it be expected that the introduction of VTOL services would modify the pattern of tourist travel, whether on scheduled or inclusive tour services? There can be few additional tourist destinations to which flights with conventional aircraft are not already operating or could be operated. Airfields in Switzerland, Austria and Yugoslavia have opened up tourist regions during the last decade which have stimulated travel. However, such island resorts as Jersey, Elba, Corsica and Rhodes may in certain cases have difficulty in offering runway space for the larger jet aircraft which are now moving into the IT sphere of operations. While farther destinations may be envisaged in the Mediterranean area, the limits of range for the first generation of VTOL aircraft design may restrict the operating radius to 550–600 miles (Manchester–Geneva is 620 statute miles). Further operations into Austria and Yugoslavia could certainly be considered if VTOL sites alone were required. However, the half hour to one hour drive by coach or car to or from an airport is not a serious obstacle to the average family on holiday.

The very real attraction of jet transport to and from the foreign airport is now freely available, and the saving of time in days as well as the simplicity of travelling without concern for food and train connections in a foreign country, has already been provided by the Inclusive Tour operator. A possible future growth in the short 2–4-day holiday would probably be stimulated by the time-savings inherent in VTOL services. Such holiday trips are already being sought by a small and growing section of the community: the commonest destinations from the UK. Northern regions are Paris (especially at Easter and Christmas), Scotland (Edinburgh, Dundee for St Andrews, Cairngorms in January–March), Channel Islands (Spring and Autumn). Such generalised considerations cannot readily be quantified. It may be most realistic to presume the steady growth of IT business through the 1970s, which the potential offered by VTOL aircraft of 90–160 seat capacity will continue to exploit in the 1980s. One important consideration is that the inclusive tour operator might well be keen to offer VTOL travel as a competitive factor just as he learnt to use jet aircraft in the late 1960s. A more vital competitive factor, however, is cost, and the VTOL aircraft must have comparable costs of operation per seat-mile and offer an adequate seat capacity to provide

economic group handling and low levels of d.o.c. These principles apply to private use of VTOL services, where cost becomes
a predominant factor on routes which are essentially business
routes. Note also I.T. discussion in Chapter 4.

Air cargo

The criteria for air cargo transport development have
many similar characteristics to those applicable to Tourism. Here also time saving is significant only in its economic
context, and air terminal proximity to the origin and/or destination of the shipment will be of less importance than the relative
costs of collection and delivery and transit costs (by road truck
usually) to and from the airport offering the most convenient
scheduled flights. If VTOL transport costs can reduce the total
costs of distribution, then this form of transport will be used.
We do not see a strong likelihood that air cargo service could
be rendered at a lower cost through use of VTOL aircraft, but
clearly (as in the case of IT passenger services) as VTOL comes
into general use with high frequency schedules on key industrial
routes, greater use will be made of the capacity for freight
carriage which could then be offered as soon as large VTOL
aircraft are available, and when technological advance allows
operating costs to be acceptable to the shipper. It seems most
probable, therefore, that high frequency services with large
aircraft (probably exceeding 160 seats) giving high utilisation
and improved doc will stimulate the use of VTOL services by
the air cargo shipper and his agent, rather than that he will
seek the inherent merits of VTOL as an end in itself. Unlike the
IT passenger who may be buying with his ticket an enjoyable
personal experience, the air cargo customer (the shipper)
seldom sees the vehicles which carry his goods. Thus, the forces
at work on the development of air cargo are less emotive than
those which determine the movement of passengers. A recent
study on the location of cargo airport sites to minimise the cost
of total transport to UK industry has suggested that no more
than five sites are required to cover the whole country. One of
these is in Northern Ireland. Thus, a close pattern of cargo
depots at many VTOL sites seems to be little justified. How-

ever, if a considerable capacity at a high frequency is to be provided at a low marginal cost on major industrial routes because of the large business passenger traffic, the interest of industry would be rapidly aroused, and road truck costs (including drivers' night stops) might be seriously challenged.

As emphasised above, the total cost to the shipper will be the sole determining factor in the long run.

Air Mail will almost certainly be carried by the GPO and by European Post Offices on high frequency scheduled VTOL services. This will form an important source of revenue not yet of importance to UK domestic service operators, although important on the international European sectors.

Operating Patterns and Schedule Reliability

With any radically new form of transport such as VTOL aircraft, the opportunity presents itself for a re-examination of first principles of operations to ensure that the advantages and flexibility inherent in the design are exploited to the full, and are not hampered by techniques which may no longer be applicable.

Most of the serious VTOL studies of the past few years have highlighted the potential savings to be gained by taking this opportunity. Some of these have, however, ignored the practicabilities of large-scale aircraft operations, and some of the rather more academic American reports have based their operational proposals on optimistic techniques which are mainly applicable to present-day North American operations, and do not take account of the facts of current North Western European practice, or of probable developments in the USA itself.

The detailed study of problems relating to practical operations has emphasised the need for caution in assuming that all the potential flexibility of a VTOL aircraft can be exploited when it is integrated with the air transport system as a whole.

Take-Off and Landing Techniques

Some thought has been given to what might be termed the

departure and arrival 'hover height', i.e. the height to which the aircraft ascends vertically after lift-off from the pad, and from which it descends vertically to touch down. In the city centre, the selection of this height will presumably depend primarily on noise characteristics and acceptable noise levels and data now available suggests that this will be about 1500 ft. On co-located VTOL and CTOL airports, and on some peripheral sites, noise considerations would not necessarily be so dominant and much lower hover heights could be considered, which might be as low as 50 ft. Lowering the hover height would have the following advantages:

1. It would provide a more economic operation, in that fuel and time would be saved. Optimum procedures would have to be based on detailed performance assessments.

2. It would monopolise the take-off or landing pad for a shorter time period, and this could be an important factor in assessing pad and VTOL airport capacity.

3. It would provide the pilot with visual reference on more occasions allowing precise manoeuvre, which is always advantageous, whether or not auto landing aids are available.

Jet efflux effects from the lift engines might have to be considered at these low altitudes and might entail defining approach and take-off paths that were insensitive to the effects. Such paths, however, would be short and would not need to interfere with the approach and departure funnels.

Approach to, and departure from, the hover height point could presumably take place using a wide range of angles depending on stability and transitional requirements. The three-degree conventional glide slope would possibly be inapplicable for standardised VTOL operations because of obstacle clearance in the more confining area of a VTOL city centre or suburban airport, and perhaps one of the order of $10-15°$ would be both more appropriate and economic.

Holding

The requirement for holding, particularly in the terminal area, will be reduced by several factors. Firstly, UK ATC future plans envisage the gradual elimination of holding at destination, aircraft being sequenced farther and farther back down the airways until, ideally and as currently happens in some situations in the USA, arrival sequencing will take place at the originating airfield. Other factors will help to reduce VTOL holding:

1. Its separation from conventional aircraft and runways.
2. Its wide speed-range.
3. The elimination of the approach bottle-neck by use of multiple approach and departure paths.
4. Minimum pad-occupancy time.
5. Advanced navigational and guidance systems.

A high measure of service regularity could be achieved with VTOL aircraft and in many of the operational regimes discussed considerable economic advantage is likely from the operation of these aircraft. Their major *raison d'etre* is likely in the business passenger field where they may break into the inter-city traffic now dominated by rail services. Operating costs thus become even more critical with VTOL than with CTOL aircraft. High traffic sectors may well be fed by CTOL feeder services.

The future for VTOL

It can now be accepted that it is technically feasible to design and develop civil VTOL aircraft based on jet lift and/or vectored-thrust engines which could operate with direct operating costs within 15–20 per cent of conventional subsonic jet transports. Quite conventional passenger layouts could be provided and block times shorter than those required for existing aircraft would be possible. Studies indicate that it would be quite realistic to cut six to eight minutes off the block time of VTOL aircraft and this is a major contributor to the reasonable operating costs of this type of aircraft.

A study published by Trans-Australia Airlines (Watkins, 1963) estimated that an improvement of at least 20 per cent in cruising L/D ratio should be possible at a Mach number of 0·88 if the wing were not designed to compromise with landing and take-off. It is certainly true that weight savings including reduction in flap and undercarriage weight may make significant contributions. Costs for such an aircraft will inevitably be higher since the power requirements are increased and certain aspects of maintenance costs such as the overhaul of jet lift engines will increase. However, no new development in aerodynamics or airframe design should be called for although aircraft control and stabilisation in the hovering condition still requires a high investment both in time and resources.

The main operational programme which is outstanding is that of noise which is still felt by most workers in this field to be sufficiently serious to rule out the possibility of city centre operations for perhaps two decades. A high possibility exists, however, for the development of VTOL airports in the suburban areas which should assist air traffic control problems and allow special airways to be introduced below the level of the existing long take-off aircraft movement channels and assist in the segregation of VTOL traffic. Helicopter experience has found this to be highly desirable. The principal operational advantage of VTOL aircraft which may have important economic significance is the lesser time lost in ground manoeuvre, climb to, and descent from, cruising altitudes. It is this which makes it economic for this aircraft to land for traffic reasons at smaller intermediate terminals. The development of a number of VTOL terminals outside the main city centres may be the answer to air transport growth on short-haul operations in the new era. This equally suits a STOL system.

It is certain that the VTOL aircraft can, in the long term, provide a realistic answer to the intensive growth of short-haul services which otherwise must be limited by available space for landing facilities near major cities. It is also clear that the only true comparison between VTOL and conventional jets must be based on a wider concept than one which is limited to the comparison of direct operating costs alone. We must study the terminal area, its landing pads, passenger facilities, road access, air traffic control and the air/ground systems of navigation. The VTOL aircraft may appear to provide no obvious economic advantage to the airline operator with his already heavy terminal investment and his established support from national authorities who up till now have provided airport facilities at less than cost. In the long term, however, VTOL must be recognised as the more flexible technique for high-density inter-urban transport services. Initially, we may see meagre official support, but the increasing investment in VTOL for purposes of defence will in time provide the opportunity for commercial operations to provide higher standards of public service. Only this new form of transport will make this possible.

N. E. Rowe's Wright Brothers address (1964) has set the keynote for the next steps in this era of air transport: 'We must turn our ideas to VTOL and STOL and thus garner the benefit of military advances along these lines, following historic precedent. . . . VTOL provides us with a new datum of departure for further advances in aeronautics.'

BIBLIOGRAPHY

D. KEITH LUCAS, 'The Role of Jet Lift', *Jnl. Roy Aero. Soc.*, May 1962

B. LUNDBERG, *Speed and Safety in Civil Aviation*, Third International Congress of the Aeronautical Sciences, August 1962

N. E. ROWE, 'A time of Transition', 52nd Wilbur Wright Memorial Lecture, *Jnl. Roy. Aero. Soc.*, March 1964

I. C. CHEESEMAN, 'VTOL Aircraft: Some Characteristics for Civil Use', *Jnl. Roy. Aero. Soc.*, July 1963

W. J. STEPNIEWSKI, 'Some Design Problems of Tiltwing VTOL Aircraft', *J. Helicopter Ass. Gt. Br.*, 1957

F. H. ROBERSTON, 'The Helicopter: Has it a Future?', *Jnl. Roy. Aero. Soc.*, Nov. 1955

R. L. CUMMINGS, 'Vertical Transport Business', *Jnl. Roy. Aero. Soc.*, April 1960

A. E. SLOCOMBE, 'Heliport Location and Design', *Jnl. Roy. Aero. Soc.*, Aug. 1964

R. HAFNER, 'The Domain of the Helicopter', *Jnl. Roy. Aero. Soc.*, Oct. 1954
'The Helicopter – First of the VTOL Aircraft', *Jnl. Roy. Aero. Soc.*, Dec. 1961, and 1970 in Second Century Papers.

R. A. FITZEK, 'Lessons Gained in Helicopter Air Traffic Control from Federal Aviation Agency Activities', *Jnl. Roy. Aero. Soc.*, Aug. 1962

W. O. W. CHALLIER and A. J. HEYWARD, *V/STOL Transition*, Soc. of Automotive Engineers, Detroit, Jan. 1964

C. S. COCKERELL, 'The Hovercraft and its Place in the Transport System', *Jnl. R. Soc. Arts*

Civil Aerodromes and Air Navigational Services, Cmnd. 1457, HMSO, 1961

'Symposium on Cheap Short Range Air Transport', *Jnl. Roy. Aero. Soc.*, Nov. 1965

H. ZIEGLER, 'Developing Short Range Transport by V/STOL Aircraft', *Jnl. Roy. Aero. Soc.*, May 1961

W. T. IMMENSCHUN, *V/STOL by Vertifan*, Flight International, 1 Oct. 1964

Report on the Planning of Helicopter Stations in the London Area, CAP 173, HMSO, 1961

R. L. TRILLO, *What Price Hovercraft?*, Air Cushion Vehicles, Aug.–Sept. 1963

J. L. WATKINS, 'Australia's Internal Air Transport', *Jnl. Roy. Aero. Soc.*, Jan. 1963

C. D. FOSTER and M. E. BEESLEY, 'The Social Benefit of Constructing an Underground Railway', *Jnl. R. Statist. Soc.*, Part 1, 1963

Systems Analysis of Short Haul Air Transportation, Massachusetts Institute of Technology, Aug. 1965

STOESSEL and GALLAGHER, *A Standard Method of Estimating VTOL Operating Expenses*, AIAA, Oct. 1967

MILLER and SIMPSON, *V/STOL in the North East Corridor*, Aeronautics and Astronautics, Sept. 1968

A Study of Aircraft in Short-Haul Transportation Systems, Boeing, Jan. 1968

'V/STOL and the Third London Airport.' A brief to the Roskill Commission. Hawker Siddeley Aviation, 1970

'STOL and STOL-ports.' Papers by E. J. Dickie, B. J. Davey and Others. Aerodrome Owners Association Conference, Oxford 1970

'A BAC View of V/STOL.' *Roy. Aeronaut. Soc.* Conference, May 1971. J. H. Quick

9 Supersonic Transport

First thoughts on supersonic transport

In the mid-fifties the supersonic transport aircraft became a possibility owing to the mastery of supersonic flight in the military field. A high degree of confidence, moreover, was soon reached in the design of the first supersonic aircraft of considerable size, the B 58 or Hustler which flew in 1956 and achieved a speed of $M = 2\cdot0$, or twice the speed of sound. Prior to this no aircraft had been able to fly for as long as an hour at $M = 2\cdot0$ although US, British and French fighters had begun to amass considerable flying experience in short bursts at these speeds. The supersonic transport, is, however, a quite different matter and there has never been any inclination to minimise the problems which it might create. It is one thing to develop a sophisticated vehicle which is technically capable of long-distance flight at the highest speeds then achievable by man, but it is quite another to meet the operational requirements of the world's airlines for a competitive aircraft which makes economic sense, which they would be able to finance, and in which the public would have the confidence to travel.

No project has ever come before the world's airlines with more of a fanfare. Never before have so many arguments, technical, commercial and political, been used to support or to decry a new development in aviation. Emotion has been mixed with the rationale. Though aeronautics has thrived on controversy, it is perhaps doubtful if the supersonic debate will in the long run be thought to have added greatly to the economic growth of air transport in this decade. Indeed, the full exploitation of the supersonic transport is unlikely to be achieved until the 1980s when a second generation of SSTs may come into operation. The many aspects of the supersonic transport problem have, however, had to be brought out into the open from the beginning and it will be necessary for us to deal briefly

359

with the principal ones. The final issue, however, is whether an economic transport vehicle can be developed in the supersonic regime, and to answer this we must consider certain technical aspects of the subject. In this chapter we shall attempt primarily to assess the commercial feasibility of the projects recently under development and to consider the special operational problems which will arise in the exploitation of this new mode of aviation. It will be seen that we are in fact only putting to use the principles which we have introduced in earlier chapters. It is a major conclusion of most supersonic studies that, just as previously in the case of the introduction into service of subsonic jet aircraft, few new problems are likely to arise. It is primarily the old problems in a more exaggerated form which will demand the more rapid location of solutions. But far-reaching questions soon present themselves.

If the supersonic transport can now reasonably be accepted as the natural next step in long-haul air transport and thus the optimum vehicle to meet certain prescribed requirements within some determined region of operations, what form will its impact take and how favourable or otherwise will be the economic consequences to the long-haul airlines of the world? We shall accept here the technical feasibility of the supersonic transport, and discuss the economic and operational factors which will be crucial to an assessment of its commercial feasibility.

The decision by US Congress to prevent the development of the large Mach 2·7–3·0 SST project in the early 1970s has not in any way made it irrelevant to consider Mach 3·0 transpots in the present era. They must be considered just as viable, and in many respects more viable in the long term than the aluminium structures of the Mach 2·0 transports such as Concorde and TU 144. This viewpoint has been retained throughout this chapter and adds, it is thought, to the value of the discussion.

Basic considerations

The first steps towards a supersonic transport were being taken in 1955 when the project staff in the US NACA, and the then UK Ministry of Supply were studying possible designs for transatlantic aircraft. With the Lift/Drag ratios at first assumed and with specific fuel consumptions thought likely to be achievable at that time, the full North Atlantic range with an economic payload was not possible, but it was clear that the probable development of the key parameters would in due course lead to a feasible technical solution which might have important commercial applications. Both the traffic potential and the handsome time savings which would be possible, made the North Atlantic a natural first objective for a supersonic transport project.

From the basic analysis it may be shown that for a given ratio of the fuel weight to the gross take-off weight of the aircraft the range should be proportional to

$$\frac{M}{c} \times L/D$$

M being the Mach Number or ratio of the cruise speed to the speed of sound.

c the specific fuel consumption, and

L/D the Lift/Drag ratio of the aircraft.   (Chapter 2)

It is of interest, therefore, to plot the above expression against Mach Number so as to indicate for other given factors the most likely optimum speed for long-range cruise in the supersonic regime. Such a curve is shown in Fig. 9.1 from which it may be seen that the Mach 2·0–3·0 region might be the most suitable,

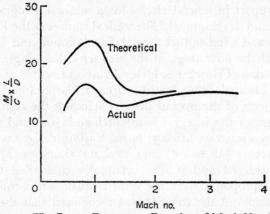

FIG. 9.1. The Range Factor as a Function of Mach Number

361

from the performance aspect, for design of a long-range supersonic aircraft. It was, of course, required that active steps should be taken to ensure that the decrease in L/D was not too steep as the speed increased in the supersonic regime, and that the design of engines was so directed that an adequate specific fuel consumption could be maintained at these speeds. Fortunately, the overall thrust efficiency of the turbo-jet engine almost doubles in the speed range shown in this figure.

The choice of wing shape was hotly debated in the earlier days of discussion and in the meetings of the British Supersonic Transport Aircraft Committee in 1956–8, the possibilities of an 'M' wing plan form were canvassed at one stage as the natural outcome of the aero-dynamic advantage (but structural disadvantage) of the well-swept wing up to speeds in the order of $M = 1\cdot2$. It has now become clear, however, that the slender delta wing of low span and small aspect ratio possesses considerable advantage in the $M = 2$ and $M = 3$ regime and also acceptable low-speed characteristics.

Variable plan form designs, incorporating means for changing the wing sweep angle in flight so as to give better low-speed handling performance (and less compromise at high speed) have been developed and were at one stage favoured by Boeing. Military experience (F 111) has also given confidence that this step is technically acceptable. The need in the UK to establish a major civil aircraft project which would exploit advanced technology, and offer opportunity in overseas markets led to strong support in official circles for a national programme of research and development. Theoretical studies at the RAE and the NPL and wind-tunnel tests at Farnborough and Cranfield confirmed the advantage of the slender delta wings, and the design studies of Hawker Siddeley Aviation Limited and Bristol Aircraft Limited (now British Aircraft Corporation) investigated aspects of the overall design including the comparative advantages of the integral wing-fuselage layout and the thin wing with a separate fuselage form. Various designs with light alloy structure ($M = 2\cdot0$) and steel and titanium ($M = 3\cdot0$) were considered and it was eventually concluded that the $M = 2\cdot0$ proposals were the most realistic when considering all the factors in the case. It was recognised that the cost of development of an $M = 3\cdot0$ aircraft would be considerably greater, due not only to the use of steel and titanium of lighter gauge, but also to the need to develop the electrical, fuel, air conditioning and flight control systems for safe operation in an environment subject to greater kinetic heating. Moreover, the time scale was longer and far more difficult to analyse precisely at $M = 3 \cdot 0$. The British Aircraft Corporation to whom the design was finally entrusted was moreover determined not to move beyond a speed range within which they and the engine manufacturers had had a good deal of experience. (Edwards, 1964.)

The need for collaboration with a major overseas manufacturer had been recognised at an early date, and while the US industry was convinced that theoretical studies combined with the well-advanced B 70 (under development by North American Aviation Inc.) justified their $M = 3 \cdot 0$ designs for supersonic transports, the French industry were far more conservative. Quite independently the designers of Sud Aviation and their colleagues in Dassault, with experience of the Caravelle and the Mirage III and IV behind them, had concluded that $M = 2 \cdot 0$ was the correct speed for a first-generation supersonic transport. Their thoughts had surprisingly been directed towards a smaller aircraft than the British designers (about 70 seats) and for a design range considerably less than the North Atlantic. Close collaboration between the British and French teams led to a design which was smaller and lighter than the earlier BAC proposals which had largely ignored the effects of flying weight on the ground overpressure or sonic boom, and yet larger and of longer range than the earlier French project of 1959, the Super Caravelle.

Concorde project

In November 1962 a formal Anglo-French agreement was signed which launched the first supersonic project 'Concorde'. Subsequent amendments to the design have increased its payload-range capacity characteristics and provided an unequivocal transatlantic capability under adverse wind and temperature conditions. The payload-range diagram for the prototype is shown in Fig. 9.2. As was explained in Chapter 2 the payload and range can vary considerably with changed operating and weight assumptions. The first flight of the Concorde was achieved in the summer of 1970.

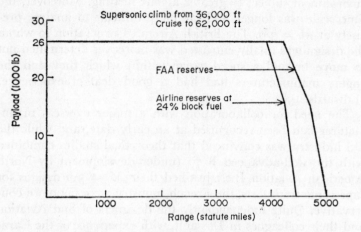

FIG. 9.2. Concorde Payload and Range

While progress in the USA was in the early stages not so apparent as in Europe, the objectives set by the major manufacturers there were from the beginning more ambitious. The field of economic and operational study as well as engineering research and development has been explored for over ten years with immense thoroughness and expertise. The $M = 3 \cdot 0$ target had been accepted by all the major US manufacturers as the choice which is most realistic having regard to the long-term development of civil aviation. Although for a given payload capacity the $M = 3 \cdot 0$ project might be less economic in terms of the specific direct-operating cost, as well as in relation to the return on average investment, than an $M = 2 \cdot 0$ transport, the higher-speed project is widely held to be the correct first step for the US industry. This view seems to be based mainly on the belief that only such 'ultimate' transports will command, on an economic time scale without serious competition, the major trunk air routes of the world where the great mass of the traffic will continue to lie. Though technologically it may be a far more challenging project, it is claimed to be well within the scope of the US industry whose supersonic flight experience is vastly greater than that available in Europe, and which can well afford to take a rather longer period to confirm its research and development results in the new areas. The US supersonic transport programme in 1965 moved into a stage where the FAA, not fully satisfied with the design proposals of the two principal consortia (Boeing, Lockheed, Pratt & Whitney and General Electric) requested supposed deficiencies in economy, range and payload capability to be made good.

The Boeing and Lockheed supersonic projects

The project which was under development by the Boeing Company was formulated in a proposal to the FAA in 1964. This stage of the US supersonic programme was superseded by the Phase IIA which sought to improve the economics of operation of the aircraft and to spell out more precisely the acceptable noise levels, and the compatibility with current operating criteria, including airport facilities. The rapidly moving technology made it difficult to establish a level of advance at which to freeze the design, but the later stages of the work in Boeing and Lockheed, and in the engine manufacturing groups Pratt & Whitney and General Electric, gained considerably from the discussions with the FAA, airline operators and organisations such as IATA. The later stages of design incorporated improvements in aerodynamics (high and low speed), propulsion and systems. In particular a deeper understanding of the sonic boom problems were achieved in this time.

The main characterisation of the Boeing design at this stage were a cruise speed of $M = 2\cdot7$ (1800 mph), a variable-geometry wing and the use of titanium as a principal structural material. Two versions of the aircraft were proposed. The standard version at a gross weight of 430,000 lb (giving a payload of 30,000 lb for 4000 miles) and an intercontinental version at a gross weight of 520,000 lb (giving a payload of 43,000 lb over the same stage length), incorporating turbo-jet or turbo-fan engines with after-burners. With an approach speed of 136 mph, the Boeing 733 project incorporated variable sweep of the wing with a single pivot well outboard from the fuselage which allows a high aspect ratio for the take-off and landing phase, and the fully swept configuration for supersonic cruise. Considerable development effort was extended into the tooling and fabrication of the titanium structure. In the use of titanium it is likely that Boeing hoped to find some considerable weight advantage to help towards the achievement of lower direct-operating costs.

A final stage in the Boeing SST development was reversion to a fixed wing of highly swept plan form and comparable to the Lockheed designs. It was this project, the 2707–300 that was receiving US Government support and the tentative approval of 26 airlines who had been prepared to pay deposits for a position on the production line, when Congress refused to sanction farther financial support for the project. This act of immolation is in the author's view a tragic error in American domestic policy stemming from the current trend of exaggerated environmental thinking no less apparent in Western Europe than in the USA. With a reasonable record of success with Concorde there can be no doubt that the US Government and industry will soon again receive the financial and political support necessary to re-enter SST development. Supersonic transport is quite inevitable as part of the long-haul civil aviation pattern and how could the USA elect to remain out of this field of activity for more than a few years.

Lockheed also based its design on the use of a titanium structure of which considerable experience was gained on the A 11 projects,* but in this case a fixed double-delta plan form is used. A design cruising speed of $M = 3 \cdot 0$ was specified and a payload-range of 46,000 lb for 4000 miles is provided for a 450,000 lb take-off weight. The Lockheed design emphasises simplicity and low wing loading, and the fuselage volume offers seating for up to 220 passengers in a five-abreast layout. No leading or trailing edge high-lift devices are employed, but combined elevators/ailerons are fitted to the wings. A drooping nose section caters for the high incidence in the approach phase.

It is characteristic of the two US designs for $M = 2 \cdot 7 - 3 \cdot 0$ supersonic transports that the use of titanium was accepted in spite of all the problems inherent in its development, and the size of the payload was increased to a value about 30 per cent above that of the early subsonic jets on intercontinental

* Long-range reconnaisance aircraft.

operations. It remains to consider in the later analysis whether the lower density of titanium and the larger payload capacity can provide the degree of improvement in the operating economy which is necessary for an approach to the levels of specific costs already achieved by the Boeing 707 and the Douglas DC 8 and comparable to the wide-body jets.

The USSR is the one other state with the incentive to develop a supersonic transport project in the near future. The prestige

TABLE 9.1. *Principal Stage Lengths of Significance to the Supersonic Aircraft*

Great Circle Distances in Statute Miles	
Eastward from London	Miles
London–Rome	897
London–Beirut	2163
London–Cairo	2194
Cairo–Karachi	2211
Bombay–Singapore	2432
Singapore–Sydney	3915
London–Nairobi	4250
London–Bombay	4481
Atlantic routes	
London–Montreal	3241
New York–London	3442
New York–Paris	3625
Copenhagen–Washington	4053
New York–Rome	4281
Frankfurt–Chicago	4334
Lisbon–Rio de Janeiro	4794
London–Mexico City	5534
South and West from New York	
New York–Chicago	738
New York–Miami	1092
Miami–Caracas	1362
New York–Los Angeles	2469
Los Angeles–Honolulu	2553
Honolulu–Nandi (Fiji)	3171
Honolulu–Tokyo	3848
Miami–Rio de Janeiro	4173
Honolulu–Sydney	5076

value to the Soviet Union of mounting early supersonic transport services is immense, and the Tupolev TU 144 with a specification and general appearance extremely similar to the Concorde claimed first flight and Mach 2 records for a Supersonic Transport. Plans exist for the entry into service of the TU 144 in 1974.

It is estimated that Aeroflot might have a requirement for about twenty SSTs in the early 1970s and the design range might not be in excess of that planned for the Concorde. There is likely to be a need for a capacity of 150–160 seats at least but the first version is likely to be based on an aluminium structure to meet a competitive time scale with the Mach limit set as high as Soviet technology will allow and capacity of 125 seats on 3000 miles.

At a later date, probably in the mid-1970s, newly designed Soviet $M = 2 \cdot 0$–$2 \cdot 2$ light-alloy aircraft might be capable of meeting the airworthiness requirements of the Western Air Transport Agencies. In some quarters it is thought to be unlikely that the Soviet Union would be prepared to deliver aircraft to countries in which it cannot prevent the dissemination of information on its aviation technology. This view we believe to be ill-founded, and in due course Soviet-built $M = 2 \cdot 2$ and $M = 3 \cdot 0$ aircraft of a size and economy likely to be of first importance on the long and dense air routes of the USSR may well be on the world market in competition with the products of the USA and Western Europe.

Choice of the technical solutions

The success of the subsonic jets has now been so universally accepted that it is natural enough for serious consideration to be given to the next possible step forward in air transport development. Steady advance has been made in speed and payload capacity ever since the early days and no sudden burst that can in any way be compared to the proposed increases in speed has ever been proposed before. However, subsonic speeds are limited to about $M = 0 \cdot 92$ because of the steep increase in drag due to compressibility as the speed of sound is approached, and the improvement in economy due to the increase in air speed will come to an end, unless a step of considerable magnitude is taken. It is about the magnitude of this step that much of the technical discussions have revolved. It must be recognised at once that even on the longer stages which are most likely, to be predominant in the schedules of the supersonic operators, the time spent in supersonic flight is less than half of the total flight time.

Consideration of the time saved by operating at the higher supersonic speed has led some critics to the conclusion that the advantage is unimportant, and that from the passenger's point of view the immense gain in time compared with the subsonic jets on London–New York (6–7 hours) is little bettered by the increase of the supersonic cruise speed from $M = 2 \cdot 0$ to $M = 3 \cdot 0$. This can be viewed realistically from the passenger's viewpoint in Fig. 9.3 where the total journey time between London and New York for the air traveller is shown for three transport aircraft stages: (1) The piston engine stage, for example the Lockheed Constellation L 1049 on North Atlantic Schedules in 1950. (2) The subsonic jet stage, example the Boeing 707–420, BOAC 1960. (3) The supersonic stage, examples, the $M = 2 \cdot 2$ and $M = 3 \cdot 0$ SST. Fig. 9.3 says all that needs to be said on the subject of the time saving to the pas-

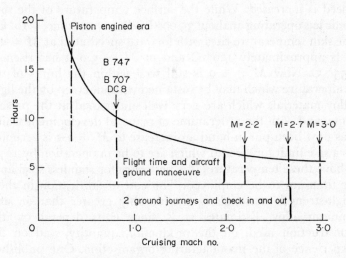

FIG. 9.3. Journey Time between London and New York

senger. Even if fares were to remain constant and the standard of comfort and convenience were not to be changed, there is little doubt that the $M = 2 \cdot 2$ timing is likely to be just as acceptable as that of the $M = 3 \cdot 0$ to most passengers. The state of diminishing returns which is illustrated in this figure may, of course, be viewed differently by the air carrier finding himself in an intensely competitive situation on a major trunk route. In this case, even the difference of fourteen minutes on the London–New York sector between an $M = 2 \cdot 7$ and an $M = 3 \cdot 0$ cruise speed might be of some consequence.

The city centre journey time which has so aggravated the short-haul air passenger in the past is now likely to be a potential irritant also to the transatlantic supersonic traveller. A more intensive drive to deal with this problem must be expected in the new era when the SST has converted the long-stage flight to the form of a short-haul operation. However the journey time may be viewed by the passenger or by the promotional departments of competitive airlines, it must be of crucial significance whether the choice can be entirely free or whether greater technological difficulty and cost would arise if the need for higher operating speeds is to be met. This unfortunately proves to be the case, due largely to the considerable increase in operating temperatures when forward speed is increased. While the surface temperature of the subsonic jets operating at about 35,000 ft is below freezing (-10° C), the skin temperature rises with forward speed until at $M = 2 \cdot 2$ it is approximately 120° C and at $M = 3 \cdot 0$ it has risen to 255° C. Now $M = 2 \cdot 0$ is still well within the limits of the temperature which may be sustained without creep by the light alloy materials which are very well understood at the present time, and with the programme of material development which has now been put in hand an increase to $M = 2 \cdot 2$ is accepted as a safe limit for aircraft which are to be in operation by 1973. Above these temperatures it is necessary for stainless steel and/ or titanium to be employed. The cost of fabrication in these high-strength materials is considerably greater than in aluminium alloy. Estimates vary, since costs depend on the construction used, on the production quantity, and on the experience of the manufacturing organisation. One published estimate by an experienced designer gave corrugated sandwich titanium and brazed honeycomb steel as £30–£35 per lb compared to a skin and stringer construction of aluminium alloy at £11 per lb.* In Europe the experience in the construction of aircraft structure in these new materials is slight compared to that in the USA. For these reasons, the US designers have been little deterred by the problems associated with the development of structures for $M = 3 \cdot 0$. It is important to note that the other materials for use in the aircraft are, in most cases, limited to a temperature which is well below the skin temperature at $M = 3 \cdot 0$ (255° C) without such lengthy and special development. However, such development, especially in the cases of transparencies (optical and radio), fuel and air systems, insulating materials, etc., has been actively pursued especially in the USA under the spur of the B 70 (Valkyrie $M = 3 \cdot 0$ bomber) and the A 11 ($M = 2 \cdot 0$ reconnaisance) programmes.

The costs incurred by such development, much of which has regrettably not been called for in European military aviation programmes, is discussed in a later section of this chapter. The uncertain time scale for useful outputs from some parts of such research was an important factor in the choice of speed for the Concorde.

Of no less importance in the choice of cruise speed are the problems set by the power-plant design. The lower speed favoured in Europe allows engines of well-established design to be used, requiring development on known lines and posing few special problems in intake design.

The decision on the cruise speed may, in the final outcome, be based on considerations which are not essentially technological. The development of speed in the aluminium $M = 2 \cdot 2$ aircraft will be as limited as it has proved to be with the subsonic jets. No development in propulsion, or in the thermal properties of materials, can hold out any hope of extending the thermal range of the light alloys which are the principal structural materials. The $M = 3 \cdot 0$ steel/titanium aircraft is in few ways thus restricted. Gains in propulsive efficiency, in output or in aerodynamic refinement may be converted at a later date into higher speeds and/or range, or in a combination of the two. Whether the longer-term development potential of the higher speed aircraft can justify the higher development costs and

* 1965 price levels.

perhaps the higher operating costs, we shall need to consider more fully in a later section.

The airfield requirements for supersonic transport aircraft

There is no inherent problem in designing a supersonic transport to achieve a take-off performance as good as or better than that of the subsonic jets. The take-off field performance for the Concorde is quoted as 9500 ft, and the landing field required 7550 ft, in ambient conditions more adverse than the standard atmosphere. The take-off and landing performance of the US Mach 3·0 projects is estimated to be even better than this and to be less critical than the Boeing 707 or 747 aircraft on maximum gross weight take-offs, and in landing at the maximum certificated landing weight. The high installed thrust takes good care of the take-off case, and a conservative attitude towards the approach speed, whether through high-lift devices and variable geometry (Boeing first phases), or by the use of low wing loading (Lockheed), gives a landing performance for the projected US aircraft which is some advance on the subsonic jets and possibly on the $M = 2·0$ Concorde with its higher approach speed and wing loading. (For one projected design of the L 2000 the wing loading at landing weight was 32 lb per sq. ft.)

FAA design objectives for the SST laid down 10,500 ft in ISA + 15° C ambient conditions at sea level as the take-off requirement at sea level. The maximum runway length required for landing under wet conditions was to be 8000 ft. When reduced power is essential to meet noise-abatement standards, the performance level may be more difficult to meet, but certainly when stage length falls in any way below the intercontinental range the margins for take-off are immediately increased.

Great efforts have been made to ensure that the airport facilities which have now been installed at great expense in so many of the major world air traffic centres will be suitable also for supersonic aircraft. The dimensions and weights of the Concorde have, according to Mr P. Satre, Technical Director of

Sud Aviation, been considered specifically in terms of the existing 'runways, taxiways, ramps, aprons and hangars available today for the DC 8 and B 707 type of aircraft' (IATA, 1964). This might be extended into the areas of tools and handling equipment, passenger loading ramps and servicing equipment with advantage, but much compromise is inevitably required in this field owing to the conflicting claims of the advance in design towards potential economy and the need to cut the cost here and now. New equipment and new concepts, automatic flight programmers, auto-landing, auto-check-out equipment and the new inertial and auto-astro navigational aids open up new areas for economic advantage and likewise of high cost in development, training and maintenance which all require the most careful assessment.

The insistence of the FAA that the Phase 2A studies of US SST should closely consider and verify where necessary airport compatibility has added weight to the recommendations of the IATA and ICAO committee reports (IATA, 1961 and ICAO, 1960) which had been prepared after wide discussion of the problems. The higher weight of the US SST projects has led to the design of landing gears with four or six bogies. This complexity has been necessary in order to avoid high load intensity on the runways and taxiways thus obviating the necessity for thickening of pavements. Airport authorities in considering the operation of supersonic transport have been obliged to evaluate the geometry of the undercarriage layout in relation to the radius of curvature of the taxi-tracks and the design of the fast run-off pavements. The layouts of the passenger terminals, loading fingers and gateway systems cannot be readily modified to suit the SST. Already the investment is so heavy at the principal terminals that compatibility of these aircraft is a *sine qua non*.

A valuable characteristic of the variable-sweep wing is the capability of retraction when space is in demand at the loading bay. At the ramp when it is necessary to manoeuvre the aircraft under its own power, the size and layout of the gate position is critical. The space required depends upon the geometry of the aircraft and the permissible angle of turn of the nose wheel. The physical characteristics and undercarriage geometry vary widely between the many US and British projects, but in one

373

US design which the author studied, with a 50° nose wheel steering angle and a wheel track of 104 ft, a turning circle of 320-ft diameter is required compared with about 250 ft for the Boeing 707. The implication of these factors on the manoeuvring space and time required at the terminals can only be assessed by individual study of existing facilities. Taking as a basis for comparison an $M = 3 \cdot 0$ transport with a ramp weight of 450,000 lb and an overall length of 222 ft, wheels and tyres for a six-wheel main landing gear can be so designed that the equivalent single-wheel load (ESWL) is less than on the Boeing 707 or Douglas DC 8 at maximum weight.

TABLE 9.2. *The Supersonic Prototypes*
Some Principal Dimensions and Approximate Weight Data

	BAC/Aerospatiale Concorde		Boeing Prototype* 2707-300
	Prototype	Production	
Length (ft)	184·5	204	286·68
Height (ft)	38	40	50·10
Span (ft)	83·85	83·85	141·68
Cruise speed (Mach)	2·1	2·1–2·2	2·7
Maximum passengers	120	128–144	250–270
Range with maximum payload (statute miles)	3,300	3,800	4,500
Maximum take-off weight (lb)	326,000	385,000	635,000

* Stopped by Congress in 1971.

However, studies reported by R. Horonjeff of the University of California to the IATA Technical Conference at Montreal (1961) indicated that an increase of 15–20 per cent in the thickness of pavement for the six-wheel main gear of a 450,000 lb SST might be required compared with the requirement for dual-in-tandem' landing gear on subsonic transports at 300,000 lb. He was recommending that the minimum radius of curvature for new taxiways to accommodate supersonic transports should be of the order of 600 ft. This would mean that many existing taxiways would need to be widened. Manufacturers may claim that 90° turns between taxi tracks can be negotiated with radii less than 100 ft but airport authorities now take into account high-frequency operations under adverse weather conditions and the need to maintain reasonably high taxiing speeds under peak conditions at busy terminals.

Noise in the vicinity of airports

It may be said with reasonable certainty that the noise level of the $M = 2 \cdot 2$ type aircraft with engines of 160,000 lb combined static sea level thrust will provide a take-off and landing noise level which, over wide areas will be lower than that achieved with most subsonic jet aircraft. Only the new generation of wide-body jet aircraft are able to show a marked advance on SST noise levels. The form of the contours of noise level for the SST is such that the terrain on either side is more afflicted than with the subsonic jets, but owing to the high rates of climb possible, the ground noise level falls very rapidly along the axis of the runway. At a point located four nautical miles from the start of the ground roll on take-off the perceived noise should be no more than 103 PNdb which is only slightly above the night take-off level permitted from London at the time of writing. Improvements in the Concorde noise level through exhaust nozzle silencers were under development at the time of writing.

Some increase in the airport noise level (on either side of the runway) might need to be exchanged for a reduction in the community noise along the line of the runway. A significant advance is being made in the study of noise suppression in the vicinity of airports (HMSO, 1963 and FAA, 1964). For example, a gain in approach noise is possible by use of steeper glide angles in the final landing phases, subject to the handling qualities of the aircraft in the configuration and adequate margins in the flareout. Special noise abatement procedures after take-off will undoubtedly give rise to greater economic penalties with supersonic transports than with existing subsonic jets.

US and UK noise certification standards are discussed in Chapter 10 in some detail. There also the position of the Concorde is discussed, especially the level of noise in the airport environment in comparison with existing 4-engine jets and the new generation of wide-body tri-jets and other aircraft.

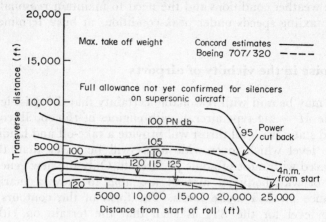

FIG. 9.4. Noise Levels in the Airport Area

Local reaction to aircraft noise, however, is difficult to assess and measurement of community discomfort is still not successfully conducted. Use of indices to measure the degree of exposure to noise has been attempted, and a Noise and Number Index (NNI) which quantifies annoyance in terms of the average peak noise level of the aircraft and the number of flights per day has been used by UK authorities. A social survey in the vicinity of London Airport (Heathrow) in 1961 lead to the derivation of this index to measure the overall nuisance at that time. An extrapolation to 1970 was carried out taking account of the increased air traffic forecast and the greater incidence of large jet aircraft. The final report of the UK Committee on the Problem of Noise (Chairman, Sir Alan Wilson) (HMSO, 1963) gave a full account of the principles of noise measurement and the concept of the NNI. One of the outstanding recommendations of this Committee was that grants on a varying scale should be paid towards the cost of improving the sound insulation of existing dwellings in areas near Heathrow Airport where noise is unreasonably high. Action to implement these proposals was taken by the British Government in 1965. Contrary to original estimations it is now likely that the proposed SST projects, in spite of their large installed power, will in fact contribute to an overall reduction in community noise levels owing to their enhanced capability of steeper descent into and climb out of the ground-level environment. Fig. 9.4 shows the noise contours drawn for an $M = 2 \cdot 2$ SST and a subsonic jet aircraft under landing and take-off conditions at maximum transatlantic weight. These figures should be considered as purely illustrative since the noise abatement programme and Concorde development is currently moving at a high rate, and the most recent available data should be consulted before comparative conclusions are reached. It is, of course, the sonic boom which raises for the SST the central problem in the field of noise. Before dealing with this, however, it is thought more convenient to consider first the operation of the aircraft in its various aspects. The trajectory of the supersonic aircraft, the route systems on which it is likely to be considered, and the influence of the sonic boom on these two aspects of the general problem are naturally related closely to each other.

The trajectory of the SST

In the flight plan for a long-haul sector, the principal characteristics of the SST stand out most clearly. We have already indicated the breakdown of time on a typical North Atlantic journey from London to New York in Fig. 9.3. We should now consider the way in which the time is spent from 'chocks-away' to 'engines-off'. Aerospatiale and the British Aircraft Corporation have published estimated flight plans for the Concorde (IATA, 1964 and Edwards, 1964) and a detailed break-down of the flight time for other projects have been presented in the literature. Some comparisons with the Mach 3·0 trajectory and the conventional subsonic flight plan can be now made. The experience gained by the US Air Force in the limited operations of the B 58 (Hustler), which achieved a transatlantic crossing using supersonic speed for much of the time as early as June 1961, is of special importance in the history of SST development and acceptance. The Concorde flight test programme however has confirmed the principal data, considerable experience of Mach 2 flying having been obtained by the end of 1971.

Mach = 2·2

If we consider an SST such as the Concorde operating at maximum weight on a London–New York stage the optimum flight plan with a 50 kt headwind at cruise altitude would be likely to show an elapsed time of about three hours six minutes excluding six minutes for start-up and taxi to the take-off point and with no allowance for hold in the New York area. This would allow for a climb at constant EAS to the tropopause (about 36,000 ft in the standard atmosphere) until a Mach number of about 0·9 is reached. At this altitude an acceleration through the transonic region at a considerably reduced rate of climb might be initiated with a higher EAS of about 500 kts. The trajectory at this stage and the altitude selected for supersonic flight will depend on a number of factors of which the take-off weight, wing loading, power loading and the need to consider the ground level over-pressure are the most important. The climb is maintained until a height of approximately 50,000 ft is reached when the cruising climb itself is initiated. At $M = 2·2$ the cruise is maintained at a constant L/D, that is with a gradually increasing altitude (never greatly exceeding 60,000 ft), until the let-down procedure is put into operation. Alternatively, and depending upon the Air Traffic Control procedures in operation at the time, a stepped climb or constant-altitude cruise may be initiated. The last of these would incur considerable fuel penalty. A descent at 350–400 kt EAS is commenced from about 250–300 miles from New York and the transition to subsonic flight is performed at a height determined largely by the over-pressures generated by the sonic bang. A height of 40,000 ft would probably be selected. A final descent phase under Air Traffic Control would occupy the last seventy miles before arrival at the final checkpoint.

Fuel reserves will be carried for a 200–250-mile flight at subsonic speed to an alternative, with an hour's holding fuel between 20,000 ft and 5000 ft. Probably 5 per cent of the planned fuel will be carried as a reserve in addition to the minimum landing reserves and *en route* allowances. What is significant is that only about 54 per cent of the fuel carried is used for supersonic flight, the remainder being used for subsonic climb, descent and for reserves in a flight condition for which the air-craft is not ideally suited. It is for these reasons that the variable-sweep wing is an important contribution to operating economy, especially in the case of $M = 3 \cdot 0$ designs whose flexibility is otherwise considerably less than that indicated in the typical $M = 2 \cdot 2$ flight plan summarised above. It is imperative that SSTs of all types should provide flexibility in range and ade-quate lower-altitude subsonic capability to allow shorter stages to be operated profitably for traffic reasons. The need also exists for subsonic phases of longer flights to be extended in special circumstances. A 500–600-mile subsonic continental over-pass phase may be an essential requirement for North Atlantic flights originating, for example, in Milan or Chicago so as to restrict ground level over-pressures.

The immense fuel loads required to be carried by the SST for strictly optimum flight plans, militates against the transport of additional loads. J. F. McBrearty, previously SST General Manager of Lockheed Aircraft Corporation has warned the airlines of the high costs of SST operation at subsonic speeds. 'It is essential' he said (IATA, 1964) 'that the airlines schedule the SST to maximise the number of stage lengths permitting supersonic cruise. By the 1970s there will be enough traffic on enough world routes to provide high utilisation for a large number of SSTs without resorting to planned subsonic segments. However, a certain amount of subsonic operation for tag-end flights and for positioning is practicable and feasible.'

John H. Shaffer, FAA Administrator, in reporting on the US SST programme in 1969 noted that it was based on super-sonic operations only on overwater routes and unpopulated areas such as those north of the Arctic circle. This did not mean, he added, that it could not be flown subsonically over land or that it could not serve major inland cities. The 2707 project was designed so that it could be flown efficiently at subsonic speeds for considerable distances. The Mach $2 \cdot 0$ aircraft how-ever is less sensitive than the faster aircraft to subsonic flight stages. Such a comparison is still important since it is certain that the US decision to stop development of the Mach $3 \cdot 0$ SST in the early 1970s has not put paid to such a project for all time. It should be clear that the higher the transition altitude to supersonic flight the lower the over-pressure value reached on the ground. This is a question involving compromise between the demands of operating economics and the degree of acceptance by the community. Studies of the total fuel requirements and block speed effects of changing transition altitude on climb and descent suggest that for the $M = 2 \cdot 2$ aircraft an altitude between 35,000 ft and 40,000 ft should provide an adequate compromise.

The trajectory of the $M = 3 \cdot 0$ supersonic transport

In brief terms, a 3000-mile flight plan of a 400,000-lb aircraft of delta-wing type designed for $M = 3 \cdot 0$ cruise has been tabulated in Table 9.3.

We should note that as in the case of the $M = 2 \cdot 2$ flight plan, only just over 50 per cent of the flight plan fuel is consumed on the supersonic cruise stage. If we include transition and the supersonic climb and descent phases, a very much higher proportion of the fuel is accounted for. The altitude of transition is not increased in this flight plan. This helps to economise in fuel, but because of the considerably greater installed thrust and weight of the $M = 3 \cdot 0$ aircraft it is apparent that very much higher levels of sonic boom over-pressure will result

TABLE 9.3. *Possible $M = 3 \cdot 0$ Flight Plan*

Altitude (ft)	Time (min)	Fuel (lb)	Distance (miles)	Over-pressure (lb/sq ft)
1. Start and taxi	6	2,000	0	
2. 0–36,000	11	26,000	95	Up to 2·0
3. Transition and SS climb to 67,000	16	53,000	295	Down to 1·5
4. SS climb/cruise 67,000–75,000	79	109,000	2,155	1·5 to 1·2
5. SS descent 75,000–45,000	20	17,000	400	1·3 at transition
6. Descent to S.l	10	10,000	70	To zero
Totals:	142	217,500	3,015	

compared with $M = 2\cdot2$ designs such as the Concorde. The cruising heights finally achieved are clearly considerably higher than those indicated previously for $M = 2\cdot2$. This, however, will only partially alleviate the over-pressures at ground level.

Air traffic control and flight planning

It is not intended to do more than establish some of the principal factors arising in this area of study. When flying in terminal control areas supersonic transport aircraft will have performance characteristics which are in general similar to those of other aircraft types in order to avoid delays to all users of the airspace and to ensure most economic use of runways and approach facilities.

Problems of traffic control, separation, navigation and communication may be generally intensified by the introduction of supersonic transport aircraft into the flow pattern, although in the cruise flight phase segregation of these aircraft, because of the higher altitude of operation compared with subsonic aircraft simplifies one aspect of the problem. It is apparent already that existing Air Traffic Control problems, associated with the greatly increasing density of subsonic jets, will need solution well before the onset of supersonic transport aircraft operations. Similar solutions may be appropriate, although clearly when at one time on the Atlantic we reported every 10° of longitude (about every half hour) this would no longer be possible on supersonic transport aircraft operations (about every ten minutes). A big advantage in our favour is that the wind and temperature effects on supersonic aircraft will cause relatively little change in estimated time of arrival, and accurate ETAs become possible, for the first time, after long-distance flights.

One problem may be the transition phase to supersonic flight which may take place in the altitude band 35,000 ft and above. This is the cruising height of current subsonic jet aircraft. No improvements in air traffic control can be allowed to conflict with the need for the supersonic transport aircraft to achieve the optimum flight trajectory so as to ensure economy and fuel safety. It seems to be now accepted that some form of ground control will be essential since the supersonic aircraft will lack the handling characteristics and probably the visual means for initiating avoiding action. Table 9.4 shows one aspect of low-altitude manoeuvring with the supersonic aircraft in comparison with the current jet aircraft.

TABLE 9.4. *Radius of Turn as a Manoeuvring Criterion. Comparison of Subsonic Jet and* $M = 2\cdot2$ *Transport*

	Miles		
	At economical holding speed	At 75% economical speed	At cruising speed
Subsonic jet	5·5	—	10·5
$M = 2\cdot2$	11	6	72

Supersonic transport aircraft will undoubtedly be required to take their turn in the landing cycle along with other aircraft in all conditions, except in emergency. No special dispensation can be expected for these aircraft and it is not easy to see how any special niches in the holding pattern can be reserved for our more sophisticated transports. For the most part, the designers seem to have been conservative in their assumptions on fuel reserves, and current criteria in use with subsonic jets have been adopted in the project design stage. The potential for improvement in this area, due to automatic landing techniques and automatic control of the flight trajectory, will in due course pay out an important dividend in operating economy.

An inertial reference system is now widely considered as the type best suited to meet the supersonic transport aircraft's primary navigational requirements. An automatic gyro will align the platform on the ground, and the short flight time should ensure adequate accuracy. Apart from this an inertial system provides azimuth and altitude reference for other equipment in the aircraft. Dead reckoning by a central computer gives accurate navigational data owing to the insignificance of the wind vector as previously mentioned. The availability of wide coverage artificial satellites for navigation in the 1970s is now assured. Many varying views exist as to the desirability of electronic control for aspects of supersonic transport management. Propulsion system control, pre-flight check-out or maintenance control, fuel management and navigation from air data computation, many such areas are now open to auto-control techniques which will be justified economically by the early 1970s. The full gamut of electronic management covering phases of operation such as take-off, climb profile, passenger cabin and cockpit environment and automatic landing, still require much technical analysis. Intensive development is still necessary to bring fully automatic control up to a civil airline acceptance standard, so that it would be unwise to modify fundamentally the supersonic transport aircraft design philosophy at this time.

Winds at the cruising altitude of supersonic flight are generally less strong than at the 30,000–40,000 ft levels used by subsonic aircraft. Nevertheless, polar jet streams exceeding 100 kts have been reported by airlines including SAS. In flight planning, however, wind becomes a factor of minor significance to the SST. Outside air temperature is, on the other hand, of crucial importance since it will affect the ground level over-pressure and the speed of cruise. It is now well established that the tropopause, or boundary level for the isothermal stratosphere, varies in altitude both seasonally and with change of latitude. In the latitudes of London and Paris the height of the tropopause falls from the height of the standard atmosphere (36,200 ft) or thereabouts in summer to little more than 30,000 ft in winter. Moreover, the isothermal temperature falls about 10° C from summer to winter conditions. A prevalent summer condition, however, is the movement of tropical air streams which, at the lower latitudes, induce high temperatures at the lower altitudes, a high tropopause and very low temperatures at high altitudes. Col. W. L. Polhemus (1962) quotes a typical situation of this kind at Fort Worth in October when the tropopause was at 49,000–50,000 ft; the temperature was isothermal at $-75°$ C and the supersonic acceleration altitude temperature was 12° warmer than the standard atmosphere. The higher temperature may necessitate the choice of a higher altitude for transition to supersonic flight with a resultant increase in the fuel consumption per mile which would eat heavily into fuel reserves. Fuel consumption in the transition phase acceleration may exceed 3000 lb/min for the $M = 3\cdot0$ transports. A loss of cruising speed at altitude due to the higher temperature, even though alleviated by some reduction in the fuel consumption per unit of time, will result in an overall loss in specific range. It will be an important criterion of the supersonic transport that a margin of thrust is available to make up for changes in ambient temperatures, as for excess headwinds, with minimum penalty when operating away from the design Mach number. The overall effect of elevated ambient temperatures on supersonic aircraft operations is likely to be considerable especially when these are in the terminal areas and particularly in the altitude belts giving the most economic and the lowest over-pressure transitions to supersonic flight. The supersonic aircraft is so much more sensitive to high temperature than the subsonic jet that particularly accurate information on temperature in the alternative climb zones may need to be made available for safe operations to be scheduled. Work at the Ames Research Centre in California has suggested that changes in the flight profile by extending the subsonic flight stage into cooler air space will not often prove to be worthwhile.

The market for the supersonic transport

The SST must be closely integrated into the structure of international air transport if it is to play a fully effective part in its development. While so much depends upon the economic feasibility of the vehicle, the capability of the aircraft to be introduced into air traffic control systems, into airline engineering facilities and into the highly developed traffic system of the world airlines, must be established without question. It will be assumed at this point that the overall commercial feasibility of certain supersonic projects is acceptable to national authorities and major airlines, and that means can be found for financing the cost of development and production and, if necessary, of meeting the higher costs of operation. Let us then consider the pattern of operations which would be likely to develop and how the supersonic services might be integrated with other scheduled operations.

Figure 9.5 provides a measure of the relative operating economy of supersonic transports ($M = 2 \cdot 2$ and $M = 3 \cdot 0$)

and the subsonic aircraft likely to be operating in 1973. Our principal interest here lies in the change in the relative economy with decrease in the stage length below the 3000–4000-mile stages for which these aircraft were designed. The basis on which these curves were prepared is described in a later section of this chapter, and the reservations which may need to be held are there pointed out. Here we need only emphasise that the overall pattern of operations will be largely determined by the need to concentrate the SST on long-haul routes and to mini- mise the sectors below 1500 miles in the case of the $M = 2\cdot2$

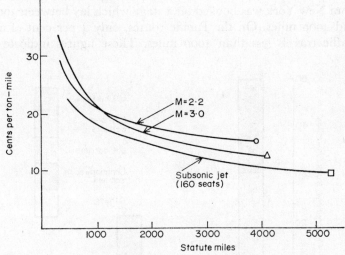

FIG. 9.5. Variation of Specific Cost with Stage Length

aircraft, except for really important traffic reasons. For the $M = 3\cdot0$ aircraft, a sector less than about 1800–2000 miles would only be undertaken for traffic support on longer sectors. This rather drastic limitation of the use of the SST may need to be substantiated when we consider the economics of these aircraft more fully, but in spite of the concentrated efforts of the US manufacturers to improve the economics and the flexibility of the $M = 3\cdot0$ aircraft in the Phase IIA programme, only limited room for advance is thought to exist in this area. In the finely conceived study of the economic consequences of introduction of SST, published by ICAO (August 1960) certain calculations were based on a minimum range of 1800 miles. Our reassessment of the problem in the light of later information on costs of subsonic as well as supersonic aircraft leads us to a similar result modified only by the need to consider the shorter commercially important traffic sectors such as Frankfurt–London, Hong Kong–Bangkok, and New York–Miami, which may need to be integrated into a real-life commercial situation.

On the US domestic trunk routes only about 16 per cent of passenger-miles are generated on stage lengths greater than 1800 miles. On the North Atlantic routes, on the other hand, in the same year, 77 per cent of the passenger traffic generated from New York was booked on a stage which lay between 3000 and 4000 miles. On the Pacific routes, only 4 per cent of air traffic travels less than 4000 miles. Those figures indicate a

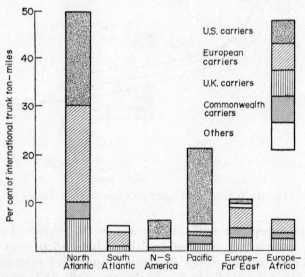

Fig. 9.6. Estimated Traffic Breakdown on Scheduled Air Services, 1974–5

likely application of the SST on the ocean routes, but on the Pacific this would be possible only if stages longer than 4000 miles can be technically achieved with an economic payload. Although refuelling stops are available on the Pacific routes the time lost would favour through flights with longer-range subsonic aircraft. On the basis of these considerations a study of the world's air routes was carried out in order to assess the market for supersonic transports in the early 1970s. The results are shown in Fig. 9.6. This shows a breakdown of the international trunk line traffic estimated for the year 1972–3, subdivided into the various world areas and into the nationality of the carrier. In all areas a continuance of the last five years' traffic growth was assumed. The predominance of the North Atlantic is very evident from these results, as also is the strong position of the US operators on the Pacific routes. We have already noted the greater suitability of the SST projects for the Atlantic rather than the Pacific routes. Other dominant factors, however, such as the sonic boom may reduce the significance of the SST to US trunk operators who, moreover, are likely to demand such flexibility of operation that the use of the $M = 3 \cdot 0$ SST may be limited to the principal transcontinental services and links to the transocean routes. The Concorde on both these counts may be of considerable interest to the US domestic trunk carriers. Later development of a very much larger $M = 2 \cdot 2$ aircraft now seems highly possible.

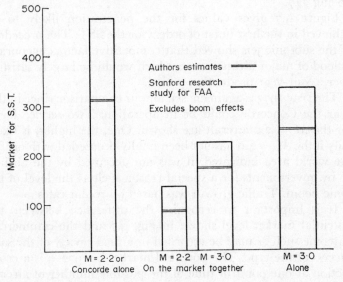

FIG. 9.7. Potential Market Penetration of Supersonic Airliners, 1974–5

From these results it is possible to assess the potential market for the SST in the years ahead. Some difficulties in analysis are, however, at once apparent. We are in doubt as to the effect of the sonic boom on the acceptance of the SST and, although preliminary results from experimental tests and flight experience in the UK and the US are now available, it is still not possible to assess the success of the designers in meeting the limitations of over-pressure suggested by the FAA ($1 \cdot 5$ lb/sq ft in cruise: $2 \cdot 0$ lb/sq ft during transition) on domestic operations, with increases in these figures to $1 \cdot 7$ and $2 \cdot 5$ respectively for flights over 3000 miles. We are in doubt as to the relative market penetrating potential of the $M = 2 \cdot 2$ aircraft (of lower first cost and greater operational flexibility) and of the $M = 3 \cdot 0$ designs (of greater size and speed – if and when these are built). In addition to these factors, the ability of the subsonic jet to maintain its passenger and airline appeal may be greatly augmented by its continued development, its continually reducing operating cost and its high flexibility in operation and integration. Moreover, the competitive power of the subsonic jets has been augmented by aircraft manufacturers' decision to develop a new series of 250–500 seaters exemplified by the Boeing 747.

Figure 9.7 gives values for the penetration likely to be achieved in the first burst of orders for the SST. The precedent of the subsonic jets showed that competitive factors encourage a flood of major airline orders which would be largely satisfied over a four-year production period.

The year 1973 is again chosen for our comparison since in this year the Concorde could be in operation. Two service levels for the $M = 2 \cdot 2$ aircraft are shown. One, the higher, is likely only if the $M = 3 \cdot 0$ has not been finally proceeded with or if in the world area indicated, it was not accepted by the airlines or by governments for a special reason such as the level of the sonic boom. Traffic growth was based on recent rates.

It is important to recognise the difference between the potential market level shown in Fig. 9.7 and the commercial outcome such as may be recorded in a final review of the sales success of the type. The potential market in 1972–3 is a cross-section at one point in time of the possible number of aircraft in service or the market penetration of the SSTs.

The influence of the sonic boom on the world SST market

No more than the broadest of estimates can be made of this factor, but clearly it is necessary to consider the proportional effect that might be felt on the international market for the SST if strong resistance arose in the territories over which the aircraft will fly, due to the sonic boom. If a campaign to 'ban the boom' was led by influential speakers in one or two Western countries, a strong following might be achieved which could strongly influence international conferences and perhaps lead to unilateral action to prevent overflights of supersonic aircraft. In this eventuality the effect on the overall demand for aircraft could be serious especially if the countries straddled the main trunk routes which we have considered. Some rational arguments are developed for the allocation of public resources to other aviation projects posing comparable technological challenge and perhaps offering greater commercial prospects (Lundbert, 1962, Beaufort, 1962, and Anti-Concorde papers 1969–71).

If supersonic flights were prohibited over all highly populated land masses the global pattern of operations would be drastically altered. A study conducted by the author for a Royal Aeronautical Society Symposium (February 1961) showed that for BOAC and the British Commonwealth air carriers, although a theoretical requirement for 24 SSTs in 1970 was established, only 59 per cent of these could be used if they were limited to overwater operations in supersonic flight. For the US overseas airlines, only 49 per cent of the 31 aircraft estimated to be required would be usable because of similar worldwide restriction. The US domestic operators would be most seriously affected. The table below shows these results:

The lack of economic flexibility of the SST when required to fly even short subsonic sectors, makes it a serious matter to remain at subsonic speeds in order to postpone transition and generation of the sonic boom. Even on direct flights such as Frankfurt or Zurich to New York, the necessity to fly subsonically over France for an additional 250 miles would cause an increase of 7 per cent in the direct operating cost and comparable increases in the sector flight time.

TABLE 9·5. *Restriction on Use of the SST Due to Sonic Boom.*
$$M = 2·2$$

Area	Percentage use
BOAC and British Commonwealth	59
US International	49
US Domestic	16
Other World Carriers	62
Total:	43

The sonic boom

The problem of the sonic boom or over-pressure which may create acute discomfort to communities spread over a wide area under the path of the supersonic aircraft is one which was not fully recognised in the first stages of the development. The relatively small size of early supersonic military aircraft gave little warning of the effects on the human ear and on sensitive materials of the pressures which would be felt at great distances when heavy high flying aircraft operated above about $M = 1·2$ The so-called pressure signature, an N-shaped wave of pressure rise and fall, is created by the shock waves thrown off from the aircraft when at supersonic speed. These coalesce at a distance of tens of thousands of feet from the aircraft into two shocks, a bow and a tail shock of approximately equal magnitude. Theoretical methods have been evolved for computing the pressure rise and it is found that the predominant factors determining the magnitude of the pressure rise are the instantaneous weight of the aircraft, the altitude and the Mach Number. To be more precise, the pressure rise (lb/sq ft) on the ground directly on the aircraft track and due to the passage of the shock wave is given by:

$$\Delta p = 0·363 \, K_R K_A K_L \left(\frac{M^2 - 1}{M}\right)^{\frac{3}{4}} \frac{W^2}{l_W^{\frac{3}{4}}} \, P_a^{\frac{1}{2}} h^{\frac{3}{4}} P_g$$

where K_R and K_A are reflectivity and attenuation factors respectively.

K_L is the lift slope factor
l_W is the wing length in feet
M is the Mach Number
W is the aircraft weight in lb
P_a is the ambient pressure at aircraft altitude (lb/sq ft)
P_g is the ambient pressure at ground level (lb/sq ft)
h is the altitude in feet

The theoretical pressure rise is given by this formula for cruising supersonic flight when the lifting effect (i.e. weight) predominates. The reflectivity factor is generally taken as 1·8 or 2·0, but tests showed that many situations exist where the value will be considerably higher or lower than this.

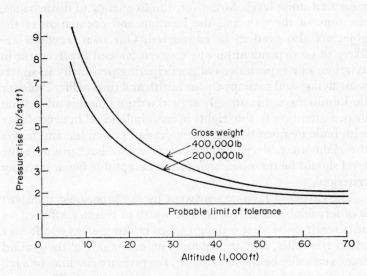

FIG. 9.8. Intensity of Boom Overpressure Due to Lift. $M = 2·0$

By simplification of the equation and introduction of approximate values for typical SST projects, the above expression can be plotted as shown in Fig. 9.8. This chart, based on the investigations of J. Morris (1960) when Special Projects Engineer of Hawker Siddeley Aviation, shows values for typical $M = 2·0$ projects. The very much higher weights envisaged for the US $M = 3·0$ projects may create a higher boom intensity on the cruise than will be experienced with the Concorde. However, calculations show that the effect of Mach Number for a given weight and altitude is not very considerable. As already stated, it was a requirement of the FAA Phase II programme for a US SST that the limits of sonic over-pressure should be 2·0 lb/sq ft during transonic acceleration, and 1·5 lb/sq ft during cruise (for domestic US operations).

Experience already available, based on the test programmes, shows that the threshold of possible damage lies somewhat higher than 2·0 lb/sq ft. In spite of this, the community response to the sonic boom has been far from favourable. People hear, feel and observe vibrations and may be psychologically disturbed in a way which cannot be judged purely by a carefully measured noise level. Moreover, the frequency of disturbance, the time of the day and the location and occupation of the objectors also need to be considered. Our own reactions are likely to be dependent on our concern for and involvement in aviation, our expectations of participating personally in supersonic flying, and perhaps on our health and time of life. Professor Bo Lundberg, in his strongly argued writings on this subject has drawn attention to the 'rights of each individual in accordance with basic democratic and humanitarian principles' and makes the claim that 'sleep disturbance at a low background noise level should be the main basis for an acceptable boom intensity criterion'.

The carpet of land or sea swept by the supersonic transport is of formidable dimensions. The width of country affected by an aircraft of $M = 3·0$ design when cruising at 70,000 ft may reach 100 miles, and at fifty miles on either side of the ground track vertically below the aircraft, the pressure rise may be such as to disturb sleep (i.e. not less than 0·25 lb /sq ft). The extent to which we may be persuaded to accept these things and to learn, by degrees perhaps, to live with a new external fact of life, man-directed but not readily avoidable as may be the avoidance of an airport or a city centre, will become a critical question for many national aviation authorities and airlines in the next five years. To assess the magnitude of this problem with regard to the British Isles the author investigated the airline movements which might be expected over the northwestern corner of Europe in the mid-1970s. Naturally, only the flight segments likely to be flown supersonically were considered. These results are shown in Fig. 9.9. An earlier analysis with which the author was associated established a Frequency and Population Index for the British Isles. This work may be compared to that subsequently reported by the UK Committee on Noise (HMSO, 1963) in which a Noise and Frequency Index (NNI) was used in the analysis of nuisance from aircraft in the vicinity of London Airport (Heathrow).

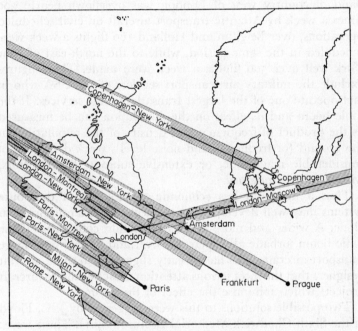

FIG. 9.9. The Pattern of Boom Areas without Operational Restriction. Great Circle Routes

In our study, the boom carpets were found to cover wide areas of north-west Europe, and the northern parts of the United Kingdom were heavily overlaid. The greatest effect was produced by the supersonic tracks of aircraft on great circle paths from Scandinavia, North Germany and Holland to New York, Washington and Montreal. Southern England and the Netherlands would be overflown by aircraft from Switzerland, southern Germany and northern Italy. There is no question that the British Isles would suffer acutely if supersonic air services are operated on great circle tracks between the European capitals and the gateways in the north-east of America. Diversions along the English Channel may allow some relief to these islands if not to the Benelux countries and to France. A very much fuller appraisal of these facts will be required before a full-scale programme of SST production and operation can be launched. Even in the summer of 1960 a wide band of country west of London was overflown nearly 300 times a week by Atlantic transport aircraft on civil scheduled operations, over Belgium and Holland 160 flights a week were scheduled in the same period, while to the north-east of New York well over 500 flights a week were made. These figures exclude the military air transport services of the USA who in fact operate one of the largest transatlantic air services. If the sonic boom and its effect on the population can be measured as the product of frequency and density of the population on the ground (or frequency and noise level), track diversions of considerable magnitude, or extensive subsonic flight sectors, will become mandatory.

Thus a new and less economic distribution of the route systems may well develop so as to meet this Atlantic problem alone. A wider and more serious restriction could arise if the sonic boom forbade all supersonic overland operation of large transport aircraft. This has already suggested to some aircraft designers that the most serious attention must be paid to aircraft projects which minimise the effect of the boom.

Two possible solutions to this were suggested by J. C. Floyd in the Sixth Chadwick Memorial Lecture (1961). These were:

(i) Laminarisation of the flow over the aircraft's outer skin which would so reduce the drag that the payload may be considerably increased for a given gross weight, thereby limiting the effect of the boom which is highly sensitive to the flying weight of the aircraft.

(ii) The design of aircraft for a supersonic speed limited to $M = 1\cdot15 - 1\cdot2$ which, together with a high degree of wing sweep, might gain considerably by the use of variable geometry.

If the sonic boom were to limit the overland speed of aircraft to about 760 mph or $M = 1\cdot15$ in the standard atmosphere, a large (150–200 seat) aircraft of this nominal speed could not be easily eclipsed in economics or in speed on overland trunk routes.

A further research programme has been developed which aims to establish the means of reducing the sonic boom shock wave at its source or during the propagation stage. One hopeful method is to modify the aerodynamic form of the fuselage so as to spread out the 'near field' of pressure patterns and ensure that the N-shaped wave does not become established until at least one thousand body lengths away from (i.e. below) the flight path. Early results suggested a probability of achieving a 25 per cent reduction in the pressure pulse rise when using these methods. An urgent need exists for the intensification of this programme.

These new approaches to the problem of achieving high economy without generating the sonic boom have received detailed attention because of increasing international concern at the implications of the boom even over sparsely populated areas.

US tests on the sonic boom

The sonic boom tests mounted by the FAA in Oklahoma City during the first half of 1964 were significant in establishing over-pressure values in relation to theory, as well as in testing community and structural response. The initial tests were conducted at 1·5 lb/sq ft and during the last few weeks the (nominal) pressure was raised to 2·0 lb/sq ft. It was found that the variance in the peak pressure was considerable and exceeded mean values by 30 per cent on 15 per cent of occasions, and by 80 per cent on 1 per cent of occasions. Such variations in over-pressure, which might cause very serious damage during the 'super-boom' at transition to supersonic flight, were not expected and were thought to be due to random changes in the temperature and viscosity of the atmosphere. Variation between flights, and at intervals of a few hundred feet along the ground track, were recorded. The over-pressures in Oklahoma City caused little structural damage and none to structures or appliances in a proper state of repair and maintenance. Specially prepared test houses as well as public and private dwellings were surveyed during this programme. None of these received structural damage. It is well known that Oklahoma City was using the 7 a.m. supersonic overpass as a daily alarum call so that some have concluded that the FAA cruise level of 1·5 lb/sq ft is too high to allow for undisturbed sleep.

UK experience

The continuing Concorde flight-test programme, as well as the operational trials such as the London–Tehran–Tokio–Sydney flight in the summer of 1972, has generated a massive body of experience on the sonic boom. Tests in the western coastal area of Britain in 1970–1 indicated the variable reaction of the public to the sonic boom and gave evidence that light damage can be inflicted upon insecure structures. It now seems quite clear that supersonic flight will not be possible over densely populated areas, but that it is fully justified and generally acceptable over lightly populated areas in any part of the world.

High-altitude hazards

Increased hazards in flight at high altitudes due to radiations of various kinds, cosmic rays and ozone are known to exist and are subject to intensive study in the physics, meteorological and aero-medical faculties. The major concern has lain with the intense high-energy cosmic events which could produce dangerous over-exposure especially in the higher latitudes (above 50–55°) during peak periods of solar activity. This normally occurs about every four years, but lower-energy emissions are more frequent if less dangerous. These radiations penetrate to the altitudes of planned $M = 3\cdot0$ operation and re-routing to latitudes below 50° or to altitudes below 50,000 ft will be essential, and in all probability, with very little warning.

It will be recognised that the exposure risks to passengers will be insignificantly small, but for flight crews on regular polar operations in flight altitudes of 70,000–80,000 ft the solar proton injury may reach the limits set for radiation workers. The interchange of crews between high- and middle-latitude flights may prove a means of meeting this problem. The necessity to develop reliable forecasts of radiation activity so that avoiding action can be taken by supersonic flight crews is apparent. Aircraft will need to be capable of lower-altitude operation (50,000 ft) without undue fuel penalty and crews may need to take account of immediate diversions to lower latitudes in the preparation of flight plans. In effect, the altitudes of supersonic flight will introduce a new environmental factor in the design and operation of these aircraft. It seems now to be generally accepted that the higher levels of ozone in the atmosphere at higher altitudes will not prove a serious problem to the SST. Although ozone concentrations of about five parts per million are liable to cause irritation and illness in some individuals, it is claimed that the ozone content of the cabin air can be chemically controlled without difficulty. It is believed that ultraviolet rays can be effectively attenuated by windscreens and cabin windows. The probability of meteorite damage at supersonic altitudes is very little different from that at present existing with subsonic jets.

Pollution from the SST

High altitude emissions by SSTs cruising in the 60,000–65,000-ft band have been under intensive study. Until actual emissions and reaction rates are known, however, the environmental effects deduced from modelling cannot be assessed. Water vapour, oxides of nitrogen and other matter is anticipated, but the emission data and dispersion mechanisms are unknown.

The destruction of ozone by photochemical reaction in quantities which might permit harmful levels of ultra-violet radiation to reach the earth has now been discounted by the MIT in a sponsored Study of Critical Environmental Problems. (Massachusetts 1970.) Similar fears of an increase in the earth's surface temperature as a result of an accumulation of carbon dioxide in the lower atmosphere (the greenhouse effect) have also been put to rest. Instrumented flight testing however is being undertaken by the National Oceanographic and

397

Atmospheric Administration in the USA through 1971–2 to measure the effect of emitted water vapour. It is unfortunate that such fundamental research gives opportunity to the Friends of the Earth and members of other well-meaning societies to repeat unconfirmed statements damaging to the natural economic development of the most advanced air transport projects.

The scheduling of supersonic transport

In the comparison between supersonic and subsonic transports it is important to establish at once the basis on which the aircraft operations are to be considered. The number of aircraft in the fleet, the route system to be covered, the degree of integration and the tautness of the schedules must be determined. The $M = 2·2$ and the $M = 3·0$ SST will require different treatment in this respect.

We have already seen that the probable flow patterns (presuming no distortion by restrictions imposed due to the sonic boom) would be principally on the North and South Atlantic, on the Pacific and Far Eastern routes and with subsidiary flows between North and South America and from Europe to Africa (Fig. 9.10). We have noted that the SST will be expected to operate primarily on stages greater than 1800 miles ($M = 3·0$), and perhaps above 1500 miles ($M = 2·2$), but for commercial reasons, particularly on routes from Europe and through the Middle East, shorter stages will need to be closely integrated into the pattern even though some loss of economy must be anticipated through the shorter stages which may require lower-altitude operation at subsonic speeds. On all stages the availability of airfields with suitable facilities will need to be investigated. This concerns runway length and strength, refuelling capability within the scheduled ground time, passenger handling, flight planning, air traffic and approach control and the large number of second-order factors each of key significance in the acceptance and transitting of a supersonic transport vehicle.

It is not possible to consider the many detailed problems of scheduling which will arise in the planning of the operations of

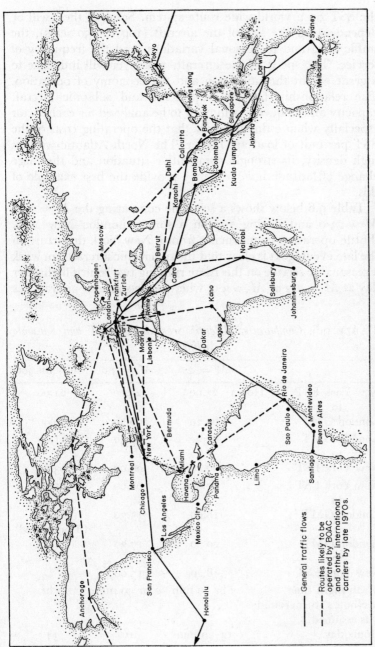

FIG. 9.10. Some Probable Supersonic Transport Routes

General traffic flows

Routes likely to be
operated by BOAC
and other international
carriers by late 1970s.

the SST on a world-wide route system. Some of these will be dependent on the size of the aircraft (100 to 250 seats), the traffic level and its seasonal variations, and the frequency of service. The speed of the aircraft, moreover will influence to a great extent the utilisation and the economy of operation. The relationship between supersonic and subsonic aircraft capacity and frequency will need to be analysed for each sector especially when estimates show that the operating costs of the SST per unit of load are higher. The North Atlantic with its high density, its strongly competitive situation and the large change of latitude involved, may provide the best example of this.

Table 9.6 below shows a schedule comparing the $M = 2 \cdot 2$, $M = 3 \cdot 0$ and Boeing 707 on a simple London–New York shuttle operation commencing from a New York departure in the late evening. It is clear that the supersonic aircraft can work a reasonable service on this route running two return flights per day at $M = 2 \cdot 2$ or $M = 3 \cdot 0$, whereas the subsonic aircraft has

TABLE 9.6. *Comparative Atlantic Schedule for SST and Subsonic Airliners*

		$M = 2 \cdot 2$	$M = 3 \cdot 0$	Subsonic jet
New York EST	Hours	23.00	23.00	21.00
to				
London GMT		07.20	06.30	09.00
London GMT		09.20	08.30	11.00
to				
New York EST		07.40	06.00	13.00
New York EST		09.40	08.00	15.00
to				
London GMT		18.00	15.30	03.00 (if permitted)
London GMT		20.00	17.30	
to				
New York EST		18.20	15,00	
Mean flight time		3 hr 20 min	2 hr 30 min	7 hr
A 2-hours' turnaround is assumed				
Hours/day		13–20 min	10	14

generated only one return flight, although the latter has rather more time in hand than the $M = 2\cdot2$ aircraft and greater economic potential for a short operation with the remaining hours of the day. It may be noted that the very considerably increased speed of the supersonic aircraft has not developed a proportionately equivalent mileage in the operating cycle, nor has the faster $M = 3\cdot0$ supersonic aircraft increased its mileage over that of the $M = 2\cdot2$ aircraft. Hence arises the problem that the increased speed of the SST, even a moderate increase in the Mach Number itself, leads to a decrease in the utilisation of the individual aircraft in hours per day or per year, unless schedules are acceptable which are very much less convenient to the travelling public than those in use today.

In the case of the $M = 3\cdot0$ when operating the Atlantic service suggested, it may be possible to schedule a 'tag-end' service to one of the following cities, if the sonic boom level permits, or a complete reshuffling of the fleet integration may be possible to include long-distance intercontinental flights of which New York–London is only one sector:

1-way Flight Time. $M = 3\cdot0$

	(Hr min)
New York–Chicago–New York	55 min
New York–Miami–New York	1 hr 10 min
London–Rome–London	1 hr 00 min
London–Frankfurt–London	45 min

It would clearly be desirable to ensure that the utilisation of the $M = 3\cdot0$ aircraft is increased beyond the ten hours indicated in the above cycle, but the economics of this aircraft on these shorter stages will need to be very fully considered. We should note especially the limitations now often imposed on landings and take-offs during night hours.

The capability of the SST to meet current noise requirements or to improve on them has yet to be demonstrated. In the FAA SST requirements, the airport noise levels were important desiderata. However, we have already noted the necessity to exchange for the improved community noise level along the line of the take-off of the SST, some deterioration of the situation to the side of the runway. The higher levels probably necessary might effect night operations of the SST;

this would have a very serious effect on the full exploitation of the available operating hours and increase specific operating costs. Movement frequency would also be restricted.

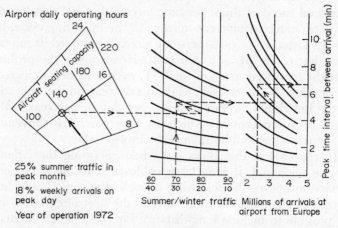

FIG. 9.11. Parametric Results of New York Airport Transatlantic Arrivals, Year 1973

Fig. 9.11 brings us to another aspect of the operational problem. If our traffic estimates can be accepted then we must face the problem of arrival and departure frequency at the peak time, and the probable distribution of the traffic. To simplify the diagram we ignore the daily and the diurnal variations that create even greater problems in airport arrivals and departures. The factors we take account of are:

1. The useful daily operating hours. This may be limited by the restriction of the hours of operation to reduce night noise disturbance as discussed above, or by the need to consider passenger travel convenience or necessity.

2. The seating capacity of the aircraft.

3. The seasonal fluctuation of the traffic, given by the simple ratio of summer/winter traffic.

Means of escape from this situation could lie in the provision of larger aircraft or in the wider dispersal of the gateways into the USA and into Europe. If keen community resistance to the sonic boom is aroused it might be that US transcontinental operations would continue to be performed with subsonic jet aircraft. Thus the natural subsonic aircraft development up towards 500 or even 750 passengers might lessen the problem of airport and terminal facility congestion. It is even possible that the $M = 1\cdot15-1\cdot20$ aircraft, which provides another solution to the boom problem, could be developed to the very large size ideally suited to the North Atlantic in the 1970s.

Body attitudes of supersonic transport

Studies of the supersonic transport in various phases of the flight trajectory have indicated the greater floor angles or body attitude which may be encountered. After take-off and during preliminary climb, small increases of attitude will arise, probably not notably greater than those on some subsonic types (probably $12-15°$). In the *en route* climb phase the attitude may still reach $12°$, accentuated by the affects of acceleration. In the approach and touch-down stages of the flight the fixed-wing double-delta $M = 3\cdot0$ SST is likely to reach attitudes of $9-10°$. Deceleration will tend to accentuate this also. It seems likely that for a rather higher proportion of the flight time, we shall require the use of seat belts. The acceleration is rarely likely to exceed $0\cdot4$ g. However, estimates by one US manufacturer have shown that if $10°$ floor gradient were the criterion then for only four minutes after take-off would it be necessary for seat belts to be fastened because of the floor slope.

The economics of SST operation

Our consideration of the supersonic project up till now has been based on the supposition that it is an economically feasible project for operation on world-wide long-haul trunk routes as a replacement in due course for many of the services currently operated by subsonic jets. How sound is this proposition and on what basis is this thesis founded?

One conclusion of our operational study was that the $M = 2\cdot2$ and the $M = 3\cdot0$ SSTs are vehicles with markedly different characteristics. We need not again explore these differences. Fundamental to the operational use of these two speed brackets for supersonic transport is that the greater flexibility and better overall operating economy of the $M = 2\cdot2$ aircraft allows it to be operated on a wider pattern of routes and with a smaller design payload than is economically desirable with the faster aircraft. It has been noted already that the US designs for $M = 2\cdot7–3\cdot0$ steel/titanium aircraft allow payloads for design range with up to 250 seats. These vehicles, therefore, would for several reasons become highly specialised and likely to be commercially successful on a fairly limited number of world routes even in the late 1970s. Their poor showing on stage lengths less than about 1800 miles, about half the design range, provides further opportunities for alternative air transport developments. These may be:

1. The lower speed $M = 1\cdot8–2\cdot2$ Aluminium SST (such as Concorde).

2. The current subsonic jet types developed in size and with third-generation engines (turbo-fan) to improve economy and reduce noise.

3. New very large subsonic turbo-fan projects with lower cost possibilities to seek out even wider markets and to provide a long-range facility. This is the family of wide-body jets.

A decade of progress is probable on all these projects which can, in many respects, be complementary. It is certain that the market for Concorde would be modified by the development of the $M = 3\cdot0$ aircraft, to a lesser extent by Soviet plans for an SST, and by the renewed impulse given in the 1965–70 period to subsonic development by the so-called C 5 A technology based on advanced subsonic turbo-fan military transport designs for the USAF. Trends indicate continued competition from subsonic aircraft until the mid-1970s. Nevertheless, a very substantial proportion of the inter-continental and long-haul international traffic could well be carried in supersonic transports by 1980 if the economics of the aircraft can be shown to be adequate for competitive services.

The cost of SST development

Since the Governments of Great Britain and France are now resolved for reasons of prestige, and so as to force the 'state of the art' to support the development of an SST programme, there is less evidence now of the efforts to win converts to progressive air transport policies. Had SST development been possible on a purely commercial basis within a reasonable time scale, it might well have been preferable to have let the natural growth in resources of the aviation industry support the programme. However, the resources required and the potential economy of the best designs were not likely to encourage the industries without government support.

In Europe this would have clearly meant no SST programme within the foreseeable future. Economic studies of the balance of payments for the USA, UK and France following SST building and export programmes have indicated a favourable outcome from the proposed levels of national investment except in the most adverse circumstances. They show that the introduction of Concordes and US $M = 3\cdot0$ projects into world airlines should generate annually for four to six years favourable balances for the UK, France and the USA exceeding £60–100 million (UK/France) and \$1–2 billion (USA).* At even half the lower figure quoted for the UK an important contribution to the balance of payments would be made. But the investment required by the nation and the industry would be formidable.

The President of the Boeing Company, William M. Allen, said in 1963 that the 'estimated peak investment by Boeing in inventory alone, assuming Government participation as proposed by the FAA (at that time \$750 million of the first \$1 billion of development funds) and assuming progress payments by the airlines of 33 per cent of the sales price prior to delivery, would exceed \$900 million'.

An earlier proposal, approved by Congress, that the US industry (airframe and engine) should provide 25 per cent of the development cost was rejected by the manufacturers who sought a Government stake of at least 90 per cent. Unfortunately, no firm interest was evinced by the Department of Defence in the SST proposals. To the military planners in the US and in Western Europe, supersonic personnel and material delivery, with range limitations as at the present state of development, do not justify the excess operating costs over the

* Prices at 1966.

subsonic aircraft which are now under development. The inflexible need for first-class airports and the small proportional effect that reduced in-flight time would have on overall deployment time explain further the lack of military support.

The cost of development of the Concorde was at first estimated at about £400 million, up to the stage of the production and development of prototypes. This estimate (February 1966) included the costs incurred after certification and all research and development on the airframe, engines and equipment. It included the full production tooling and the building of six test aircraft as well as sixty-six engines. Two aircraft, however were to be withdrawn from flight test at a later stage and furnished for delivery to customers. These costs were, of course, to be shared between Britain and France. Since the earlier estimates, however, costs have risen considerably. This, through the continuing development of airframe engine and systems, is the common pattern of all aviation development where inroads are made into new regimes of operation and with previously untested power-plant, systems and techniques. A severe inflationary trend also coincided with the period of Concorde development. By October 1970 the total estimated Concorde R & D costs, including the provision of modifications and full production tooling, the building of 66 engines and 6 test airframes, and flight and ground test programmes, had reached a level of £825 million. The actual cost incurred to that date had reached £460 million. It seems unlikely that more than one quarter to one third of the total R & D programme will be recovered from sales even if a major marketing success can be achieved. By the year 1973 an R & D cost of at least £1000 million to be shared between Britain and France can quite realistically be assumed.

The assessment of direct costs

For many reasons an assessment of the direct-operating costs of the SST projects and the comparable subsonic jet developments is particularly difficult to make. For one thing, the degree of investment of public funds in the SST programmes is not yet clearly determined, and the scale of this investment, the means devised for its recovery or partial recovery, and the anticipated orders over which it might be spread, are crucial to an assessment of the prime cost of aircraft and of the standing costs of operation. For very obvious reasons the new and unknown factors which will need to be considered, studied and controlled will make any ready-made cost formula of limited value. Nevertheless, a great many assessments have been made and in general the conclusions are consistent.

We have discussed the estimation of standing costs at length in Chapter 2, and the assessment we have made of these costs for the SST has followed the same pattern. The prime costs of the aircraft was assumed as indicated in Table 9.7 and spares of 20 per cent of the cost of the aircraft were added. We have presumed that the airframe cost would be amortised over 10 years with a 15 per cent residual value for the Concorde, but used 12 years for the $M = 3 \cdot 0$ aircraft because of its more advanced design. Engines were depreciated also to 15 per cent of their first cost, but over a seven-year life. The cost of fuel on the international route system considered was based on 12 cents per US gallon (5p per Imperial gallon) and represents an anticipated price in the mid-1970s in Europe and on the US Atlantic seaboard. Fuel amounts to 33–36 per cent of direct costs and the results are therefore sensitive to the control of price.

The need to achieve on supersonic operations adequate thermal stability in the kerosene fuels which are now in use for subsonic jet engines has been under active study in the USA and the UK. The problem is more acute at the higher ambient temperature generated above $M = 2 \cdot 7$. It is clearly most essential to ensure that the price of fuel should be maintained at a level no higher than that now existing at the principal international terminals. Some variation in the principal required characteristics, thermal stability, sulphur content and combustion characteristics, is known to exist. Leading fuel suppliers have pointed out (*Aviation Week*, 25.1.65) that sampling of fuels at terminals has indicated that improvements in the distribution and handling methods may be called for at specific points. Possibly an additive may need to be developed so as to increase thermal stability up to $M = 2 \cdot 7$. However, specially developed fuels for use in an $M = 3 \cdot 0$ transport would add seriously to the cost of the largest item of the direct-operating cost schedule.

Crew costs are assumed to be considerably escalated from current rates and we have estimated a cost which amounts to 24 c. per mile on the four-crew $M = 3\cdot0$ SST and 18 c. per mile on the $M = 2\cdot2$ transport with three on the flight deck. The insurance of the hull and public liability was taken as 6 per cent of the depreciated price of the aircraft in a given year. This will amount to approximately 5 per cent of the value of the new aircraft. When comparing the subsonic jets, the insurance cost of these aircraft was taken as 4 per cent, or two-thirds the rate for the SST. Block speeds and utilisation have been estimated from carefully prepared flight plans with adjustments for diversions, delays and contingencies approximating to subsonic jet practice except where operational study and wider discussions have suggested particular assumptions (Polhemus, 1962; Hopkins, 1964; Shaffer, 1970).

The maintenance and engineering supervision and control of the SST has been the subject of special study. There is every hope for a considerable and steady improvement in maintenance efficiency by the early 1970s. Although no major change in the basis of planning scheduled maintenance in this period is foreseen, it is possible that in airlines with worldwide networks a larger proportion of overseas maintenance will be necessary to achieve the highest SST utilisation and flexibility of service. Overseas work, however, may cost more and some account needed to be taken of this. The high speeds and more frequent landings in a given operating period will impose on the SST a higher rate of wear and tear than has been experienced in the recent past by the long-haul carriers. This will apply to systems, structure and furnishings. Furnishing materials of high quality, with hard-wearing characteristics, and of lower unit weight are required by the designers of the SST. Higher costs per unit of capacity are incurred here also.

Aspects of maintainability

Due to the exceptional rates of productivity achievable with a supersonic transport aircraft the unit of time takes on a new significance. Although the costs per mile may be comparable, nevertheless the operating costs per hour are considerably higher than for the subsonic jet transport of equivalent carrying capacity, and so is the loss of revenue through grounding the aircraft for one additional hour beyond the service schedule. Herein lies the need for a new concept of maintainability and reliability with supersonic transport. Since these aircraft will be generating the transport capability of three subsonic jets, we shall be unable to persuade the serious operator to retain standby aircraft hours to cover the unscheduled arising of technical faults. If this productivity can be achieved the supersonic transport can offer a rich reward, but if unserviceability is frequent and service delays arise then we must admit at once that the operator would be in a serious position. The operation of the aircraft will not perhaps be faultless, but it must be free from ground time delay even though it will be inevitably a more sophisticated and complicated aeroplane to maintain. Engine intake and exhaust nozzle variable geometry, the necessity for structural integrity with pressure differential beyond present civil experience, and the new complex systems of control and cabin conditioning, will require the most precise attention to detail in design for maintenance. In some designs wing flap systems may be simplified, however, or even deleted.

Proposals are now under discussion for automatic check-out equipment for the inspection and functional test of supersonic aircraft. This might be mounted on the aircraft or on the ground, or might be a combination of both. Its purpose is to check the condition and serviceability of all aircraft systems, whether electrical, hydraulic or pneumatic, and to report substandard elements or components, identifying where possible the source of trouble. It is anticipated that in due course an important use will be found for electronic computers in forecasting the probable serviceability state of components by recording the condition of a component and tracing trends towards sub-standard conditions. These concepts are not new and military aircraft in the US have already been designed with this in view. A further step might be the transmission in flight (data link) of such key component serviceability data as would prepare ground stations for the required replacement items which can be awaiting aircraft arrival. In-flight recording of

TABLE 9.7. *Comparison of the Operating Cost of SST and Subsonic Aircraft on International Operations. 1975*

Aircraft Types	Supersonic		Subsonic	
	$M = 2.7$ Now project only	$M = 2.0$–2.2 Concorde	$M = 0.85$ DC 8/63	$M = 0.85$ B 747 B
Gross weight (lb)	480,000	385,000	350,000	775,000
Max. payload (economy pass.)	250	128	250	450
Design range (st m)	4,500	3,800	4,500	5,200
Utilisation (hours p a)	2,900	3,000	3,250	3,500
Prime cost (excl. spares) $ m	50.0	24.0	12.5	20.0
£ m	21.0	10.0	5.2	8.3
Depreciation life (years) to 15% value	12	10	10	12
Direct operating cost per mile on design sector $	3.80	2.4	2.5	3.5
£	1.58	1.0	1.04	1.45
Direct operating cost per seat mile c	1.51	1.89	1.00	0.78
p	0.62	0.79	0.415	0.32
Total operating cost per seat mile c	2.59	3.05	2.20	1.90
p	1.08	1.27	0.91	0.79
Break even load factor, passenger only: at 7c per mile	36.0	42.2	30.2	26.3
3P ,, ,,				
Number of passengers to break even on design sector	90	54	75	118

system characteristics, particularly on the engine, has been in use for many years. These newer developments will be essential if we are to exploit to the full the economic potential of supersonic transport. The first cost of such equipment, and its own maintainability, shows promise of being well within the margins necessary to ensure considerable overall operating cost reduction per unit of productivity.

Table 9.7 shows the main conclusions of our estimates of the operating cost levels of the US $M = 3\cdot0$ and the European $M = 2\cdot2$ projects at 1975 prices. The US type considered is based on the Boeing and Lockheed feasibility Phase IIA studies and might be considered typical of a fixed-wing layout for $M = 3\cdot0$. The $M = 2\cdot2$ is represented by the Anglo-French Concorde production aircraft (1971).

A typical wide-body jet is also shown with a DC 8 derivative in the mid 1970s. The latter must be considered as alternative and competitive product lines which may considerably modify the demand for SSTs in the late 1970s.

Fig. 9.12 indicates the principal characteristics of the design

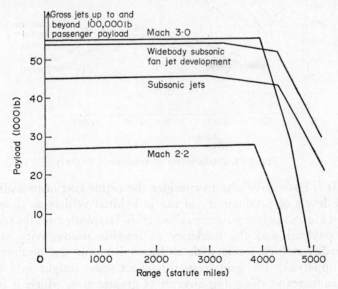

FIG. 9.12. Payload Range of Principal Long-haul Projects

payload and range of the proposed supersonic transports. Some of the principal stage lengths of importance to supersonic service were shown in Table 9.1. The limitations of the range available to the $M = 2 \cdot 2$ SST is apparent, however design development should correct such restrictions as may be imposed in the early years of operation.

The immense productivity potential of these aircraft is shown in the next figure, 9.13. It may be noted how the full effect of the traffic generation due to speed is not apparent until about 1800 miles on the $M = 3 \cdot 0$ and not until about 1200 miles on the $M = 2 \cdot 2$ aircraft. The highly effective capability of the subsonic jet is well illustrated on this diagram.

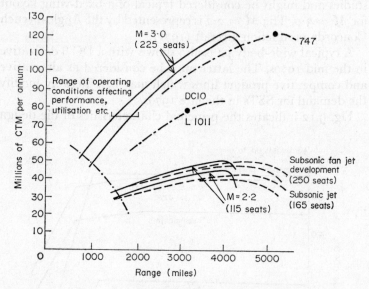

FIG. 9.13. Productivity of Supersonic Projects

It is instructive also to consider the prime cost of providing the levels of productivity of the individual vehicle as shown, and Fig. 9.14 gives an illustration of this. It is plotted as a function of payload and the tendency to provide productivity at a steadily reducing cost with an increasing unit size of aircraft is apparent. We gain from this chart some insight into the advantages of designing aircraft of greater size, which is one of the reasons for the better specific operating costs of the large

US $M = 3 \cdot 0$ aircraft compared with the smaller European $M = 2 \cdot 2$ design. In each case payload growth is expected.

It should be remembered that Fig. 9.14 brings out one factor only, although perhaps the most important one, in the direct operating cost index (or direct costs per pass. mile) and this does not illumine more than one facet of the economic problem.

An argument has sometimes been put forward on behalf of the smaller SSTs that the operating costs per mile may be lower than those of the larger subsonic jets. Clearly this may be true under certain circumstances, especially if the research and development charges are not fully amortised into the direct operating costs of the aircraft. Thus, if only a nominal proportion, say only $\frac{1}{2}$ per cent of the total R & D expended on the Concorde project, were to be recouped in the sales price of each aircraft then it may be possible to reduce the costs per mile of the aircraft on the longer stages to a level below that of

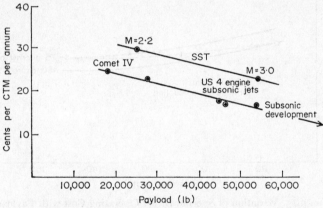

FIG. 9.14. Prime Cost of Productivity of Supersonic Projects

the Boeing 707/320 and 420. Sir George Edwards in the Brancker Memorial Lecture (1964) stated that his calculations showed a better cost per mile for the Concorde relative to the subsonic jets, down to less than 1000 miles. Our own studies based on project figures at an early stage in the UK SST programme (Henshaw, 1962) showed a similar pattern of behaviour, but our more recent calculations for this present work and other available information indicate lower direct costs achievable with the subsonic turbo-fan jet and higher development and maintenance costs for the SST. More conservative data is also provided by recent papers and probably all that could now be claimed is comparable costs per mile for these types at their respective design ranges (Table 9.7).

Concerning the operating costs of the Boeing 733, Mr William M. Allen, President of Boeing, said in January 1965 that the 'variable sweep wing design can be operated with lower breakeven load factors than existing subsonic transports on all but short ranges even after including amortisation of prototype development and testing as part of the direct cost of operation per passenger mile'. Mr Allen can have made no more than a token allowance for the heavy total costs of the research and development which would have supported the $M = 3\cdot0$ programme.

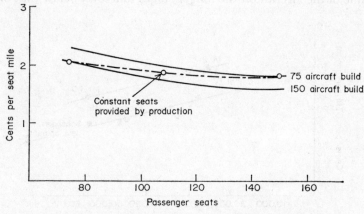

FIG. 9.15. Variation of Specific Direct Operating Cost with Payload Capacity. $M = 2\cdot2$ Transport on North Atlantic Operations

One factor of some interest is shown in Fig. 9.15 where the specific direct-operating cost for a family of $M = 2\cdot2$ SSTs is shown as a function of the number of passengers carried. A representative operation on the London–New York route was selected. Two curves are shown for production quantities of 75 and 150 aircraft. The effect of production volume on the amortised cost loading in the direct cost index is thereby evident. The line shown dotted represents a constant provision of seating capacity on the production line, the larger aircraft with its smaller market leading to direct costs which are less favourable than the lines of constant aircraft numbers would suggest. This is by no means an entirely academic modification to the assessment of overall costs. The air operators, no less than the manufacturers, are closely concerned with the scale of the market for this and for the developmental reasons which we discussed in Chapter 3.

Finally, Fig. 9.16 shows a direct comparison of the three aircraft, in the form of a histogram of cost per seat mile on the chosen system of routes. This provides one yardstick whereby they will be assessed by the potential operator. Some reservations must be held. The full potential economy inherent still in the subsonic jet is not easy to assess, but an estimate is shown here as a shadow behind the histogram for $M = 0.85$. The potential through further development to large-size aircraft is considerable, since the small increase in total costs per mile must be related to a substantial increase in the revenue potential on suitably chosen routes.

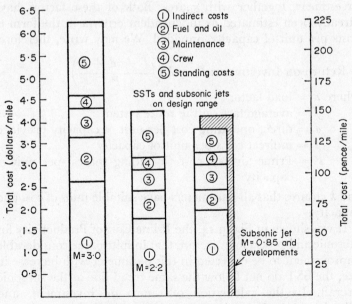

FIG. 9.16. Breakdown of Total Operating Costs

The operating cost levels are not precise, nor can they apply to all route systems or all airlines. Only an approximate assessment can be made of the probable improvements in operating techniques possible in the 1970s or of the trends in fuel prices, crew salary levels and the cost of spares. Finally, the assessment of the indirect operating cost may be open to discussion. Some improvement, shown as a reduced level of indirect costs as a percentage of total costs, has been claimed for the SST in the mid-1970s. This has been accepted since it was a notable feature of the introduction of the subsonic jets in the early 1960s. A similar tendency is thought to be most likely when the highly productive SSTs come into service a decade later.

The return on investment

A measure of economic merit which may be used to assess the value of the SST is the return on the average investment. We may consider this as the ratio of the potential profit per annum per aircraft to the prime cost per annum of the aircraft investment, together with spares. Both of these factors have already been estimated as independent criteria in the form of costs per unit of capacity provided. We may write, therefore:

$$\text{Return on Investment: } R = k \left(\frac{\lambda f - (d + i)}{P} \right)$$

where λ = load factor
f = average fare on the route system
d = direct operating cost per unit of capacity provided
i = indirect costs per unit of capacity
P = Prime aircraft cost (including spares) per unit of capacity

and k ensures that all parameters have suitable units of cost and capacity.

It was shown in Fig. 9.14, the Prime Cost of Productivity for subsonic and supersonic aircraft, that in spite of the considerable improvement to be expected in this parameter with increase in size, the SST do not follow the same trend line as the subsonic aircraft. In the calculation of return on investment, and following general practice, we can measure the average investment, and following general practice, we can measure the average investment as the average value of the aircraft following a linear depreciation over ten years to a 15 per cent residual value, allowing also 20 per cent for spares. This represents approximately 68 per cent of the first price of the aircraft. An average load factor of 55 per cent and a passenger revenue yield of 2·5p per mile were used.

Aircraft type	Block speed (mph)	Unit cost £ million	Unit operating cost per seat-mile, pence	Annual return on investment %
$M = 2·7$	1360	26	1·08	16·45
$M = 2·0$	1150	12·5	1·27	5·45
$M = 0·85$	505	6·25	0·91	44·89
$M = 0·85$	520	10·0	0·79	70·46

Note: With a 20% revenue surcharge the $M = 2·0$ project provides a 19·7% return on investment.

On the above basis our representative aircraft may be shown to provide the return on investment, when engaged in international operations, as shown in the preceding table.

The extreme sensitivity of these results to the profit margin $\lambda.f - (d + f)$ is clear from the equation given. By boldly developing the inherently high-cost $M = 3·0$ aircraft to a size great enough to depress the specific direct-operating cost to a level about 25 per cent above that of the existing subsonic jets, it is possible to achieve a return on investment which – though somewhat less – is nevertheless still very profitable and likely to be attractive to those operators who have access to the necessary capital and also the high-density routes to exploit. A reduction in the revenue yield to 2p per mile could be far more effectively absorbed by the Mach 3·0 aircraft than by smaller SSTs.

It might be difficult to recognise the economic value of the Mach 2·2 aircraft as a result of this last assessment of the comparative returns on investment, but if our earlier discussion on worldwide traffic distribution is taken as a guide we should look to find a market in the many special areas where greater flexibility and smaller capacity, combined with the immense advantage and prestige of supersonic flight, will find a ready demand.

In addition to this, a surcharge on the fare for the SST service would give the $M = 2 \cdot 2$ aircraft a greater opportunity to establish its position alongside the subsonic jet in the early years of its operation. A surcharge of the order of 20 per cent would not only greatly improve the return on investment, but would result in a lower and more workable load factor, justifying the continued operation of subsonic jets in parallel with supersonic transports. The later marks of SST would, moreover, be likely to offer improved economy through increased capacity and range just as the production aircraft will be an improvement upon the prototypes which we have considered above.

Clearly no final assessment of the economic viability of the various types of SST can yet be made, but the various methods of approach suggested above can already suggest the likely figures of merit in a relative sense, and will be used by airlines and government departments to make the final assessments when the performance data of production aircraft is available.

BIBLIOGRAPHY

Supersonic Engineering, a symposium edited by J. T. Henshaw, Heinemann, 1962

B. K. O. LUNDBERG, *Is Supersonic Aviation Compatible with the Sound Development of Civil Aviation?*, Aero. Research Institute of Sweden, 1962

R. A. E. FARNBOROUGH, *Report of the Supersonic Transport Aircraft Committee*, Mar. 1959

W. L. POLHEMUS, 'The Navigation and Control of Supersonic Transport Aircraft', *J. Inst. Navig.*, April 1962

The 14th Technical Conference of I.A.T.A., Working Papers on Supersonic Transport, Montreal, April 1961.

I. A. T. A. BOGOTA, *Commercial Supersonic Transport Projects*, Proceedings of the 20th AGM, Sept. 1964

SIR G. EDWARDS, 'Progress with the Concord Supersonic Transport', *J. Inst. Transp.*, May 1964

R. R. JAMISON and R. J. LANE, 'Engines for Supersonic Airliners', *Jnl. Roy. Aero. Soc.*, Sept. 1960

J. Morris, 'An Investigation of Lifting Effects on the Intensity of Sonic Booms', *Jnl. Roy. Aero. Soc.*, Oct. 1960

The Technical, Economic and Social Consequences of the Introduction into Commercial Service of Supersonic Transport, ICAO, Aug. 1960

R. G. Thorne, *The Influence of Some Operational Problems on Supersonic Air Transport*, 8th Anglo-American Aero. Conference, Sept. 1961

H. A. Hopkins, *Piloting Aspects of the Concorde*, Airways International, Sept.–Oct. 1964

'Supersonic Transport Aircraft, A Symposium', *Jnl. Roy. Aero. Soc.*, Feb. 1961

J. G. Borger and W. F. Hibbs, *What's an Economic S.S.T.*, Astronautics and Aeronautics, Sept. 1964

An Economic Analysis of the Supersonic Transport, Stanford Research Institute, April 1963

R. Beaufort, *Market Research – Or Crystal Ball?*, The Aeroplane and Civil Aviation News, Aug. 1962

M. B. Morgan, 'Supersonic Transport Aircraft – Promise and Problems', *Jnl. Roy. Aero. Soc.*, June 1960

Noise. Final Report of the Committee on the Problem of Noise, HMSO, Comnd. 2056, July 1963

Oklahoma City Sonic Boom Study, Deputy Administrator for SST Development, Federal Aviation Agency, Aug. 1964

Flight International. Concorde for the Airlines, 15, 22 and 29 April 1971

John H. Shaffer, FAA Administrator, SST Economics. Interavia, Feb. 1970

Sir Morien Morgan, *Impact of R and D Programmes on Economics of Future Aircraft*, Roy. Aeronut. Soc., May 1970

419

10 Airport Development and the Problem of Noise

Terminology

The indiscriminate use of the terms *airport* and *airfield* sometimes causes confusion. The term *airport* has come into usage in reference to the large air transport hub, and in the UK especially where full-time customs facilities are available. ICAO, however, still adheres to the word *aerodrome* which it defines as an area of land or water (including buildings, installations and equipment) intended for use in the arrival, departure and movement of aircraft. We find in some quarters that *aerodrome* is viewed in the 1970s as an archaic word, but we ourselves retain it. *Airfield* is used with reference to small aerodromes, generally without a hard runway or the facilities for handling transport aircraft, passengers and/or cargo.

The Prospect for the 70s

It is not the object of this chapter to explore all aspects of the design and operation of airports. This is an immense and wide-ranging subject and the reader is referred to the list of references at the end of this chapter for guidance on wider reading. For an introduction to the subject the sections on Airport Design and Operation in the *Encyclopaedia Britannica* (1974 edition), or the references hereto appended may be of value. The approach here will be to discuss the critical new factors in airport development through the 1970s in so far as they will affect the economics of air transport operations and to consider the impact of noise nuisance on the local community.

Airport development through the 1960s was accelerated by the steady increase in traffic and by the demands of jet transport for greater runway lengths, higher pavement strength and greatly increased passenger and cargo handling capacity. The arrival of the 4-engined jets especially the Boeing 707 and Douglas DC 8 family of aircraft, was the principal activating factor. A very extensive programme of airport building and development was inaugurated which in fact will continue for many years to come.

The facilities already provided form the basis of the existing airport system, but the new generation of wide-body jets is already stepping up demands in airport specification. This consists essentially in the provision of space and accommodation for handling 'theatre-sized' crowds, and in weight and dimensional criteria. In parallel with this, and to a large extent independent of aircraft types and of civil engineering work is an extensive programme of airfield approach and en route navigational aids which is in action in all parts of the world.

The fundamental design requirements of the capital city airports will not continue however to be dictated by the largest of the long-haul aircraft, since congestion is already a major factor in the costs of airport facility provision and operation, both to airport owners and to the airlines, and naturally enough congestion is caused far more by the high frequency movements of the short- and medium-haul carriers. Congestion arises not only in the air but with aircraft and service vehicles on the runway-taxiway-apron system, and in the terminal area (passengers), and in car parks and on the roads of access (motor vehicles).

No easement of the problem of congestion is to be anticipated through the 1970s. Indeed attention is being drawn in current studies to further incipient problems due to the wide-body jets because of the expected concentration of movements by these aircraft at the large traffic generating hubs. The avoidance of smaller hubs for economic reasons encourages feeder air movements to connect with the big aircraft. The concentration of such movements by smaller aircraft will increasingly cause problems in the areas of congestion and noise. This wider question of social disturbance through noise and pollution with the more frequent air movements of smaller aircraft may therefore pose greater problems than the long-haul aircraft movement pattern.

Short-term planning of airport requirements

While in the early 1970s the airport situation is dominated by aircraft and passenger congestion at the world's major airports, runway and terminal restrictions are already extracting economic penalties at the far larger number of medium-sized airports where aircraft development has overtaken the tardy planning and investment of many owners and operators. To meet this problem, in a number of countries some form of national airport development programme has been inaugurated. This has the immense advantage of eliminating the less desirable elements of competition and redundancy, but may arouse criticism in some quarters since local enterprise and insight into the special needs of a regional situation might be discouraged. National airport planning has been accepted in the USA for many years, and has worked with such effect that it has been widely proposed in the United Kingdom.

The US Airport Plan programmed by the FAA is of particular interest in this context since it is likely to be a form of organisation which will be more widely adopted in the future by states with extensive airport systems (which may have grown up from diverse origins), especially where an uncontrolled and redundant hierarchy of airports has been developed without apparent benefits to the community.

The US National Airport Programme is an annual assessment of civil airport needs for both commercial and private flying, taking into account all classes of airports. Revised assessments are based on both technological development in aircraft as well as upon projected increases in air traffic.

The plan lists facilities by location within each state, recommending new airports for the next five-year period and improvements to existing airports, including runways, taxiways, and specific airport safety requirements. The latest revision reflects various long-range requirements through 1980, considering the very large subsonic passenger jets, the supersonic transport and V/STOL, as well as the increases projected for general aviation operations. These longer range requirements emphasise the long time required to prepare master plans, acquire land, obtain financing, and begin construction of future facilities. Under the Federal Aid Airport Programme (FAAP), eligible facilities are: construction of runways, taxiways and aprons, installation of airport lighting, land acquisition for new sites, clearance of airport approaches, and the enlargement of existing airports. FAAP assistance does not include construction of terminals, hangars or aesthetic improvements. By the US Airport and Airway Development Act of 1970 financial support for the expansion of both airports and airways was to be provided by means of air passenger, freight and air operator fuel taxes.

The location and planning of airport sites and the development of facilities in all countries requires today a wide-ranging pattern of multi-disciplinary studies and research which raise formidable problems of control and integration. Fig. 10.1 shows the form of an Airport Development Programme organised in the United Kingdom by the author which embraced a Planning Region and parts of six countries. Areas of investigation included:

Population studies including forecasts up to 1985.
Investigation of industrial plans and earmarked development.
The impact of a projected new city on transport demand.
A survey of industry over the region with personal interviews to establish past use and current demands for personnel and cargo service by surface and air modes.
A study of car journey times to and from existing and proposed airport sites.
Engineering studies of existing and proposed sites.
Noise studies in regard to possible levels of air movements.
Land use in relation to NNI contours.
Meteorological studies.
Studies of air movements and ATC restraints now existing and likely in the period of study.
Operating costs and revenue estimates for the alternative sites with due regard to all sources of airport and adjacent property revenues.
Cost/benefit studies of the alternative proposals.

These areas of investigation are likely to arise in any extensively developed region in North-West Europe, North America,

Japan or Oceania. Some simplification may be introduced in less industrial zones. It is at last being realised that airport location and development is a critical factor in the planning of new regions, and if for no other reason than to minimise the nuisance to the community, the aviation facility must be correctly located at the start and the key functions correctly disposed in relation to them.

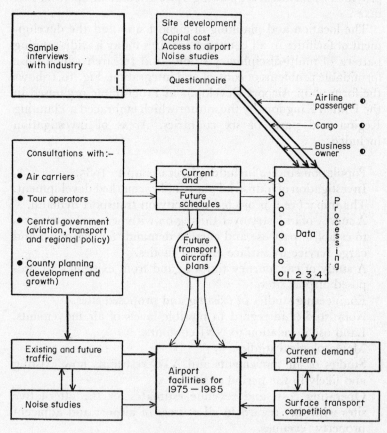

Fig. 10.1. Regional Airports Research Plan
(© Alan Stratford & Associates)

Changes in airport requirements

Studies of airport development in the short-term future are initiated by the airport owners or authorities who are under economic pressure to provide expanded facilities to meet growing traffic demands and the coming generation of transport aircraft. In the less developed countries the urge to attract air services, more especially to and from the USA and Europe, has stimulated an airport building programme on a massive scale. Nearly every major city in the world is today planning a further extensive development of its international airport (first extended probably in 1960–5 to suit the early four-engined jets), or is seeking a new site to meet the expected traffic growth of the 1970s.

According to the 1968 edition of the US National Airport Plan (FAA November 1968) more than 800 new airports are to be built in the USA in the next five years to relieve present congestion and to accommodate the forecast growth.

Covering fiscal years 1969 to 1973 inclusive, the plan recommends twenty-two airports accommodating airline aircraft and seven hundred and forty-eight new airports for general aviation including twenty-five to be used as STOL ports in the heavily congested New York–Washington corridor, and on the Los Angeles–San Francisco axis. Fig. 10.2 shows the increase in areas provided by the major world airport authorities over the past thirty years. The upper curve shows the increase in area

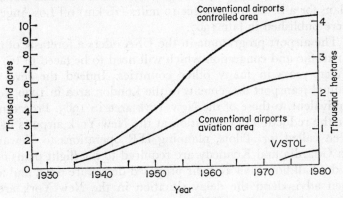

FIG. 10.2. Increase of Capital Airport Size, 1936–75

provided by the major world airport facilities including the adjacent land for aviation linked activity such as access roads, car parking and air orientated industry. The lower curve indicates the actual land in use for airport services. The extension of these curves to the right is in question.

Although runway length requirements have apparently reached a limit, parallel runway systems are now viewed with favour for new airport projects, and the acreage still grows with 15–18 thousand acres (6–8 thousand hectares) being specified for certain major airports to be inaugurated in the mid-1970s.

The Palmdale site proposed for Los Angeles requires the acquisition of 17,000 acres (68·8 km²) and the Dallas International Airport now under construction has involved planning control over 18,000 acres (72·8 km²). The scarcity and high value of land has stimulated interest in off-shore airport sites when a situation is available within an acceptable distance from the centres of industry and population. Such locations are also under active consideration because of air traffic control conflict with existing major airports near the great cities and because of increasing public pressure to reduce noise.

A study commissioned by the FAA investigated new methods of construction for off-shore airport projects. Present interest centres on airports built on piles, those built within polder dams and protected by dykes, and floating airport projects. A Lake Michigan off-shore site is favoured by Chicago; the Foulness–Maplin sands has been chosen as the site for the Third London Airport, though not without serious doubts. Plans for a Seadrome project 10 miles (16 km) off Los Angeles were published in late 1967.

The airport programme in the USA offers a foretaste of the air traffic and congestion which will need to be faced in ten to fifteen years in many other countries. Indeed the level of annual transport movements in the London area in 1970 were equivalent to those of the New York area in 1963. Procedures for the reduction of congestion at the New York airports have been called for. Pilots, planning IFR operations to Newark, La Guardia and Kennedy are required to file flight plans one and a half hours before their proposed departure time, and are then advised on the delay situation in the New York area. Times of departure (ATD) are also assigned which must be made good within fifteen minutes. Such arrangements must be expected soon in Europe.

STOL airports in the USA

The recent stimulus to establish STOL services in the USA has arisen largely through the need to ease airport congestion at the principal air centres on the East and West Coast. No less than nine STOL Airport sites are now planned in the New York area, including four in Manhattan. At present the city's only STOL facility is one runway at La Guardia Airport. FAA plans include $126 million expenditure in New York State. Washington National, Dulles, and Friendship International airports are already linked with regular STOL services offering high frequency daily services. The Los Angeles airport master-plan calls for V/STOL metroports to relieve Los Angeles International and the proposed satellite airfields at Van Nuys, Ontario and Palmdale.

These plans are an important part of the pattern of airport development for the immediate future in the USA. Relief from congestion, from noise and from regional planning obstruction will be sought by the promotion of STOL services until the next stage of the international airport programme is fully prepared or until V/STOL aircraft of an economic size are on order on a considerable scale.

Guidance material already issued by the Federal Aviation Administration (FAA) has recommended runways 1500 ft (457 m) long and 100 ft (30·5 m) wide; 60 ft (18·3 m) taxiways, pavement criteria for 150,000 lb ramp weights; and 150 ft (45·7 m) over-runs at each end. Recent trials with the 53,000 lb prop-turbine McDonnell-Douglas 188 (Breguet 941) in the USA have been successful and the steep climb-out has been favourably noted in urban areas in comparison with conventional aircraft. The trials were planned to give routings clear of airways and congested terminal areas, offering segregated and more direct tracks, and favourable flight profiles with minimum delay. The development of navigational aids is of special significance and Decca Omnitrac pictorial display equipment with data-link was put to use with good effect.

Evolution of worldwide airport systems

The growth of airport size and investment has been a natural reflection of the increase in air traffic which has been characteristic of the last 20 years of civil aviation. But the variety of air operations has encouraged many different levels of airport and airfield type with a wide range of facilities for passenger and cargo handling and for the operation of aircraft from advanced jet types to single-engined light aircraft. The simplest grass airfield now used by general aviation differs in few particulars from the city airports of the pre-war era when runways were rare, and when 500 acres sufficed to meet the requirements of the air carriers.

In the pre-war era capital city airports became important social centres, and Templehof, the Berlin Airport constructed in 1929, provided restaurants and roof-top observation areas, receiving in its first year of operation over three quarters of a million visitors. Since 1945, however, the story has been one of constant growth, investment and obsolescence.

To set the scale of world-wide airport traffic Table 10.1 indicates the passenger, cargo and aircraft movements recorded in the year 1969 for the ten airports handling more than 10 million passengers in that year.

In this Table of total air traffic only one airport appears which is outside the United States. In a listing of the five airports handling more than 100,000 *international* air transport aircraft movements in 1969, however, New York's (J. F. Kennedy) is the only North American airport in a list which includes London (Heathrow), Paris (Orly), Frankfurt (Rhein-Main), and Copenhagen (Kastrup). The US airports, as may also be seen in the table above, handle an immense number of general aviation movements.

The annual growth and the monthly distribution of the movements throughout the year is also significant, and Fig. 10.3 shows how the air transport movements as well as the total aircraft movements have flowed during the last three years in the premier airports of New York, London and Paris. Several interesting characteristics are at once to be noted. Most significant of all is the large scale of air traffic in categories other than air transport, at the US airfields. This traffic predominantly general aviation, was growing faster than any other sector of commercial aviation in the 1960s and is likely to become a dominant factor in the airport movement pattern before the end of the 1970s. We should note, however, some hesitation in the sales of light aircraft as recorded in 1969 and 1970. Note also the gradual decline in the peak monthly movements at the US airports as congestion has made itself felt.

TABLE 10.1. *Airport Traffic in 1969*

Airport	Passengers (1,000)	Freight & Mail (1,000 short tons)	Air Transport movements	General Aviation movements
Chicago-O'Hare	31,443	562	637,939	40,093
Los Angeles-International	21,310	478	411,215	147,863
New York-J. F. Kennedy	19,508	753	351,999	58,954
Atlanta	15,513	157	367,496	57,920
San Francisco-International	14,473	313	306,929	78,277
London-Heathrow	14,315	379	237,068	18,000
New York-La Guardia	11,736	59	238,459	71,880
Miami-International	10,563	269	275,443	93,059
Washington-National	10,248	83	221,831	109,727
Dallas-Love Field	10,010	57	242,700	141,967

Such a view of the principal world airports, however, gives no true impression of the world-wide airport situation. For the countries of the 117 member governments of ICAO an immense variety of airfields and strips have been provided which in some areas are only slowly being brought into line with the requirements of jet transport. In the less developed areas, as in parts

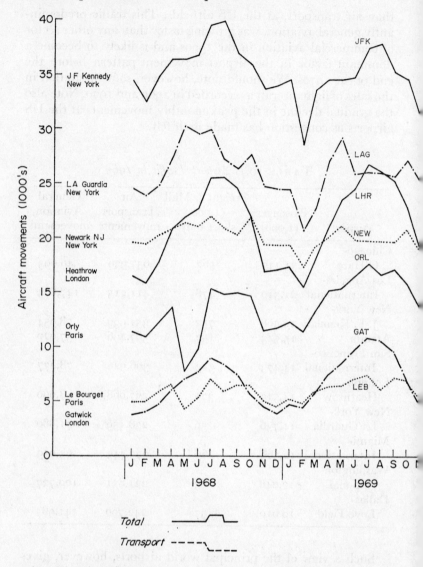

FIG. 10.3. Total Aircraft Movements 1968–71 at the Airports of New York (J. F. Kennedy; La Guardia; Newark, N.J.); London (Heathrow, Gatwick) and Paris (Orly, Le Bourget). Showing also for 1970 and 1971 the purely transport (scheduled, charter, etc.) movements for JFK, Heathrow and Gatwick (i.e. excluding light, business, military, etc.). *Sources:* Port of New York Authority, British Airports Authority, Aeroport de Paris

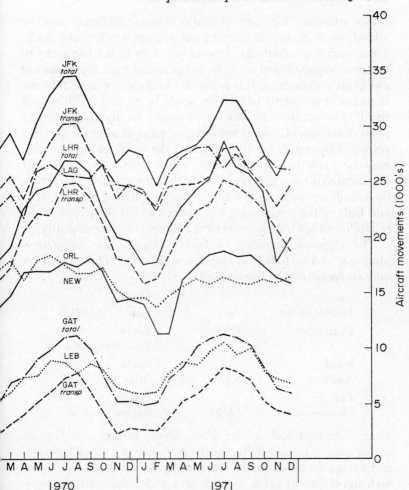

of South America, Central Africa and the Far East, the preparation of airfields is simple in the extreme, labour is cheap and the aircraft types in use have few demands upon the ground facilities beyond a level stretch of ground with reasonably unobstructed approaches. A beacon, with primitive lighting of the strip for night landing is generally all that is required for light transport aircraft operations.

Some elementary buildings for the reception of passengers and for the airfield personnel to supervise operations with a

431

tower structure for ease of radio communications, may be added when transport movements are on a scheduled basis. From such basic facilities airports move up in the hierarchy to the most sophisticated air hubs in operation near the centres of our great populations. It is primarily in these key areas that the immense investments have been made in ground facilities and the infra-structure of aids for air transport. In the less developed parts of the world, which are often in great need of the services provided by organised air transport, the facilities and the aids may be inadequately provided. When money is scarce and technical skills are not available within the country there may be a tendency to provide a fine terminal building and runway, and little of the engineering equipment which the security and reliability of air transport services require far more urgently.

The regional divisions of ICAO provide air navigation planning and technical advice for such areas. These divisions may conveniently be listed as follows:

Africa–Indian Ocean	AFI	Middle East	MID
Caribbean	CAR	South East Asia	SEA
South America	SAM	North Atlantic	NAT
Europe Mediterranean	EUM	Pacific Region	PAC

Many countries such as the USA, Great Britain and France with a sense of responsibility for the provision of ground facilities and navigational aids make loans and give free financial aid for such development often as part of a wider national aid programme in the undeveloped world.

Sources of finance

For airports in current operation the possible sources of capital are clearly: 1. Their own self-generated funds. 2. Government or local authority (municipality) grants or loans. 3. Private loans which may be raised domestically or on the international market.

While the most desirable situation is that of creating adequate reserves for development, it is rare indeed for major projects to be financed internally by a favourable cash flow. The scale of work generally required for limited development, such as the expansion of smaller facilities, car parks, fire stations and the replacement of operating equipment, should normally be met from revenues, subject always to a favourable traffic development and presuming adequate prime facilities (e.g. runways, taxiways, aprons, terminals, car parks, and navigational aids).

Airport revenue arises from four principal groups of sources:

1. *Airside Revenue*
   Aircraft fuel sales
   Landing and parking fees
   Handling and apron services
   Hangar rents and charges

2. *Terminal Revenue*
   Desk and shop concessions
   Bonded stores revenue
   Passenger taxes
   Restaurant profits

3. *Car Park and Services*
   Car park revenue
   Garage services
   Car hire

4. *Cargo Areas and Industrial Rentals*

The expansion of such revenues to maximise their value to the airport is a principal task of airport management. Rent reviews will always be an important means of revenue increase.

Clearly the control of costs is no less critical and methods for the minimising of running costs, for reassessing labour requirements, and for acquiring more cost-effective equipment as traffic develops, will always be under the review of an alert management. Methods for the comparison of airport costs are valuable, and the figures circulated by the Airport Operators Council International are commended. Systems of uniform accounting moreover have been developed. These allow further analysis and useful comparative allocation of costs and revenues for airport financial control.

Government or local authority grants or loans

Sources of international loans exist in the USA, UK, West Germany, and France; the basis of these is generally political or economic. In the United Kingdom, the Overseas Development Administration (Foreign and Commonwealth Office) advises the relevant governments on the allocation of funds for airport development in British Commonwealth territories. The Agency for International Development in Washington serves a comparable purpose in promoting US influence within undeveloped countries overseas. In Ottawa the Canadian International Development Agency is also active.

The US Airport and Airway Development Act of 1970 created revenue sources for the expansion of the US national airport and airways system. Federal funds are provided but these are based on the financial support from the users of such facilities by means of passenger, freight and fuel taxes.

In the United Kingdom the ownership of airports is in many hands. The British Airports Authority, the Civil Aviation Authority (taking over from the DTI), Local Authorities and Private Companies are the respective owners of the various civil airfields in the country. Cases of joint use with the Ministry of Defence also exist. The British Airports Authority set up by the Airports Authority Act of 1965 owns five UK airports and possesses powers for capital raising which are defined and revised from time to time by Parliament. The UK municipalities were in 1970 restricted in their loan powers by instructions from the DTI which has defined the key projects which are reserved for central Government loan sanction.

In the development report for Luton Airport, 1969, the Consultants recommended that for the project envisaged, which required a total capital investment of £16·5 million ($39·5 m), it would be desirable to consider establishing a separate corporation or statutory body issuing stock under the guarantee of the Luton Corporation and as a separate investment operation. Such schemes have as yet found little support in the United Kingdom.

Private loans

Such loans have been raised largely in the USA in recent years. These have been raised as:

General City Obligation Bonds   Widely used for financing US City Airports, and based on the full tax income of the Authority concerned.

Revenue Bonds of a Port Authority or Airport Based, as at Chicago, on the airline revenue at the airport and guaranteed use of facilities for a period of years.

Special Facility Bonds More restricted in range and secured against rental from airlines and others for the special facility to be provided.

Such loan schemes are critically dependent upon a soundly based domestic airline industry, which is as yet rarely found outside the USA. For this reason private loans have not yet risen to significance outside the USA. The references given offer a fuller exposition of the US situation.

Airport design standards

The standards required for the design of airports have important economic influences upon the airport operation itself and upon the operator of transport aircraft. The increasing sophistication of the requirements introduce costs which must be met in the first instance by the airport authority and will in most cases be passed on in the form of increased landing fees/or other charges to the airport users. Longer runways, wider taxiways, increased radius of turn-off fillets, increased apron areas, car parking extension and multi-story schemes, improved lighting, higher technical standards of the instrument landing aids, new terminals and access roads – all such developments incur high levels of capital expenditure. To plan the effective amortisation of such costs in the light of the forecast growth in airport traffic requires considerable experience in airport engineering, economics and project management. It is our object here to discuss the factors which contribute to the effective economic control and evolution of the airport. The basic categorisation of civil transport airports will first of all be considered.

Categorisation of airports

Over twenty years of experience has enabled ICAO to establish standards of operating practice for the design and layout of airports and runway systems. These are incorporated in Annexe

14 to the Convention on International Civil Aviation. These requirements have been incorporated in the airport licensing and air navigational regulations of most member Governments of ICAO.

The codes of practice relate to runway, taxiway and apron layouts, navigational and airfield approach aids, lighting and obstruction marking. Noise standards are to be incorporated in a farther Annexe. IATA, with the extensive experience of its airline members in operations from airfields in all parts of the world has also provided extensive guidance material for the airport designer, developer and operator. These latter recommendations have, of course, different objectives and are not mandatory. The most relevant documents are listed in the references given at the end of this chapter. ICAO has categorised airports in respect to the overall length of the main runway. This parameter, having a reasonably clear relationship to the size, weight and flight safety standards required for the largest aircraft able to make economic use of the airport, and hence to the likely passenger and cargo loads associated, is used to define a code which determines other major design requirements (see Table 10.2).

TABLE 10.2. *ICAO Aerodrome Classification*

Code	Runways Basic Length		
A	2100	m	(7000ft) and over
B	1500–2100	m	(5000ft–7000ft)
C	900–1500	m	(3000ft–5000ft)
D	750–900	m	(2500ft–3000ft)
E	600–750	m	(2000ft–2500ft)

The principal factors so determined are:

Taxiway width
Runway Gradients. Average and Local Slopes
Width of Overall Strip
Transitional Slopes for Obstruction Clearance
Approach Surface Slopes. Instrument Runway and Other
  Runways
Take-Off Surface Slopes
Navigational and Approach Aids

Obstruction Marking and Lighting
Runway and Taxiway Lighting.

For a full exposition of all requirements in relation to the Airport Category, Annexe 14 of the ICAO Convention should be inspected. In the UK the relevent document is the Licensing of Aerodromes (CAP 168) published by HMSO. This follows very closely the ICAO code and standards but minor differences have to be considered.

The classification of aerodromes in France

The classification of aerodromes in France is based on functional considerations, and relates to the nature of the facilities which must be provided to cater for the types of aircraft which frequent and determine the specification of the aerodrome. This classification is defined by the ordinances of the Code de L'Aviation Civile (Sept. 1959). These may be summarised as follows:

Category A Aerodromes destined for the use of long-haul air services (2100–3000 m).

" *B* Aerodromes to be used for medium-haul aircraft and for certain services by long-haul aircraft (1500–2100 m).

" *C 1.* Aerodromes destined for short-haul and for limited medium- and long-haul operations (900–1500 m).

2. For General Aviation (900–1500 m)

" *D* Aerodromes to be used for training, sports flying and tourism, as well as for some short-haul services (390–900 m).

All such lengths need to be corrected for altitude, temperature and gradient.

This more pragmatic approach to the definition of airfield categories may indicate less precision in the specification of requirements but offers greater flexibility in categorisation and in development. For example, an aerodrome in Category A must in practice be able to provide a runway of at least 2500 m and the site must be capable of permitting an extension in due course to 3000 m. For this category, in certain situations a potential for extension to 3500 m may need to be demonstrated.

Runway categorisation

Runways may further be categorised as
* Non-Instrument Runways, intended for the operation of aircraft using visual approach procedures, and
** Precision Approach Runways, intended for the operation of aircraft using visual and non-visual (instrument) aids providing guidance in both pitch and azimuth (yaw) adequate for a straight-in approach.

Instrument Runways are divided further into three major categories defining the minimum meteorological conditions under which safe landings may be attempted.

Category I   Intended for operations down to 60 metres (200 feet) decision height and down to an RVR of the order of 800 metres (2600 feet).

Category II   Intended for operations down to 30 metres (100 feet) decision height and down to an RVR of the order of 400 metres (1200 feet).

Category III   *A* Intended for operations down to an RVR of the order of 200 metres (700 feet).

   B Intended for operations down to an RVR of the order of 50 metres (150 feet).

   C Intended for operations without reliance on external visual reference.

N.B. RVR denotes Runway Visual Range.

Airport planning

For the layout of the Airport Master Plan critical minimum dimensions need to be specified and these form the basis of the ground plan arrangements within the defined requirements of the critical aviation and ancillary demand functions.

In our own work we define these functions as:

I. Terminal buildings

Reception	Catering	Other Services
Departures	Other Concessions	Airport Management
Arrivals	Customs	{Airport Maintenance
{Airline	Concourse	and Servicing
{Functions		ATC and Control Tower

II. Aircraft services

Aircraft Stands	Fuel Farm
Aircraft servicing/Supply	{Air Taxi, Club and other
{Hangars and Engineering	{Flying Services
{Services	Meteorological Services

III. Airport services

Air Cargo Zone	Electrical Supply
Freight Customs	Heating Plant
Industrial Zone	Police and Security
Car Parking	Fire Fighting
Access Roads	

Depending upon the category of airport under consideration the above groupings would be refined or cut down so that only the relevant factors apply in the detail required by the project.

In the preparation of the Master Plan a very thorough engineering exercise is called for involving the combined efforts of many disciplines, including specialist engineers, economists, accountants, regional planners, air transport specialists, and systems analysts. Scientists in fields as diverse as noise physics, meteorology, soil mechanics, air traffic control and sociology may be involved. The complexity of the problems may be comprehended by a study of Fig. 10.4 which sets out in some detail a work plan for an integrated airport study which was schemed by the author and his associates for an international project.

The simplified flow chart there shown demonstrates the factors which need to be considered in airport planning and development. Its content will, of course, be modified by the nature of specific requirements: a small extension to an existing runway, or a forecast of future traffic does not require the same amount of work and effort as a complete locational and construction study for an international airport. The availability of comprehensive experience is, nevertheless, essential for even the smaller tasks because it is necessary to study carefully all the

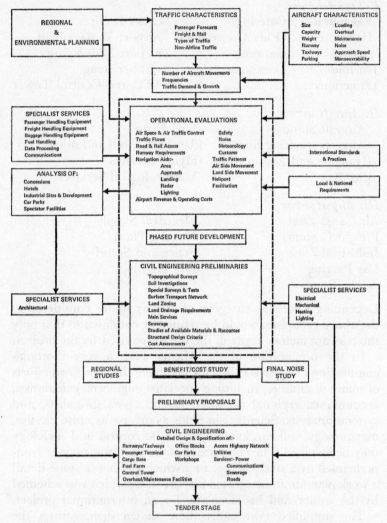

FIG. 10.4. The Comprehensive Approach to Airport Planning
(© Alan Stratford & Associates)

inter-related factors in aviation. Due to the rapid rate of growth
of air transport, any omissions or underestimates of individual
factors can have cumulative effects on the overall operation of
an airport. There is, therefore, no satisfactory alternative to the
comprehensive approach.

Airport economics and planning

One essential part of the multi-disciplinary approach to airport planning, as illustrated in Fig. 10.4, is the assessment of the air traffic potential in its various forms such as passengers (business and tourist) freight and mail. It is essential to bring together a team with extensive experience in this field of work, and an effective air transport group must keep in touch with current and future developments, preferably by acting as professional Consultants in the Air Transport field.

At an early stage there must be fed into the studies the requirements arising in the particular airport situation: these may include movements of supersonic transport, the new generation of wide-body jets, the many types of conventional large and small transports, and where called for, executive, private or military aircraft. Provision for adjacent sites for Vertical Take-Off and Landing aircraft in the late 1970s and an analysis of the long-term competition from air cushion craft (Hovercraft) or from advanced passenger trains (APT) may become part of such a study. Other forms of transport are now often key factors in the development of air services.

Experience in Hydrofoil, Hovercraft and Container ship economics may need to be brought into play in air transport projects in Western Europe when over-water traffic development is significant.

Two further aspects of airport economics may strongly affect major decisions on airport planning and the detailed specification of the project. These are air cargo development and the potential for industrial activity in the vicinity of the airport itself.

While air traffic and aircraft characteristics, especially in the future decades, are essential factors, studies concerned with road traffic and airport terminal access have in many projects a major contribution to make. The increasing scale of recent airport schemes, and expansion of long-established sites near urban and industrial areas, has emphasised regional and environmental planning. Noise problems have created serious difficulty in most recent major airport studies, and the relevant specialists need to keep in touch with aircraft and engine manufacturers with particular regard to aircraft-engine noise / engine thrust characteristics.

441

Operational evaluations are noted in the foregoing chart as central to the phased development of the airport plan. These include many studies specific to the needs of an individual project.

These assessments are brought together with the civil engineering evaluations for the final analysis of benefit and cost. The comparison of alternative projects and investment plans should be based on discounted cash flows.

Civil engineering

The growth of air transport during the last twenty years has created a continuing and increasing demand for ancillary construction work on and in the immediate vicinity of the larger airports. There is a need for access roads within the airport which create their attendant traffic problems. Adjacent public roads must be designed to cater for an increasing car owning population as well as the increasing traffic in service vehicles and cargo to the airport itself. Car parking for passengers as well as airport staff and visitors has become a problem in every major airport. Land values and space available will determine whether open parking, multi-storey or off-airport private venture parking arrangements are optimum, and how their distribution will effect the airport economy.

Hotel accommodation for transit passengers and short-term businessmen and tourists must also be taken into consideration in overall planning. Tourism has now become a major factor in the economy of all countries, both large and small, and this is evidenced by the increasing investments in the construction and operation of hotels adjacent to airports by airport authorities and the airlines, as well as by private concerns. The success of such hotels depends to a large extent on their close integration into the airport complex and, in turn, the economic viability of the airport itself is greatly increased by such amenities. Tourism development is discussed in more detail in Chapter 4.

All too often such planning has been done piecemeal over a number of years, with the attendant disadvantages of greatly increased capital cost, and compromise solutions have to be found which fail to achieve the standards which would have been possible had skilled airport planners and engineers been engaged at an earlier stage of the project.

Nearly every major airport at the present time is an example of insufficient vision in achieving at an earlier date a more flexible plan at less cost. In many cases, the main runway/taxiway system may need to be realigned and the airport terminal itself abandoned, requiring a new location to be found. The passenger and aircraft services must be closely integrated with the airport management and other specialised services.

In Chapter 6 will be found a discussion of air cargo terminal layout, the functions of the cargo terminal, uses of automation and computer control of air cargo in the terminal. Loading studies on the apron and aspects of the London Airport (Heathrow) EDP scheme are also considered.

Airports for aircraft in the new categories

It was shown in Table 4.2 that the new generation of widebody jet aircraft possess certain characteristics which are more demanding than those of their predecessors. These include aircraft length and overall wheel base, wing span and wheel track, turning radius with its effect on runway-taxiway fillet design, and height of the cabin floor with its demand for direct-access specialised loading ramps. Greatly increased apron areas and taxiway clearances are required. It is noteworthy that runway length and strength has not been a critical factor in the introduction of these aircraft, whose predecessors set demands never likely to be exceeded.

A higher degree of compactness has been achieved with succeeding generations of jet aircraft. However we are not in sight of the limit of aircraft size and the many favourable economic factors due to size make it clear that very considerable farther increases are likely through the 1970s.

Justifying the cost of airport development

No major airport development can be assessed without a rigorous analysis of the cost involved and the timing of the

443

expenditure in relation to the revenue earning potential of the project. Thus the costs of the civil works, the land required, and the equipment must be ascertained, to the degree of accuracy required by the nature of the study, and the phasing must be determined in relation to the need for increased capacity and facilities.

A planned programme on the lines of Fig. 10.5 will therefore need to be drawn up which will be subject to revision and refinement as a fuller appreciation of the project and its traffic generating effects become more fully understood and enumerated. In the Figure the quarterly capital costs are shown for a UK Civil Airport planned by the author's firm in 1970/71.

Proposed capital expenditure in each quarter is shown. Quarterly depreciation sums were computed with land written off over 40 years, civil works over 20 years and equipment over 10 years. Interest in practice becomes a major item at current rates of 8 to 10 per cent.

The cost of any development are significant only in relation to the capital available and the revenues which are likely to accrue. The reader is referred to the literature for a detailed considera-

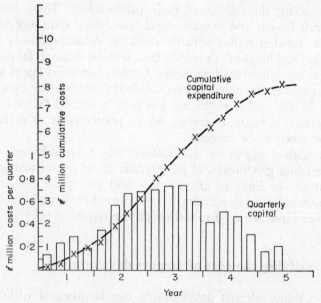

FIG. 10.5. Airport Capital Costs

tion of the methods in use for the appraisal of the optimum project. We must here, however, re-emphasise the need, already noted in relation to aircraft projects, for a proper assessment of demand and for adequate operational evaluations. Clearly if the traffic growth is self-evident and no doubts exist with regard to the next stage of a well formulated development plan, then the problems should be few. A constantly up-dated airport traffic forecast is, however, the essential first stage and this requires an analysis of the types of air passengers by reason of the journey (business, private or holiday), origin and destination information, and details of freight, mail and aircraft movements. In recent studies undertaken by specialist economists the tendency has been to consider air travellers, now and in future, as the natural outcome of an economic process which stems from gross national product and the distribution of population and income in the particular country, with a total disregard for some of the other most significant factors in the choice of air as a mode of transport.

Foremost among the factors at work are the financial and technical resources within the country, the availability of operational skills in air transport, and the initiative among the air carriers themselves to acquire aircraft and to promote air services on the routes concerned.

Airfield and route facilities must be provided and paid for, and services must be offered with a high standard of proficiency but at a frequency and fare which will meet the demand at the time. Moreover, and very significantly, the aircraft which would be required to operate the service must be of a type and size which can expect to pay a reasonable dividend to the operator – if not at once, then certainly within a short period of years – when the fares are set at the level approved by the licensing authority and acceptable to an adequate public. These conditions are not always easy to meet, as was shown in earlier chapters when aircraft size was shown to be a critical factor in unit operating costs and fare levels. Indeed in the domestic United Kingdom these viable conditions can scarcely be met at all except on the key traffic routes; in the USA on the routes of the local service operators they can be met only with a subsidy. This does not, however, make the necessity for a full assessment of all traffic growth in the airport context any less real, but it means that the economic basis for growth must be

445

established in terms far more precise than those employed in some academic methods for the economic assessment of industrial projects.

Thus the growth of air traffic in a given airport situation is dependent upon a wide range of factors which need to be carefully evaluated in order to determine the most cost-effective plan for promotion. Some recent assessments of airport planning problems are here discussed with indications as to the validity of the methods used.

Studies of air terminal location

Many studies have been undertaken on the optimum location of airport terminals, and Adib Kanafani at the University of California has formulated particular methods developed from other transport fields. Total feasibility requires a solution of a number of component problems. Using simple one-dimensional assumptions of one airport linked to one terminal with a certain percentage of travellers going direct from point of origin to the airport, he showed that the location of the off-airport terminal need not always be in the city centre, and 'down-town' terminals became optimal only when certain limited trip density and city size relationships can be shown to exist. Such studies show the sensitivity of total travel cost to terminal location. A network approach was also formulated as a mathematical programme which with simplification leads to a simple linear programme. The network formulation is likely to lead to more useful solutions of the problem since actual data can be introduced more realistically, however the need for simplification has to date reduced the value of such work and research is required if multi-airport and terminal problems are to be solved. The author takes the view that this important work still requires considerable development and will not for ten years be readily useful to the metropolitan planner so tightly hedged with the pragmatic restrictions to his options.

Airport accessibility studies

These have also become an important part of airport locational work where new airport sites are being sought or developments on existing airports are being subjected to close cost-benefit examination. Accessibility, may be measured as the reciprocal of the weighted average total journey time for the many trips (road and rail) to and from airport terminal areas, and for the many kinds of passengers, cargo and airport worker who may use the particular site. We must note the different scales of values which may be set on the journey time by the different groups of airport users, and add that in numerical analysis care must be taken to ensure that an increase in user journeys does not necessarily suggest a decrease in accessibility to the individual, although congestion on a restricted road network will decrease accessibility. Airport accessibility from the air is also of great economic significance.

Richard de Neufville and Edward Mierzejewski of MIT studied the cost-effectiveness of airport access modes for 'old' and 'new' type cities. They assumed that the density of a city not only affects the amount of traffic but also the cost of establishing new systems. They defined the density D of a city as a negative exponential of distance x, evolving $D = Ae^{-bx}$ allowing total costs to be calculated. In considering the various modes of access, high speed rail, busway (on separated tracks), VTOL aircraft (helicopters), conventional bus, taxi, limousine (microbus), motor car and express auto (on separate tracks), the speed and cost of each were computed for peak and off-peak times. Various levels of traffic volume, airport distances and city types were used to calculate optium modes for travellers with and without motor cars. The authors emphasised the importance of those to whom a car is not available, since it includes the majority of non-residents of any city.

Overall regions of dominance for the transport modes were established, a principal presentation being the value of time plotted against distance for the variable modes in the new and the old cities for those with and without an automobile. In a more developed form the analysis could be used to marked effect in establishing the overall value of the different modes for airport development and surface transportation planning.

Among recent theoretical studies of special value in the field of airport access, K. R. Sealy and H. Armstrong carried forward work on airport location theory by presenting a method allowing the weighting of access time by the population with a propensity for air travel. This study was part of the work of Alan

447

Stratford and Associates on airport development for the South Hampshire Plan (1970). Data requirements for such an analysis are severe and, as is generally the case, the data available was a severe constraint. This was true of the future road networks and populations (1980) and their future distribution through the region. Simplification of road networks and populations allowed a matrix to be produced which could be handled by the computer available. Nodes were defined at all junctions on the A and B graded road systems, at all airport sites under review and at all road entrances to the study region. Links were the motorways and A and B roads connecting nodes in the region. Rail links were not considered. To make the population location element amenable to analysis, 'catchment areas' for each link were established. Within each such area all points are closer in time to that link than to any other, using all roads as channels of movement. Road travel times in off-peak hours were used for the various standards of roads in the period (1975–80) under consideration. These were based on discussion with the Road Research Laboratory at Crowthorne, Berks.

A population of potential air users was established in order to weight the links, and enumeration district data (as provided by the UK census) was used. Socio-economic factors, affecting the propensity to fly, were introduced from Urban and Rural district data of lesser detail than the population itself but thought to be adequate in an expanding population situation. Use was made of the Roskill Commission findings and ASA reports and surveys with respect to the propensity to fly on business trips (see Bibiliography). For potential non-business air users data from the Family Expenditure Survey of 1966 was used. By combination, a road travel time and air-user population was established for each link.

It was realised that there might still be an uneven population distribution within the catchment area. To overcome such irregularity, each link was considered directionally whereby the weighting for movement in each direction could be made. Conclusions from this work are illustrated in Fig. 10.6. It should be noted (1) that urban congestion as represented in the analysis by the road speeds, influences the weighting of the links and moves the points of maximum accessibility well away from the main centres, and (2) that the population weighting makes city peripheries more accessible since these are the residential areas

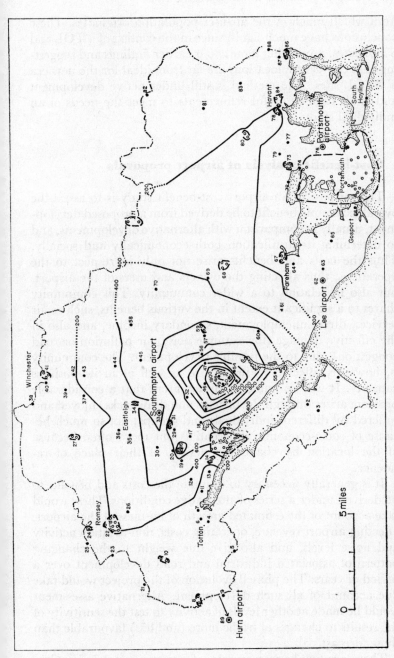

FIG. 10.6. Airport Access, Solent Region: Chart of Node Accessibility Surfaces. The black dots or ringed areas are the nodal points; the heavy figures 200 to 2,000 define contours in millions of accessibility units

from which much of the air-user population originates. These conclusions have much significance in the context of VTOL and STOL sites, supporting some of our earlier findings and suggesting that city centre locations are far from ideal for the new era V/STOL sites. The method is still under active development and lends itself to useful refinements to meet the needs of an individual study.

Cost-benefit analysis of airport proposals

The purpose of an airport cost-benefit study is to assess the overall economic benefit to be derived from a proposed development, usually in comparison with alternative developments, and to determine its justification both economically and socially. Thus the costs and benefits arise not only in respect to the operations, thus affecting the owners and users of the airport, but also in relation to a wider community. This community shares to a significant extent in the various benefits, such as air services, direct unemployment, secondary income, and also in the effective damage (for example noise, air pollution or road congestion), due to the possible development. The community is, however, affected in its private as well as in its business capacity. It will be immediately apparent that a considerable problem arises through the benefits and drawbacks enjoyed and suffered by different individuals and groups; not so much because of socio-economic differentials but more often because of the location by chance or design, of their place of residence.

It is generally necessary to estimate the costs and benefits to be derived under a series of alternative conditions. These would take account of the estimated growth of business at the airport, affecting airport revenue, operating costs, non-aviation activity and noise levels, and also give due weight to the changing pattern of associated industrial and road development over a period of years. The phased evolution of the project would take due account of all such development. Alternative assessment would be made at other levels of activity to test the sensitivity of the results to changes of traffic more (and less) favourable than those forecast.

There are two basic categories of persons and organisations

(namely the users and non-users), which need to be considered as directly affected by an airport development. Other secondary effects may also be important.

Users Airports affect public authorities, firms and private persons and there is therefore a public and a private sector. The public sector includes the airport owners and airline management, tour operators and other providers of services at the airport for passengers and cargo shippers. The private sector includes the individual air passenger and the cargo shipper.

Non-users This covers a very wide sector of the population which may be affected in employment, business and social life by the activity through the airport. Non-users of the airport, though more remote from its activity, may none the less be very convinced that they would be benefited or handicapped by the development.

Secondary effects

Apart from the above direct effects, changes in the use of one facility may affect the utilisation of other facilities in the same field. For example, the development of one airport whereby jet aircraft may be handled with greater economy, will discourage the use of another airport. Many instances of this will come to mind in the UK and in the USA, which have caused major diversions of traffic from less well-sited airfields. A further secondary effect will occur as a result of the impact of various stages of airport development upon local employment and income, and the effect of the spending of this income in the local area. This is known as the multiplier effect.

The influence of transport development upon regional development has generally been omitted in these studies: it was not considered by Beesley and Foster in the M. 1 Motorway and the Victoria Line Rail studies. The multiplier effect analysed at length by the Port of New York Authority for the fifth New York airport suggests that this is a considerable issue. The question remains whether we can yet quantify the effects for any area with adequate precision. In general this has been difficult to do because of lack of data and the high cost of acquiring it. Bearing these points in mind, it is essential to prepare draft schemes at a very early stage of a cost-benefit study so that we can take stock of the questions and data it pre-supposes, and define the required survey plans and costs for carrying them out.

Scheme for a cost-benefit airport study

As we approach the most cost-effective survey plan, a frame-work may be built up with three main groups of transactions which may yet need to be pruned quite drastically as the work proceeds because of the sheer scale of the computations. We need to bear constantly in mind the relation between the work load (staff and cost) and the ensuing accuracy of the acquired data. We believe that a comparative answer is the most valuable outcome of the methods, and the degree of accuracy to be achieved would allow us to disregard differences of less than 5–8 per cent. A discount cash flow method over the selected period will probably be used, touching those cost/benefit items which show a differential value and which are amenable to evaluation.

The Roskill Commission

It is important to establish the significance of the Roskill Commission in the progress of airport development and cost-benefit technique since its activity and its findings have drawn about it an aura of mysticism which is in danger of destroying much of the invaluable work. That the recommendations of the Commission were not acceptable to the Government of the day nor to a large body of public opinion, should not alter the fact that the methods of cost-benefit analysis on which the Commission's research team based their quantitative assessments were highly developed in their three-year programme, and provided certain conclusive answers within the framework of their assumptions. Unfortunately some of these were extremely tenuous, and the recommendations went beyond the conclusions of the cost-benefit studies. It is essential to recognise in any analysis of this kind the critical nature of the assumptions, and those made by Roskill were dominant factors. There was too limited an analysis concerning the development of other airports in the South-East Region, e.g. Luton, Stansted, Southend, and Gatwick, and a nearly total disregard of the overall development of airports through the UK.

Many assumptions critical of the conclusions were challenged in public enquiry and stood up well to this, but others were modified in the final reports. Important contibutions were made in the areas of traffic forecasting, studies of airport capacity, assessments of journey costs, the value of time, and the costing of noise. But very inadequate regional planning investigations were conducted. This was apparent at all stages of the public enquiry, and gave subsequent opportunity to the well-organised opposition parties favourable to remote coastal sites to press home their arguments, for the most part not based on factual data, that inland sites were unduly damaging to the environment. This also presented the opportunity for a minority report which emasculated the recommendations.

A quite fundamental weakness in the work of the Commission was the tacit assumption throughout that knowledge and experience of air transport and airport operation, as well as regional planning, were secondary factors compared with the disciplines of economics and cost-benefit which are as yet raw and at best only partly disciplined. Cross-examination is indeed not an adequate replacement for knowledge and experience. It is also far more costly to bring to bear on any problem. There is little doubt that the aeronautical aspects of airport siting (excluding Air Traffic Control which was extensively, but conservatively studied), were inadequately covered. Regional planning was not in fact introduced quantitatively. The expenditure of time and money was lavish and very comparable results could have been achieved using simplified methods and procedures. In any case the overall cost of the selection process has never been assessed since the team of contending lawyers, witnesses, study groups and interested parties have not all divulged their scale of activity. It is most likely that the overall cost exceeded twice the total costs incurred by the Commission which was reported to be over £1 million. It seems unlikely that any such airport exercise will ever be performed again. ... indeed the Government Report on the Foulness/Maplin sites published in April 1972 uses a very simplified method of gauging the relative factors of cost and benefit. The work plan of the Roskill Commission was as follows:

Stage 1. The public hearings and consideration of preliminary

453

written and oral evidence. First research studies and determination of a short list of sites:
Thurleigh (Bedford), Cublington (Wing), Nuthampstead, Foulness (Essex).

Stage 2. The local public hearings at the selected short-listed site areas. Special reference given to Airport Layout, Runway alignment, Airport Siting, Noise and Disturbance, Airport Employment and Surface Access.

Stage 3. To make a comprehensive comparison of the costs and benefits relevant to each of the four short-listed sites and to assure the timing of the need for a Third London Airport. Specially commissioned studies were put in hand.

Stage 4. A detailed consideration was taken of all Stage 3 material from the Commission's own technical team and from outside work, and differences identified.

Stage 5. Public hearings to test the validity of all the research studies and to finalise the assessments of the Commission.

The programme for the cost/benefit analysis comprised three main parts: 1. The identification of the relevant factors; 2. The quantitative measurement of their significance; 3. The evaluation in financial terms of all measurable factors, and their aggregation as costs or benefits.

No new principles were evoked and it was clearly established that things cost what one has to pay for them, and benefits may be assumed to be worth at least what one is prepared to pay for them. 'The cost attaching to some non-material factor, such as the imposition of noise on a previously quiet area, may be assumed to be equivalent to the sum of money which might be subscribed to preserve the initial state of affairs.'

Roskill Commission. *Papers and Proceedings*, Vol vii.

The evaluation of the cost or nuisance from aircraft noise was given careful consideration by the Commission's evaluation team. The method used again fairly established long agreed principles, and the loss of damage was assessed under three headings: (a) Fall in freehold property values; (b) Additional disturbance costs, principally removal expenses in transferring to quieter areas: (c) Loss of the 'Consumer Surplus' whose future enjoyment is put in jeopardy.

An example from the USA

As an example of recent work in the USA on airport development in an adverse environmental situation we have chosen the problem of Logan Airport, Boston.

A system Engineering Project of MIT in 1968 studied the Seaport and Airport development at Boston and sought an overall solution for the optimum location of facilities. Our present interest lies in the analysis of the problem of Logan Airport, which lies within four miles from the commercial, population, and industrial centres of Boston and yet is remote in terms of road access time even at off-peak periods. One study had predicted a peak hour journey time to the airport from the city centre of between 60 and 70 minutes by 1980. The Project Bosphorus report of MIT noted that . . . 'proximity of the airport in terms of audibility, however, cannot be denied'! In an attempt to meet the overall objectives of a fully acceptable urban development which sought concurrently reasonable economic, technical and sociological solutions, a carefully ordered priority list of aims was established. This in the author's view, was well conceived and is of wider application and interest.

1. The prospect must spring from widespread need; it must reflect the desires of a large segment of the population. It would also be desirable that such a need was felt by the physical neighbours of transportation facilities.

2. Its service must be relevant to people as individuals both to the shipper a thousand miles away and the citizen whose back yard it passes.

3. It should promote positive social interaction and be a source of pride to the community.

4. It should be directed not only at the problems for which it was originally intended, but also at the problems of its immediate surroundings.

5. If some citizens fall victim to severely adverse affects, they must be compensated. This may involve possible recompense spelled out in the design. In the eyes of those affected a fair repayment must be achieved.

6. There must be preservation of the natural resources of air, water, and land, and the possibility of additional use of these resources for the community.

455

7. The impact of the design upon the city during construction must be fully explained and as innocuous as possible.

While the objectives may be to some extent idealistic, they provide an important assessment for present thinking on the vexed question of airport development criteria. In the study in question they were to a considerable extent achieved. Using techniques, such as we have discussed earlier in this chapter and introducing results from other studies by Boeing on STOL aircraft, and by SARC on inter-city passenger travel, a computer model was determined which defined a dynamic transport system for airport and seaport demand and optimum location. A principal conclusion was that a Jet port would be most effectively sited at Brewster with a high speed link, and with passenger and cargo handling facilities retained in a part of the existing Logan site. Improved shipping facilities with 20 berths could be built on the southern edge of the Logan site. We would not wish to argue here with the various input data which so powerfully affect the output from such studies. The economic viability of STOL vehicles were favourably interpreted in relation to known CTOL evolution, and the evaluation of noise was inevitably arbitrary. Probably the assessment of the value of time needs refinement and the costing of civil works and of handling procedures might well be in error to some extent but the approach and methodology is invaluable. Airline and airport executives will argue for many months on the practicality of Jet port facilities on remote sites (remote though rapidly interconnected) with centralised passenger handling facilities. The answer can only lie in the most thorough analysis of costs based on the soundest market assessment that can be made.

The cost of congestion and delay

We have already noted that the cost of congestion in the air and on the ground may rise very considerably when short-haul operations are based on large international airports. Due to the increase in block times and reduced productivity of the aircraft, the direct operating cost per mile flown rises and higher indirect costs must be allocated to each completed flight schedule. Estimates show that an average delay of 15 minutes per flight may raise doc by 39 per cent on 200 statute mile sectors and by 21 per cent on 400 mile sectors. Since on US domestic flights 50 per cent of passengers (1969–70) travelled less than 500 miles and 30 per cent travelled less than 300 miles predominantly on single sector flights we can recognise at once the scale of diseconomy which is already arising. The FAA have estimated the cost of wasted fuel due to this cause alone in the USA in 1970 to be $140 million. The loss of potential revenues which will be caused by airport saturation must become even more severe since remedial action can be taken only slowly, and cannot be effective immediately. The overall annual loss has been estimated to exceed $500 million in the USA by the mid-1970s with little hope of alleviation in this time scale.

The principal areas of potential congestion and delay are:
1. ATC congestion in the terminal control area.
2. Runway approach separation due to the proximity of aircraft of varying approach speeds in IMC.
3. Runway occupation and taxiway congestion in preparation for take-off and after landing.
4. Apron congestion: aircraft and vehicles.
5. Terminal congestion, affecting passengers, visitors, airline staff, passenger service staff, customs, police, and all other airport officers.
6. Air cargo base, engineering and maintenance facilities.
7. Car parking, hire-car and taxi stands.
8. Access roads.

Restrictions on airport movements, acquisition of larger aircraft, the provision of new facilities, terminals, runways and car parks, and the location of new airport sites have all been employed as methods for easing the problems. The essential need is to recognise the complexity of the situation and to seek solutions to the many congestion problems within the context of a wide-ranging programme of development.

An overall programme of such research and development would comprise three major sections:
1. Assessment of air transport growth within a total transport complex including business, private and holiday travel on domestic and international journeys.
2. A planned programme of air vehicle development within the framework of international commercial aircraft competition to cover problems of SST, V/STOL and large subsonic aircraft development with due consideration of noise level licensing.

457

3. A programme of international and national airport planning to meet the needs of the air carrier industry, the essential requirement for economic aircraft development and the justified claims of the public and the regional planning authorities.

Unfortunately no national or international body has the competence or the potential resources to implement and direct such a programme.

The extensive and intensive use of civil aircraft now makes it virtually impossible to study effectively any one of the above major elements in isolation. This situation unfortunately is likely to persist. Perhaps the insistent problem of noise nuisance with its strong political overtones in democratic states, has brought governments together more effectively than any other area of air transport development in the last decade.

Airport noise

This highly complex subject cannot be treated in this book with the precision demanded by the physicist, and the reader is referred to the various references given at the end of this chapter for a more detailed consideration of the scientific basis of noise and sound transmission.

In the first place, five aspects of the discomfort due to sound may be identified:

1. The intensity of the physical loudness, in decibels (dB).
2. The pitch or frequency of the sound.
3. The complexity of the frequency spectrum.
4. The duration of the sound.
5. The number of repetitions.

The well-established unit of measurement, Perceived Noise Level in Decibels (PNdB), defines an approximate level of acceptance or discomfort which is of value in the assessment of the individual noise. A more refined unit, the EPNdB, super-imposes upon the more familiar PNdB further corrections to allow for the separate tones in a noise effect, and takes account of the duration of the noise. These noise units may also be combined with the number of repetitions to locate areas acceptable for different types of land use. Thus a Boeing 727 jet aircraft at 1500 ft after take-off (about three miles from the start-of-roll point) may produce a peak PNdB value of 105 for about 25 seconds.

A repetition of such occurrences under given conditions, say take-offs in daylight or night hours, would amount to a noise situation which could be rated on a scale of nuisance which could be calibrated against community reaction. On such a basis the FAA Composite Noise Rating Scale, the CNR, was established. Thirty-two repetitions of the above aircraft take-off cycle amounts to 100 on the CNR scale. Between 100 and 115 units, individual persons are likely to complain, even vigorously, and concerted group action may well be taken. Below 100 the impact becomes progressively less objectional to the majority of people.

Procedures for estimating land use compatibility with aircraft noise have been developed and are in extensive use more especially in the USA and in Europe. Details of the pattern of flight operations including aircraft type, number of landings and take-offs, runways in use, wind patterns and the direction of use, as well as flight paths before landing and after take-off are required. Information on engine testing areas for run-up, the types of engine, location on the airport, orientation of the run-up bay and the run-up thrust-time cycle is also needed. Total activity in the day-time and night-time periods is called for and the data is tabulated for computation. The perceived noise level contours for the various aircraft categories are then obtained from the manufacturer for landing, take-off or run-up, and in relation to the location under consideration in the airport environment, the PNdB level for a given aircraft operation can be assessed.

The composite noise rating (CNR) for the sum of the various aircraft noise inputs is obtained by adding to the perceived noise level in the particular case, various tabulated corrections arising from operational factors which influence community reactions to noise. For landing and take-off such factors are frequency of movement and runway in use. For engine run-up the hourly running time is the critical factor. Rules applied in this system of Noise Rating require that if there are 3 or more aircraft type/runway/flight path categories within 3 units of the maximum CNR then 5 units should be added to the highest CNR for take-off. If there are less than 3 cases then the highest CNR applies.

The US Consultants Bolt, Beranek and Newman studied 28 airports by means of a noise exposure contour technique to provide guide lines for land-use planning and zoning as well as for airport development. This later method is based on the subjective level of aircraft flyover noise.

The US Noise Exposure Forecast Index (NEF) is based, like the CNR upon the aircraft take-off and landing noise level, which in this case however is defined by the effective PNdB with corrections for the number of operations by flight paths in day and night periods. To systematise the computation it is convenient to allocate the aircraft types to a limited number of classes with mean noise and flight path characteristics, which are developed as a function of the sector length flown. The continuous correction for frequency of movement and for summing the various noise contributions by the various aircraft classes makes it difficult to draw the NEF contours directly from EPNdB contours. Contours are most conveniently plotted by means of a computer programme, the complex flight path network having been broken down into a simplified system of flight segments.

Many attempts have been made to establish the acceptable activities which could justifiably co-exist with various noise levels and frequencies of repetition in the vicinity of airports, railways and motorways. In older cities and urban areas the lack of planned areas of activity is a principal difficulty in this work.

Various types of activity may be considered which are then zoned as follows:

Residential Areas
Out-door Theatres and Arenas
Schools, Hospitals and
    Institutions
Hotels and City Terminals

Business and Commercial
Zones
Offices and Public Buildings
Theatres and Halls

* Outdoor Recreational Areas   * Industrial Zones

When the CNR rating exceeds 100 but does not exceed 115 only the starred zones (*) are likely to be suitable. In some cases, such as hotels, office blocks and public buildings due account should be taken of the effects of noise in the overall design of the buildings, the orientation of the structure, height, windows (e.g. double glazing). This also must be fully appreciated; the vitality of air transport is such that the number of aircraft movements is likely to grow. Careful assessment should be made of the future spectrum of air movements, their number, the types of aircraft and the routings, including any possibility of new runway alignments.

Earlies studies had shown that the perceived noise level was augmented by 3 PNdB when the duration of the noise doubled. Becker of the Aeroport de Paris showed that the level of discomfort from airport noise was related to its discontinuity, and could be represented by a value of PNdB related to that of a continuous noise (lasting 8 hours) by the equation $N = N_1 + 10$ log t/T where N_1 is the PNdB for the continuous noise, and t is the total duration of noise from aircraft movements each being assumed to last 30 seconds, and T represents 8 hours. Times are of course expressed in common units.

Noise and number index

This method of quantifying the long-term exposure of populations to the effect of aircraft noise was developed in the UK by the Wilson Committee (1963) which was set up to examine noise in all aspects. The NNI is, like the CNR, a composite figure which takes account of the basic PNdB level generated on a number of individual flights and the number of such flights performed during a given period. The index was based on a day-time social survey undertaken in the London (Heathrow) area, and was used subsequently to correlate the annoyance experienced with the physical characteristics of the noise to which the population were subjected. A scale was devised which corresponded to the various levels of annoyance aroused, this being determined by answers to a series of questions.

The NNI was defined as

Average peak loudness (in PNdB) $+ 15 \log_{10} N - 80$

Where N is the number of aircraft heard per day.

Dr E. J. Richards, a member of the Wilson Committee on noise, has in various papers drawn attention to the difficulty of drawing conclusions from one survey and extrapolating to other conditions. Moreover it is not possible to obtain evidence

461

from the survey which would be strictly applicable to night flights, or which would allow safe predictions for different regions of the same country, or even for communities with different levels of background noise. Other UK surveys have more recently been put in hand but few results are yet available. The second Heathrow Survey, 1971 (see Bibliography below), gave some support to the earlier survey, 1963, but results showed an unchanged sensitivity to individual aircraft noise, and a lesser concern for the number of movements.

It is certainly a considerable weakness of the method that it allows only an imprecise prediction for night flights, since the original survey obtained no firm reactions to night-time aircraft noise. Night noise, however, has become a matter of very considerable importance in the 1970s.

It is found that in the prediction of the effect on schools and institutions of all kinds, other assessments must be made. It has been stated for example by some authorities (*vide* the Southampton Airport Enquiry 1969), that if aircraft movements giving a peak PNdB exceeding 85, occur less than 35 times a day, or 4 in a peak hour, the likelihood of interference with oral teaching would not arise and sound insulation might not be justified.

A criterion for night movements on a similar basis may well be reasonable. For example, the dominant effect of an occasional high noise level overflight might suggest that 2 movements in the hour by night at a PNdB exceeding 90 might be a justified upper level to adopt. This indeed approximates to the 3500 movements in the 7-month period which was adopted as the limit to night movements at Heathrow by the UK Board of Trade (now DTI) under Section 14 of the Airports Authority Act, though now replaced by a summer night jet take-off ban.

It will be noted that the principal consideration up to this point has been the intensity of *air transport* movements which are generated at the airport. The traffic in smaller aircraft will however predominate in many airport situations, but the noise level will, in general, be below the threshold of noise nuisance except in the case of executive jets, and certain types of twin-engined business aircraft. Accurate forecasting of the scale of traffic in the various aircraft categories for 10–15 years ahead is clearly an essential for such investigations. Other criteria for the assessment of aircraft noise have been suggested. Two of these have been proposed by Dr E. J. Richards of Loughborough University. These are the Index of Community Noise (ICN) and the Airport Noise Efficiency Factor (ANEF).

The ICN was based on the concept that noise nuisance is proportional to the total noise energy received by a population in a given period. Dr E. J. Richards concluded that the principal factors contributing to this are (a) population density, (b) number of movements, (c) a 'path factor' which includes spread of movements, height, acoustic absorption, and atmospheric refraction, (d) engine power divided by aircraft speed, and (e) an 'acoustic conversion factor', relating to the subjectively weighted acoustical energy radiated during climb and a function of the power of the engine on the ground. By analysis he showed that the ICN can be defined as:

$$\text{Constant} + 10 \log_{10} \text{(population density)}$$
$$+ 10 \log_{10} \text{(total daily static thrust)}$$
$$+ 10 \log_{10} \text{(forward speed factor)} + 10 \log_{10} \text{(path factor)}.$$

It can thus be shown that if the total daily thrust is doubled without change in the other variables, the nuisance in the area is increased by an equivalent of 3 PNdB.

The ANEF relates the number of people adversely affected by noise to the annual air transport movements at a given airport. The basis of this criteria needs further development. It certainly has the value of ready computation and rapid application for comparative purposes.

In the author's view the NNI concept of the Wilson Committee still provides the soundest basis for application in the airport environment and leads to the most effective noise control procedures and to positive land-use planning.

On the NNI scale it has been concluded that exposure to aircraft noise reaches an unreasonable level in the range 50–60 NNI and this is generally adopted as the maximum acceptable level for day-time operations. Although the Committee were imprecise on the subject of night movements, they suggested tentatively the corresponding limit of annoyance might be 15 to 12 NNI lower.

In our own work, undertaken in many cases in conjunction with the noise specialist team under Mr C Waters at Loughborough University we have adopted the following criteria for disturbance as a result of the computation of NNI contours in a given airport traffic situation.

Within the 55 NNI Contour
Unacceptable for schools and all residential planning Worthy of compensation. Industrial uses considered.
Between 55 and 45 NNI
From unreasonable to moderately annoying. Undesirable for planning except with sound-proofed buildings (since traffic may grow), and unacceptable for schools and Institutions. Compensation should not be required.
Below 35 NNI
Adequate for the great majority of land uses.

The Surrey County Council have been foremost among Local Authorities in the United Kingdom in adapting NNI Contours as the basis for urban development. Their zones for planning purposes at Gatwick are based broadly on the above principles giving due weight to the NNI bands (day and night), land use, and the potential value of sound-proofing.

The author is aware that advanced work on noise control and land use planning is in progress in Germany and France, and it is likely to be in hand elsewhere Little of this is yet published in English. A great need for international dissemination of interim reports on the most outstanding work now exists.

As part of the work of airport site selection in the Bristol Region and Severnside which was carried out in 1970–1 by the author for the Bristol Corporation, noise studies of Filton and Lulsgate airports were undertaken using a NNI computer programme designed by W. G. Batchelor and W. Nash employing an advanced print-out technique.

The NNI contours are shown in Fig. 10.7 which indicates the serious impact which civil air development at Filton might have upon the population in North Bristol. For comparison Fig. 10.8 shows NNI contours prepared by the Technical Team of the Roskill Commission on one of the recommended Foulness four-runway sites for London's projected Third Airport. Air operations on a very much larger scale are indicated in the latter case for the year of assessment 1999. Such contour work should be the basis of all noise control programmes and lead to more effective and rational land-use planning.

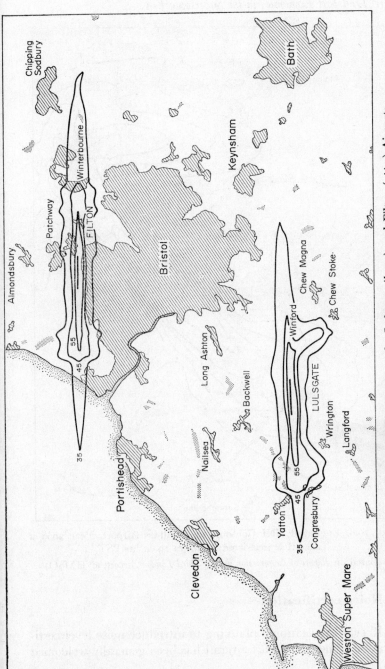

Fig. 10.7. Envisaged 1980 NNI Contours for Lulsgate (*lower*) and Filton (*upper*) Airports. (Noise contours © Alan Stratford & Associates; based on HM Ordnance Survey)

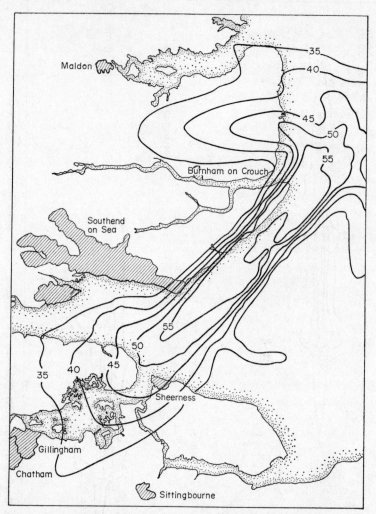

FIG. 10.8. Envisaged NNI Contours for Foulness Airport, Year 2006 if Take-off Unrestricted; 07.00 to 19.00 hrs BST.

(Based on *Report of Commission on the Third London Airport*; © HMSO)

Noise certification

Recent international planning to introduce noise level certification in new transport aircraft has been generally welcomed as a step forward in implementing current objectives of noise reduction at the source.

The UK Government in the Air Navigation (Noise Certificate) order of 1970 promulgated noise standards required for the issue of a noise certificate as a result of preliminary international discussions and recommendations of ICAO. It relates essentially to subsonic aircraft exceeding 5700 kilograms (12,500 lb) of gross weight, fitted with turbine engines with by-pass ratios exceeding 2. The exemptions, however, should be examined. These include the earlier types of jet aircraft representing a large proportion of existing air fleets. It also excludes all supersonic transport aircraft.

The noise levels are required to be measured in EPNdB:

(*A*) on take-off, at a point on a line parallel to and 650 metres (0·35 nm) from the extended centre-line of the runway where it appears that the noise after take-off is greatest;
(*B*) on take-off, at a point on the extended centre-line of the runway, 6500 metres (3·5 nm) from the start of the take-off run; and
(*C*) on the approach to landing, at a point on the extended centre-line of the runway, 120 metres (394 ft) vertically below the 3° descent path.

As shown by flying trials these noise levels should not exceed the following, under the weight conditions noted. For intermediate weights, the noise level should not exceed a linear variation of the logarithm of the total weight.

Maximum total weight authorised of aeroplane	Noise level in EPNdB		
	At point (*A*)	At point (*B*)	At point (*C*)
272,000 kg or more (598,000 lb)	108	108	108
34,000 kg or less (74,800 lb)	102	93	102

The noise levels specified may be exceeded at one or two of the measuring points if: (*a*) the sum of the excess does not exceed 4 EPNdB; (*b*) at no measuring point is the excess greater than

467

3 EPNdB; and (*c*) the excesses are completely offset by reductions at the other measuring points.

The existing jet aircraft noise monitor locations in the vicinity of London Airport (Heathrow) are shown in Fig. 10.9.

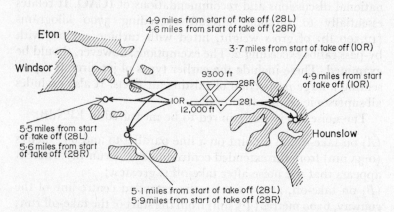

FIG. 10.9. Noise Monitor Locations, Heathrow Airport, London. Noise-sensitive areas shaded. Distances shown in miles from start of take-off from Runways 10 R, 28 L and 28 R respectively

US Federal Aviation Regulations Part 36 have enunciated noise level standards required for the certification of airworthiness, which are closely related to the ICAO recommendations but are slightly higher than the UK requirements. Approach, take-off and side-line noise levels are specified in relation to maximum aircraft operating weights, and trade-off is also allowed so that noise levels measured at one or two of the measuring points may exceed the prescribed limits.

Certain allowances were given for 4-jet aircraft applying for certification before 1.12.69. The regulations exclude SSTs. In the formulation of these standards, however, little attention has been paid to the problems of the aircraft designer working on a project often with unproven engines and with airframe development potential not readily foreseen. On a given aircraft/ engine combination it may require a 2 per cent weight reduction to reduce flyover noise by 1 EPNdB so that the errors in noise assessment might have a catastrophic effect on operating economics. Moreover noise requirements may prove unduly severe in the case of high powered aircraft, using steep climb and approach angles with unconventional ILS glide-slopes.

Current jet aircraft operating at noise levels above the requirements for new projects will provide a large part of airline fleet capacity for a number of years. Legislation does not require modification kits to achieve lower noise levels but some attempts have been made, notably by ICAO and by the FAA, to encourage the retro-fitting of so called 'hush-kits' to achieve improved levels (probably 3–4 dB lower). Such moves have been viewed anxiously by the CAB, and naturally, also by IATA. Cost estimates have shown excessive financial penalties due to installation costs and aircraft time out of service, and because of the payload decreases due to weight modification.

In general proposed noise target levels are between 5 and 10 EPNdB below the levels of jet transport aircraft flying with the airlines in 1970–1.

Due to increasing engine by-pass ratios over the period 1965–1975 there has been and will continue to be a steady reduction in jet noise, probably about $\frac{1}{2}$ dB per annum. In 1968 there was a large step favourable to noise reduction because of the introduction of the single stage fan engine without inlet guide vanes. The further 5–10 dB reduction called for to meet the requirements is possible on most new engine designs but implies weight and specific fuel consumption penalties which in 1970 were estimated at over 1000 lb and 3 per cent s.f.c. on the Rolls Royce type 211 engine (Lockheed 1011) but which in the next generation of transport engines might exact less than one third of this penalty.

There is little doubt that the new requirements will in due course provide considerable improvement in the airport environment, but that airlines and the airline customer will be required to pay increased fare levels for the resulting environmental improvement.

Meanwhile existing situations require all possible steps to be taken for the amelioration of the airport noise problem. At the present time the principal methods in use are:

1. Operational noise abatement procedures, whereby the least noise sensitive runways are used, least sensitive directions on

runways are employed (subject to wind), and the most intensively populated areas are avoided in the approach and take-off flight phases. A total ban on night movements in extreme cases.

2. Engine power may be reduced over sensitive areas especially after take-off and climb to a safe altitude.

3. The discouragement of development, especially of residential areas, schools and institutions, in the immediate airport environment with collaboration of the local or regional planning authority.

4. New airports to be sited only after a careful assessment of the many factors including environmental damage from noise and disturbance.

The control of noise is in many large airports being monitored by noise measuring devices at carefully located points under the approach and take-off paths of the aircraft. However, the required minimum noise flight procedures which result in improving the noise situation close to the airport boundary, will have a deleterious affect upon those living farther out. As an example, in studies undertaken for the Surrey County Council we found that the power reduction enforced after take-off from Heathrow in the interests of residents west of the airport caused considerably increased discomfort in the Surrey towns, mostly lying 200–300 ft above airfield level. Over this region, which suffers from the predominant south-bound flights, aircraft are at a lower altitude than they would otherwise have been (because of power reduction), and at this point in their trajectory open up their engines to higher climbing thrust.

Supersonic transport aircraft

The supersonic transports, Concorde and the US projects, were originally designed to meet the airport noise level of the early 4-engine jets in the early 1960s. The world wide concern with noise which led to the promulgation of regulations for the control of noise at airports and in the design stage came upon them when at a late stage in their development. The FAA and the UK regulations in fact specially exclude the SST from the necessity to meet the full noise requirements. Certainly the

Concorde (fitted with the Olympus 593 MK 601 engines) with an improved exhaust silencing-system will be of comparable noisiness to the currently operating 4-engined jets on flyover and approach even though the lateral noise will be about 6 PNdB higher than that of the current fleets. Work has been in hand to produce the most effective retractable silencing system for production aircraft. In this system, known as the 'spade' silencer, a series of retractable spade-like devices are deflected into the jet efflux to divert some part of the high velocity exhaust gas into the annular space between the primary and secondary flows. Some loss of thrust is thereby incurred but this is acceptable in a retractable system which will have a negligible effect in cruising flight.

In the full take-off power case – when lateral noise is critical for the SST – estimates have shown that the spade silencers should show a 4·5 PNdB improvement for a loss of thrust of 5 per cent. This should reduce lateral noise to 114 PNdB which is still above the 707–320 and the DC 8–60 series aircraft. Further noise reductions are anticipated from later exhaust nozzle designs including the TRA design, the buckets of which are used for thrust reversal and vary the final nozzle area.

Even were a new SST project to be conceived today it is difficult to see how a major breakthrough in airport noise levels could be achieved when the critical cruise requirement for power plant design are a high thrust/drag ratio, implying high jet velocity and a straight-through turbine cycle. The Director General of SNECMA, M. Garnier has noted that 'if the principle of a straight flow cycle is maintained a significant gain on s.f.c. in supersonic cruise and in subsonic flight could be expected by raising the temperature from 1100° to 1300°, and the pressure ratio from 14:1 to 23:1. This could result in a load improvement of some 15 per cent. . . . I can only confirm today the validity of the decision made by Rolls Royce and SNECMA as early as 1961 to adopt a straight-flow cycle for the Concorde's engine.'

The problem of airport noise nevertheless remains and in the first years of Concorde service, the new generation of wide-body jets with greater operating weights will be flying from the same civil airfields as Concorde and with a much more acceptable level of noise.

Noise levels estimated for the Concorde in comparison with other jet aircraft are shown in the following table. (No simple relationship can be established between PNdB and EPNdB for *all* aircraft.) Concorde figures are with the improved 'Spade' silencers and specified in EPNdB.

These figures were issued in 1971 by Aerospatiale with reference to the US. FAR (Part 36) regulations applying to aircraft for which application for certification was presented after 1967. Thus the Concorde is not required to meet the rules but will naturally be operating in an environment increasingly dominated by turbo-fan engines with high by-pass ratios.

TABLE 10.3. *Comparative Community Noise (EPNdB)*

		Boeing 707-320 B	DC 8-50	Concorde
Side line	0·35 NM	108	106	111
Flyover	3·5 NM	114	115	114
Approach	1 NM	120	117	115
Total		342	338	340

It is estimated by the manufacturers that Concorde side-line noise will be less than that of the VC 10, each operating at maximum take-off weight. Fly-over noise will also be comparable with the 707 and DC 8, while on the approach it will be measurably quieter than these aircraft. A direct comparison with the Boeing 747 and the large Trijets is of course less favourable to the Concorde, the Trijets being likely to achieve a 5 to 10 PNdB improvement in approach and up to 15 PNdB improvement in take-off.

Noise control at airports

Stuttgart Airport in West Germany is thought to be the first European jet airport to install a computer-controlled system for monitoring aircraft noise. This has been in operation since 1969. Weather-proofed microphone terminals acquire and feed noise data to a centrally disposed Hewlett-Packard computer. Noise is measured at 7 points near the airport, each being monitored twice a second throughout the 24-hour period, and prints-out on receipt of any data which exceeds a predetermined threshold level. With such information available it is possible to devise the most effective noise abatement procedure, and to determine more precisely the capacity limitations of the airport. Such data is also clearly of value for land use planning.

The United Kingdom Government in the Civil Aviation Bill of 1971 extended their powers for the control of airport operations beyond the airports of the British Airports Authority, so that they may intervene in the control of noise at all airports in the United Kingdom. A system of graduated penalties for airlines may be introduced and aircraft movement limitation and weight restriction may be forced upon airport authorities. Airport managers will be required in specified cases to provide and maintain noise measurement equipment open to inspection by Government Officials at any time.

Already under Section 15 of the Airport Authority Act of 1965 the Department of Trade and Industry had powers to require the BAA to make grants towards the cost of noise insulation of buildings. A scheme for sound-proofing houses around Heathrow was introduced in 1966. It applies to all buildings erected before 1 January 1966. In specified wards, which came within the estimated daytime 55 NNI contour for Heathrow (1970), a grant of 50 per cent of the cost of sound proofing to an approved specification including double glazing, sealing of windows and the mechanical ventilation of three rooms. A scheme for houses around Gatwick (London's Second Airport) is now also in operation.

Noise and community objections

The subject of noise is one which causes considerable and sometimes unreasonable emotion in certain circles, but it may be quite rationally viewed as an agonising matter by those living in the immediate vicinity of a major airport. It is apparently of far more concern to the democratic nations than to states with less press freedom, and it is certain that political pressures require us to pay full attention to demands which often reach excessive proportions. It is probable that the decision of the British Government to locate the Third London Airport at Foulness was due to the pressure of opinion from a limited number of people who live in the vicinity of alternative sites, and of others across the nation who value traditional and regional amenities far higher than the technological progress and economic growth of the United Kingdom.

There is no way of proving that they are right or wrong but the significant fact is that they are able to demonstrate an ability to determine government action against the best interests of air transport development. In the New York State Legislature the proposed Anti-Noise Bill (1971) would effect all noise which is 'injurious or would reasonably interfere with the comfortable enjoyment of life and property'. No noise levels have been set, unlike the earlier Stein proposals, but clearly the objective is to prevent the natural development of air transport in the vicinity of one great centre of population. A Road Research Laboratory working group estimated that at least 19 per cent of the UK urban population are subjected to traffic noise which should be unacceptable in a residential area. This and other assessments indicate that road traffic creates a great deal more noise nuisance than the widely publicised air traffic. In the first case little action can be taken by the individual, in the second case he can express his feelings against a specified organisation (the airport authority) and national or commercial interests (the airlines).

For such reasons, there can remain no doubt that the need is urgent to improve the environment in the vicinity of airports, and the industry must prove itself equal to the heavier task which it has been set, *viz.* to develop a range of economic transport vehicles of many sizes and capabilities, with far lower overall noise creating characteristics. A recent study published in 1971 by NASA into US aviation and research has described aircraft noise abatement as the most crucial requirement for US civil aviation, and recommends an annual research and development effort of 100 million dollars to reduce noise by 10–15 decibels per decade 'until aircraft noise is suppressed into the background'.

Population affected by noise

It has been our practice to count the houses and the number of the population living within the NNI contours and likely to be resident there within each future period covered by the Survey. Such an assessment is related to the significant population forecasts which are available, but a 10-year period is generally required. Schools and other institutions are also counted. Clearly the population within each band of contours will not all be equally affected by a given level of noise, but a uniform level of acceptance within each band is presumed. However the percentage acceptance will clearly be greater as the NNI level decreases. We could consider for discussion one hypothesis which is that the number of people adversely affected by noise = $(0.75 \times NNI)$ per cent of the people exposed to noise. This suggests that in the 45–55 NNI band about 38 per cent of the population would be adversely affected, but this almost certainly over-estimates the noise-nuisance below 30 NNI. Clearly far more social research is required to elucidate the position in this twilight area between technology and sociology.

Not only is it desirable to assess the population which is affected by noise, but an attempt must be made to evaluate the contribution that is made by noise to the total costs, or dis-benefit, of airport development for a number of years ahead, so that the present value of the dis-benefit may be computed. As part of the cost-benefit exercise noise may assume a considerable importance. In the Roskill Commission studies, the evaluation of noise was a major area of work and contributed significantly to the final recommendations. Noise in the first place was a primary factor in excluding sites from the final short list of alternative locations, which were essentially low noise level sites. In the second place careful assessment was made of the noise cost elements in the discounted total present values of each project.

Air pollution

A detailed consideration of this subject is not justified at this time since its impact upon the economics of air transport is

475

minimal. Nevertheless a high degree of co-operation and financial support has been forthcoming from the aircraft manufacturing industry in a voluntary retrofit programme to combat smoke emissions in certain twin and tri-jet aircraft. The overall costs are understood to be in the order of $10,000 per engine. There is constant reference in the literature to the subject and in comparative studies considering air and surface transport modes there is justification for careful quantification; this is an intangible subject and one requiring considerably more analytical study.

Research, principally in the USA has shown that the atmospheric pollution caused by transport aircraft of current types and affecting the ground environment in the vicinity of airports is not serious. In cruising and orbiting flight the emission from jet engines is negligible, and the visible product often noted during the climb-out and approach of jet aircraft (the main factor which has caused public comment) is now being rapidly eliminated by more careful attention to the combustion process in jet engine burners.

In fact the combustion in the reciprocating engine (especially in the motor car) is far less complete than in the turbine engine and there is greater emission of carbon monoxide and other constituents such as hydro-carbons and the oxides of nitrogen. A recent study by the Flight Transportation Laboratory of MIT into urban transport showed that when comparing automobiles and jet aircraft in the airport environment the pollutant yield (1 lb per passenger-mile provided) was, in all the cases considered, greatly in favour of the aircraft.

In the case of executive aircraft and general aviation which is still dominated by the piston engine, the case is less clear-cut. The pollutants are higher per seat-mile than for the motor car, but the very much lower intensity of movement and the dispersion effects of the turbulent atmosphere above ground level make this a matter of minor significance with the scale of air traffic (general aviation) within this decade.

V/STOL sites

The phased development towards a more readily adaptable air vehicle requiring less land for ground operations must be expected to take place through the 1970s. If this can be achieved with less social disturbance we must hope to find greater willingness to bring the benefits of civil aviation close to the heart of our cities.

Almost certainly the first stage in such development will be the evolution of economic short take-off aircraft (STOL). In chapter 8 we have differentiated between the various types of reduced take-off (RTOL), short take-off (STOL), and vertical take-off (VTOL) aircraft and their field length requirements. Reduced take-off and landing is now with us, and a major sector of light transport aircraft and nearly all general aviation may be placed in this category. There is wide experience of reduced field operations and the extension of the use of such aircraft, and development of the market so that designs for larger capacity vehicles can be brought forward is now inhibited largely by lack of finance suited to such projects.

The shorter taxi times required in the compact STOL port designs give a potential air operating economy. However, in times of high flow rate, delays could be caused without a stricter departure control than has been customary for equivalent flows at most conventional airports. Aircraft seating capacity, modes of loading and unloading passengers, aircraft apron servicing cycle times, gate occupancy time control, and the number of gates available are the most critical design factors in compact STOL ports for high flow rates. If no restrictions arise from the air traffic control system or from surface transport access or transport interface problems, the potential economy in the 1980s by a gradual replacement of CTOL airports by STOL ports could be very considerable. No very immediate economy however can be looked for since for at least a decade conventional (CTOL) aircraft will predominate on all services and for much longer than this, probably until well into the last decade of the century, CTOL aircraft types, subsonic and SST, will dominate the long-haul routes of the world. Conventional airports will therefore be essential for a long time to come for the long-haul carriers and for inter-continental flight operations.

STOL port evolution will be based on the economics of the case, and this presupposes the availability of economic STOL aircraft of the types already discussed in chapter 8. A requirement is likely to arise during the 1970s in these primary areas:

1. As an adjacent facility for major national airports, to ease congestion and noise, and provide a better return on investment and facilities.

2. As a primary air hub for important but small national centres, to provide direct air access to major airports and STOL ports and as a STOL service centre for other inter-city flights.

3. As secondary air hubs, peripheral to our major population centres, and more accessible than conventional airports.

The possibility of city centre sites for VTOL and STOL aircraft has been very fully analysed in the USA and in Europe in recent years. Our own work on site selection and development has required critical appraisals of road developments; from these studies peripheral sites accessible to the emerging motorway pattern in all countries appear to be so advantageous that central areas hold little appeal even with the dramatic opportunities offered by vertical take-off projects. Note also the comments on the airport location work of Armstrong and Sealy in this chapter. Land cost, noise, congested access for passengers and cargo, structural design costs and fuelling/fire risks as well as accident hazards have ruled out in our own view the serious possibility of V/STOL sites in central areas of the major existing cities. In a study undertaken for a British aircraft manufacturer in 1968 we concluded that peripheral sites for VTOL and STOL were entirely adequate for large-scale operations. For example, Speke (Liverpool), Yeadon (Leeds), Middleton–St George (Tees-side), Woolsington (Newcastle), Squire's Gate (Blackpool), Todwick (Sheffield) and Barton (Manchester), offer immediate opportunities for development in this context. Peripheral sites accessible to motorway interchanges (junctions), and in many cases close to container depots and to industrial sites, where noise is less detrimental, can expect to be located without much difficulty in the UK if decisions are not too long delayed.

Each city has its unique requirements. The need is for long range planning so that sites can be retained and safeguarded for a use which may not yet have fully emerged. At an early date forecasts are required. These should be soundly based taking due account of the alternative transport modes, the constraints of the locations under survey and the funding limitations.

The requirements for STOL aircraft are generally defined by the runway length 1500–2500 ft and already specifications have been laid down by the FAA as guidelines to development. The aircraft designer has known from the beginning that reduced take-off and landing aircraft (RTOL) offer considerable economic advantages compared with design for the more strict STOL case.

While air vehicle specifications will determine the theoretical strip requirements, inevitably a new STOL/RTOL Port will need to cater for a wide range of aircraft, including helicopters and general aviation. In this latter case the requirement may reach 5000 ft. The strictest airport building economy will always be achieved by designing for a very limited range of aircraft types. Close proximity of the site to a conventional airport will always allow the more demanding RTOL and general aviation types to use the longer runways at the CTOL site. This however will do little to ease congestion at a major conventional airport which is an important first objective for STOL evolution.

Fundamental to any plan to locate and establish a STOL port on the right site so as to satisfy a growing future demand at an acceptable level of cost and/or benefit to the community, is the need to provide such good access that the use of the facility will be maximised with minimum local inconvenience and nuisance. The STOL port will clearly be less demanding with regard to space for runways and taxiways. Aprons and the aircraft servicing areas, however, may be no less exacting (since conventional aircraft designs of all types are themselves becoming more compact), and car parking and other passenger terminal facilities may be just as critical. As in the case of conventional airport terminals the fullest possible analysis of the future vehicle operational behaviour is essential and this requires a detailed appreciation of the likely vehicle types and size, the airline route system and a full assessment of the spectrum of the passengers themselves.

BIBLIOGRAPHY

Airport Terminals Reference Manual, 5th Edition, IATA, 1969

ICAO Standards and Recommended Practices. Airports: Annex 14. To the Convention on International Air Transport

The Licensing of Aerodromes, CAP 168, HMSO, 1971

World Airports. The Way Ahead. ICE Conference Papers, 1970

United Kingdom Air Pilot, HMSO, 1971

Airport Capacity Criteria for the National Airport Plan, FAA, 1966

Planning the State Airport System, FAA, 1968

Airport Capacity Criteria used in Long-Term Planning, FAA, 1969

M. A. WARSCOW, *Capacity of Airport Systems in Metropolitan Areas*, 1964

LORD ROSKILL, *Report on the Third London Airport*, HMSO, 1971

SNOW and STRATFORD, *South Hampshire Airport Study*, South Hampshire Plan, 1970

ALAN STRATFORD and Associates, *Bristol Airport Study*, 1971

Verkehrsflughafen Frankfurt Rhein-Main. Report of the Airport Company, 1965

ROBERT HORONJEFF, *The Planning and Design of Airports*, McGraw Hill, 1962

The Airport. Its Influence on the Community Economy, FAA, 1967

R. B. ORMSBY, *Utility Airports. Air Access to National Transportation*, FAA 1968

The Airbus and the Airport. US Airport Requirements and Other Papers, BALPA Symposium, 1969

ARMSTRONG and SEALY, Location Theory Applied to a Regional Airport, ASA Report No. 162, 1970

Project Bosphorus. Boston Port and Airport Study, MIT Report No. 21, 1970

Annual Reports of the British Airports Authority

PETER G. MASEFIELD, 'The Modern Airport and its Future', *Jnl. Roy. Soc. Arts*, 1968

Airport and Transport Aircraft, *Roy Aeronaut. Soc.*, Air Transport Group Symposium, 1970

ALAN STRATFORD, *The Planning of National Airport Facilities*, Rome Air Transport Centre, June 1968

ADAM JAWORSKI, 'International Airports Allocation of Operating Revenues and Cost', *Jnl. Roy. Aero. Soc.*, 1971

EILON and MATHEWSON, *Simulation in the Design of an Air Terminal Building*, Imperial College, 1971

M. GARNIER, 'The Progress and Economics of the Aero Engine', *Jnl. Roy. Aero. Soc.*, May 1971

Airport Operators Council International. Uniform Airport Financial Reports

Aviation Demand and Airport Facility Requirement Forecast Through 1980, FAA, 1967

A. H. STRATFORD, 'Airports and Air Transport. Growth and Transformation', *Jnl. Roy. Aero. Soc.*, May 1969

Impact of the New Large Jets on the Air Transportation System 1970–73, CAB, 1969

Planning the Metropolitan Airport System, AOCI and FAA, 1970

B. L. SCHRODER, *Capital Financing of Airports*, ICE, Sept. 1969

G. MEUNIER, *Conception, Construction et Gestation des Aerodromes*, Editions Eyrolles, Paris 5, 1969

Airport Location Methodology, International Symposium, London, 1971

ALAN STRATFORD and Associates, *Heathrow Air Routings*, Surrey County Council, 1970 and Gatwick Air Routings, 1972

E. J. RICHARDS, 'Airport Noise – Mitigating the Nuisance', *Aircraft Engineering*, Feb. 1967

BOLT BERANEK and NEWMAN INC., *Analysis of Community and Airport Noise Abatement*, Vols. I and II, FAA, 1964

BOLT, BERANEK and NEWMAN, *Studies of Noise Characteristics of Boeing 707 and Propeller Driven Aircraft*, 1958

Noise. Report of the Wilson Committee, HMSO, 1963

J. G. ODY, 'Cost-Benefit Analysis at Airports', *Journal of Transport Economics and Policy*, Sept. 1969

Alleviation of Jet Aircraft Noise Near Airports. Jet Aircraft Noise Panel. Executive Office of the President, Washington DC, 1966

Aircraft Noise International Conference on the Reduction of Civil Aircraft Noise, HMSO, London, 1966

D. E. BISHOP, M. A. SIMPSON and BOLT, BERANEK & NEWMAN INC., *Noise Exposure Forecast Contours for 1967–70 and 75 Operations at Selected Airports*. Prepared for DOT (FAA), Sept. 1970

Second Survey of Aircraft Noise Annoyance around London (Heathrow) Airport. Social Survey Division of DTI, HMSO, Aug. 1971

Impact of Air Traffic on Urban Development West of London. Prepared for the Greater London Council. ASA Report No. 179, Apr. 1972

11 Future Projects and the Way Ahead

The contribution of research

Contributions to the future development of air transport beyond the first steps now being taken into SST and V/STOL operations are already being made by the research establishments in the USA and in Europe. These are not only in the national research agencies, but also in the private sector where fundamental as well as applied research and development is vital to an even pattern of advance. Although the costs of R & D have increased steeply during the three decades since World War II thereby requiring national support for all military and many civil projects, it is still apparent that in the initial stages the private development of new ideas is of the greatest commercial importance. Both the development of hovercraft and the jet engine arose from individual ideas taken a long way in their evolution by private enterprise. Though the points of growth arise in surprisingly different places, thorough scientific and engineering development demands large resources which increasingly need to be provided from public funds.

In a report published by the National Institute of Economic and Social Research (May 1962) it was shown that in 1959 both in the USA and in the UK, 86 per cent of research expenditure in aircraft (excluding electronics) was financed by government. In the US, however, the research expenditure was 4·4 times greater than that sponsored in the UK. More than 6 times as many qualified scientists and engineers were employed in the USA at that time on aircraft research, and twice as many per employee in the industry itself. This report sought to establish a relationship between the growth index of a number of industries, including aviation, and the research expenditure, this being expressed as a percentage of net output.

This relationship seems to be well confirmed as is also the conclusion that a concentration of development resources is desirable (especially when they are severely limited) upon those industries where competitive product performance is essential to overseas sales. Aviation is clearly in need of this investment both in the scientific engineering, as in the commercial field.

It is perhaps bold to suggest that in the early months of consideration of a new project, it should be closely studied for the economic implications of its development. It may reasonably be argued that limited value can be achieved at an early stage when the final form of a project cannot be identified and when the values of key operating and cost activating parameters are not well defined. Nevertheless, this is what the research scientist and development engineer is undertaking quite instinctively and, as it were, in private. This activity needs to be more fully recognised and brought out into the open, for with firmer discipline it is certain that the economic guide lines would be more effectively followed by all participants in the research.

Economic objectives are now more clearly recognised by the research establishments. More factual guidance would, however, be greatly appreciated by many of them, who may privately doubt whether the economic and operational specialists are equal to the task. It had been enlightening to hear the Deputy Director of the Royal Aircraft Establishments in the Mitchell Memorial Lecture in 1965 develop the theme of aeronautical research via economic analysis, and emphasise the need for a wider consideration of the influential factors in a transport aircraft design, and in the choice of lines of research and deployment of effort between different lines of attack. He said 'Insofar as economic or operational analysis lie behind the direction of research rather than the choice of an aircraft or other project, it is very important that such thinking should permeate through research teams and not be confined to specialist analytical teams'. Such thinking has been re-emphasised through the early 1970s when SST and VTOL projects have required special studies of the potential demand calling for advanced multidiscipliniary exercises supported by government and private funds. New areas of investigation of increasing interest to all sectors have arisen, foremost of these are airport location and noise control in the airport environment as well as noise certification of new transport aircraft.

Work in the development of large aircraft is still being actively pursued by Boeing and Lockheed. The way lies wide open to an extension of size as a major factor in the improving economy of transport aircraft. The reservations to be observed were considered in Chapter 4 but of the continuing development of aircraft size for the great trunk air routes of the world there can be no doubt.

Work on the jet flap and boundary layer control are also being considered, as most likely to lead to important advances in the economy of operation of the transport aeroplane, and the economic implications of their successful development have encouraged research effort in the most profitable directions. The determination of the exchange rate between an aerodynamic advantage and its associated structural and/or systems weight increase is a well-known method of optimising the design in a limited area, but a detailed appreciation of the operational parameters and their variance in the wide spectrum of a civil aircraft's market requires special experience. Nor, as we have shown, is the optimisation of the direct cost alone an adequate criterion.

Boundary layer control

The one element in the drag of the modern transport aircraft which holds out the best prospects for reduction is the skin friction drag which very largely determines the air resistance at zero lift (Chapter 2). Induced drag which is a function of lift is largely affected by aspect ratio and short of major advances in our knowledge of structures, it will not be easy to achieve any overall gain by increasing aspect ratio above the present levels of 10–12 for straight wings and 6–8 for swept-back wings. Form drag has been minimised for the latest commercial aircraft designs by means of slender shapes, smooth finish and minimal interference.

Although some improvement in boundary conditions has been obtained by means of careful shaping of the aerofoil section (retaining the maximum thickness to about 50 per cent of the chord length) this is not conducive to low-form drag on high speed sections and experiments have suggested that more drastic measures are required. The maximum effect for a given input of power is achieved by sucking away the layer of turbulent air either through a porous wing or through suitably located slots. A dramatic reduction in the L/D ratio for the wing can be achieved, depending of course on what proportion of the wing or other aircraft surfaces are treated in this way. Studies have estimated that with 75 per cent of the wing and tail surfaces laminarised by suction and taking account of the systems required in first cost, weight and maintenance expense to provide the necessary suction power, the direct operating cost of a transatlantic subsonic jet aircraft would be reduced by 20–25 per cent. However, there is still considerable doubt as to whether a practicable airliner can be operated in all-weather conditions without exceptional care in maintenance. The effects of ice and dirt on perforated and/or slotted wing surfaces are not yet exactly known. In the US the flight programme of the 2 Northrop X 21 (ex Douglas WB 66 D) aircraft was set up to establish facts in this area. In the United Kingdom, development work originally sponsored by Handley Page was not given the official support that many aeronautical scientists believe to be justified. There is no doubt that an important economic advance may lie in the use of boundary layer control. It should be noted that the SST will be less able to take advantage of this technique than the subsonic jets since a smaller proportion of its drag has its origin in skin friction.

The jet flap

A large theoretical advantage can also be shown for the jet flap, but this also awaits operational trials to establish its practical feasibility in adverse conditions of weather on actual service. The principle here resides in the concept that increased flow circulation, and hence lift, can be generated by an aerofoil if a high-energy airflow is ejected from its rear edge in a direction giving an effective angle of incidence to the main airstream. The deflected jet also provides a downward component of thrust, thus augmenting the lift. Although this is an

485

attractive means of providing lift without the mechanical flap systems which have become more complicated of recent years, if must be remembered that we are required to supply a high-flow jet stream or sheet, and the most natural source of gas flow suggests that a hot corrosive supply from the engine exhaust is employed for this purpose. Recent work using a cold jet efflux produced by a compressor driven independently by the main engines has overcome some of these difficulties as well as permitting the flap flow to be determined more precisely by the lift requirements at the time, excess flow being available for horizontal thrust.

Studies have shown that direct operating costs may be reduced by as much as 25 per cent when using a jet flap, presuming the wing to be reduced in size to meet the cruising requirement without compromise. Much advantage in the jet flap resides in its potential for STOL capability since small reductions in take-off weight result in considerable improvements in field performance. In this way it may offer a more flexible solution to lift augmentation that conventional flap systems. Such solutions might be expected to pay high rewards in commercial air operations but air carriers have, up till now, been highly conservative in their approach to new aircraft types incorporating high-lift devices of unproven design. Nor should we discount this policy out of hand. What may be equally decisive is that the market for small aircraft likely to use the smaller field is extremely limited and has little appeal to the major aircraft manufacturer.

Hypersonic transport and beyond

When we are tempted to speculate beyond the most immediate supersonic regime it might be thought that we are no more than doodling on the aircraft designer's or the rocket engineer's pad. But already the advanced project men are at work in the far fields for civil transport and are seeking the likely requirements of the future in speed, range, capacity and human needs.

Edward Heinemann (1965), who has designed some of the outstanding aircraft from Douglas, Northrop and General

Dynamics, expressed the belief that work on the SST in Europe and the USA would lead to such technological advancements and 'fallouts' that we shall be 'inspired to proceed in the direction of even more advanced designs and will be enabled to take even greater steps than now appear possible'. He thought it likely that we may take the very bold step of projecting an aeroplane to use the momentum principle thereby gaining 'Freedom from the Atmosphere'. Sub-orbital trajectories are under detailed investigation in the project departments of all major airframe and engine companies. The US company, North American Inc., developed under US government contract the first manned spacecraft, the X 15, which was the precursor of larger and more effective vehicles of the future. This aircraft operated at 500,000 ft and reached speeds of 3600 mph

The USSR is also deeply interested in the long-term future and a distinguished Soviet designer, V. M. Myasishchov, writing in *Izvestia* in 1963 discussed a rocket-boosted glider aircraft at 30,000 metres (98,000 ft) and speeds of $M = 4 \cdot 0 - 5 \cdot 0$. The launching altitude would be reached about eight minutes after take-off. A short period of boosted flight by the rocket aircraft would lift the trajectory to over 200,000 ft and $M = 10-12$. Gliding flight could then be achieved to all world destinations. For a winged vehicle with hypersonic L/D capability of greater than unity, calculations have shown that the L/D in subsonic flight should be adequate for landings on long runways. Variable geometry might be used, but VTOL would seem to be mandatory in this area. Control of transverse range is possible by use of rockets fired normal to the flight path. The possibilities of rocket post deliveries by these means between the USA and USSR, and the UK and Australia may be realised within the next two decades.

Hypersonic flight (the speed regime above about $M = 5 \cdot 0$) thus includes at the lower end of the scale the gliding of air-supported vehicles which can descend and associate with the traffic of the lower atmosphere. The regime includes also the early orbiting vehicles such as Dynasoar (Boeing) and Pegasus (Douglas), which were orbiting vehicles for part of their flight plan, but were subject to the forces of aerodynamics during ascent and descent. A corridor of flight as shown in Fig. 11.1 is based on the well-known concept (Heinemann,

1965) that the economic and technical possibilities for advance in speed will follow a path which is limited by the minimum speeds for aerodynamic lift (true speeds increasing with altitude) and the practical upper limits of the thermal strength of materials. This corridor leads to the escape channel from the gravitational pull of the earth. It is interesting to note that at 80,000 ft and $M = 5 \cdot 0$ (3300 mph in the isothermal standard atmosphere) centrifugal force is relieving the weight by about 3 per cent. At 200,000 ft this relief is only increased to $3\frac{1}{2}$ per cent. In the $M = 4 \cdot 0$–$5 \cdot 0$ range the ram-jet engine will find an important application. The great advantage inherent with the ram-jet is that it does not require the provision of an integral compressor. Unfortunately, the efficiency of the ram is inadequate below about $M = 2 \cdot 0$ and a composite power plant is required. Moreover, at $M = 5 \cdot 0$ a very large engine of a size comparable with the wing plan form of a hypersonic craft would be required so that some means of integrating the wing and the thrust system has to be found. One system known as the external ram-jet has been proposed for hypersonic transports. In this, fuel is ignited by the higher air temperatures at the

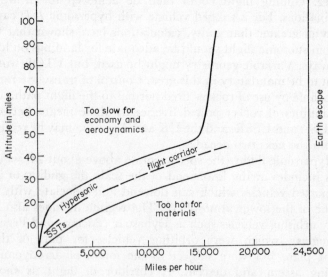

FIG. 11.1. The Hypersonic Flight Corridor

apex of a wedged section of the external structure so that both thrust and lift are generated on the rearward face of the wedge. Almost certainly higher L/D ratios can be produced in this way. The possibilities here are far reaching. Narrow delta-winged transports based on some such concepts may have L/D ratios of $2 \cdot 0$–$3 \cdot 0$. Problems of cooling after re-entry from semi-ballistic trajectories should raise few difficulties to the transport designer of the next generation since space research programmes (in the USA and USSR) have refined techniques in launching men into near space and recovering them from ballistic trajectories.

The engine manufacturers have been at work in recent years attempting to solve the problem of providing thrust from the take-off up to the lower hypersonic regime. Clearly the jet engine could undertake the job, but at a high penalty in installed weight, since the compressor system is totally unnecessary at the higher speeds. The pure rocket has a high fuel weight since it carries its own supply of oxygen. An engine known as a turbo-rocket has been proposed by Rolls-Royce (Lombard and Keenan, 1965) in order to achieve the required compromise, providing an optimum power plant plus fuel weight to meet the requirement. This engine would supply from its own resources one-fifth of the total oxygen needed for combustion. The oxygen is burned in a special combustion chamber from which the exhaust efflux goes through a turbine which drives a compressor taking in air from the atmosphere. Additional fuel may be burnt in the tail pipe. It is estimated that the weight of this engine is one-third of the rocket. It is quite possible for these engines to be used in the high-thrust form for the climb and final descent phases of the flight, while for the long-range cruise phase they would operate as ram-jets with more economical rates of fuel consumption. By these means it is not fanciful to suppose that commercial flights of two hours' duration to the antipodes might be achieved within the century.

Pegasus

In 1964 the Douglas Aircraft Company released details of a study completed to consider possibilities of a VTO rocket transport based on the structural propulsion and guidance components which were under development and test at that time for the Apollo space programme. The 'civilised' project known as Pegasus was designed as a single-stage rocket with vertical take-off and landing capability. A capacity for 170 passengers and 18 tons of cargo (or 260 passengers) was provided in a 114-ft-high, bell-shaped structure, 49 ft in diameter at its widest part. A four-decked passenger compartment was proposed. Liquid oxygen and liquid hydrogen propellants were employed to provide over 4 million lb of thrust (about half that of Saturn V) and the re-usable booster would be able to provide global payload delivery at sub-orbital speeds (17,000 mph) thus offering point-to-point speeds about twenty times faster than an SST cruising at $M = 3 \cdot 0$. Safe emergency landings were envisaged on level land or on the sea in any part of the world.

Such long-term possibilities will be very dependent upon the ability of technologists to curtail the excessive pre-flight checkout procedures and inspections which dominate all current missile and space programmes, and the need to control the launch noise which it is now difficult to believe would be acceptable in the proximity of major population centres. The principal facts in the above summary of the Douglas-sponsored Pegasus studies were published in a paper by Mr Philip Bone (1964). The author concludes 'In the absence of a clear economic stimulus, the justification for developing such a vehicle must rest primarily on the dramatic increase in speed which it offers. Perhaps the most valid reason for man's insatiable desire for ever-increasing speed is not to provide him with instant transportation, but with instant communication.'

Though these demands may initially arise through the needs of defence for antipodean delivery and 'global' surveillance, the close similarity of the needs of the military and civil user for economic transport in long-range sorties suggests that design requirements could in time cover many of the commercial operators' needs. Political and business needs will be likely to follow close behind military needs for orbital transport, as we have seen so often in the past, when they can be met at a reasonable level of cost.

Space shuttle and terrestrial transport

Space shuttle projects based on booster and orbiter units to achieve higher economy levels in the launching of space material, are now under active development in the USA. NASA's manned spacecraft centre at Houston has held management responsibility for the various design studies which have been under the critical technical analysis of the Marshall Space Flight Centres' Space Shuttle Task Team. McDonnell-Douglas, and North American Rockwell were engaged on preliminary design and definition studies in 1970–1 with various other US companies in feasibility studies.

Payload capabilities have included 65,000 lb on easterly orbits at 100 nautical miles altitude at an inclination of 285 degrees, and lower payloads at higher inclinations. Transfer to higher orbits is a requirement, using an orbital manoevring system (OMS), and shuttle re-usability for at least 100 flights is required. In case of malfunction both booster and orbiter have the capability of being returned to the launch site. The orbiter has likely dimensions of 210 ft long and 110 ft span. A high degree of directional stability is required in supersonic and hypersonic phases.

Thrust rockets exceeding 500,000 lb each are projected with vehicle gross weights of approximately 5 million lb. Both shuttle and orbiter vehicles must be capable of landing on a 10,000 ft runway. The cross-range capability whereby a vehicle can fly to right or left of a ballistic trajectory has been a paramount factor in recent designs. At least 1000 nm cross range is called for. Delta wing configuration meet the requirements.

The potential for a development of such a space shuttle vehicle for use in terrestrial journeys is considerable. The development of techniques whereby immense cargoes can be transferred across the world after launching by re-usable booster vehicles also holds important prospects for economic benefits.

The U.S.-government-initiated shuttle programme in which European states have been invited to participate has been drastically reduced in the later stages of evolution. By mid-1972, when the technical formulation of the space-aircraft system was largely complete, it had become essentially a three-part project comprising a re-usable Earth-to-Orbit ferry vehicle, an inter-orbital re-usable tug, and a shuttle-borne laboratory called the Sortie Module.

In 1972 President Nixon pledged six-year support for a phased $5500 million development programme, the first stage of which was the refinement of the North American Rockwell Corporation's orbiter design to meet new stringent economies then called for.

Hypersonic transport

Thus experience with the use of re-usable space boosters could provide the advanced technology which would allow economic hypersonic vehicles without rockets to be built well within this century. These aircraft could be available within 20–25 years able to fly to any point on the surface of the earth within one and a half hours. Using ram-jet engines and liquid hydrogen as a propulsion fuel (relatively free from pollution) and employing conventional jet propulsion for take-off and acceleration to ram-jet self-propulsion speeds it is now thought that a Mach 10 cruising speed at 110,000 ft could be achieved with a sonic boom pressure rise of approximately 1·5 lb per sq ft. Theory has shown that a Mach 15 vehicle cruising at 130,000 ft might even bring the boom signature to below 1·0 lb per sq ft. By design of aircraft form to modify lift distribution there is some further prospect that the current levels of SST boom pressure can be considerably reduced with these vehicles thus offering prospects of greater operational flexibility than can immediately be expected with the SST. R. H. Miller of MIT has reported Studies of Hypersonic vehicles of about 1,100,000 lb gross weight with half-global range capability and payload capacity of 500 passengers. Such aircraft could become competitive with conventional subsonic jets if the cost of fuel could be retained at a level at or below about 8 US cents per lb. The effect of fuel price is even more dominant than in the case of the SST, and it would clearly be necessary for a high fuel production rate to be achieved and for an adequate exploitation of the by-products to be found possible. Such questions emphasise the significance of speed in the ultimate economic value of these vehicles because of the immense productivity created by speed and the insensitivity of high energy fuel to the cost of labour which dominates most other elements in the cost equations. It seems at present unlikely that ranges of less than 3000 miles (North Atlantic) would be attractive with such vehicles, but the process of optimisation to meet the needs of a world market, acceptable climb angles and accelerations to meet passenger comfort, and design requirements for structure and propulsion as well as noise, may introduce unexpected answers in the course of development.

The application of atomic power

The theoretical advantage of nuclear power as a source of aircraft propulsion has been recognised for longer than has the potential of supersonic transport. Early optimism in the USA that the design of a nuclear power plant could be designed within the weight and volume limitations set by a large transport aircraft was however dispelled after project studies in the early 1950s. More recently the technological development of reactors in regard to size, weight and shielding has removed many problems. A major technological barrier still exists in operational safety. No full solution to the outcome of an aircraft crash on land is yet available, the danger of radiation outfall still presenting catastrophic possibilities. A first application of atomic energy as a power source in the very large strategic transport aircraft, the type C 5 A, might, however, be possible.

This project might find a civil counterpart in due course, perhaps in the form of a long-haul 600–700 passenger-transport. In due time there is not the slightest doubt that an aircraft of this capacity will be required. The specific operating economy of such an aircraft would be at a level well below, probably 25–30 per cent below, anything of which we have experienced to date. But can the traffic yet be generated on enough routes to justify the development and the civil certification of the type?

No routes in the USA or in Western Europe are yet remotely within the reach of a traffic flow able to feed such an aircraft at this time. However, normal rates of growth may well double the capacity required within 8 years (10 per cent per annum) so that an adequate number of opportunities may well exist within 10–15 years. The overall traffic-generating capability of such an aircraft will be very comparable to the US projects at $M = 3\cdot0$, and the joint operation of these two main types could well form the basis of the long- and medium-haul routes of the late 1970s. With VTO transports forming the new advance in the short-haul field, we may here recognise the shape of scheduled air transport for the last two decades of the century. These projects and possibilities must, however, be left to the attention of the air transport economist of another day.

The way ahead – Some conclusions

Work on the preparation of this study has brought home to us the immense range of civil aviation, both in the variety of its products and ideas and in the potential demand for so many different kinds of transport service. When this is linked with the high rate of technological change, of which the pace is still accelerating, we become more than ever conscious of the even greater problems that must be faced in the future by those who will be responsible for making the critical decisions. Moreover, aviation has become increasingly responsible for making the critical decisions. Moreover, aviation has become increasingly dependence on other industries, and more closely linked with surface transport and the other means of communication, quite apart from its heavy dependence upon political issues and the requirements of defence. A clear view of the right objectives for air transport and the best means for obtaining them becomes increasingly difficult to take.

There is a serious need for more basic information to guide the choice of development programmes, and national plans such as the 'Horizon' project in the USA could well be undertaken in other countries and most assuredly in Europe. The need for clear and unharrassed assessments of future needs is important in the industrial as well as in the political field, and more account should surely be taken of the contributions that could be made through commercial and economic analyses even though these may not be able to supply all the answers and should not claim a greater insight or reliability than their techniques justify.

Management at all levels should perhaps try to understand more fully the new tools that were available to them.

It seems clear from the post-war record of air transport development that technological change can be achieved successfully only when it is introduced in short and well-controlled steps. There seems to be no record of a successful breakthrough in the technology which has not been meticulously planned and introduced in carefully thought out stages. This certainly applies to the case of the subsonic jets and it is believed it will also apply in the case of the supersonic transports ($M = 2 \cdot 2$) which should be in service in the mid-1970s. A hurried jump into supersonic transport at lower speed may be less realistic than the longer-term step into the higher-speed bracket. How much do we yet know about the different markets for these very different aircraft? As has been often said the air transport industry which has found out so much about the passengers it carries, knows next to nothing about the traffic which it wants to carry. This is the task of Market Research.

Far more of it is required in Europe than is the current practice and it might be valuable if the European aviation industry studied more carefully the techniques now being used in the USA. Certainly the fine record of success achieved by the US industry, to be seen in their well-proven commercial judgment with regard to the specification and the timing of a wide range of civil aircraft, is worth the most careful scrutiny. The time has come when it must be recognised that aviation research is not confined to the physical sciences, to classical research in the wind tunnel and to *ad hoc* flight test and the rest, but has an important field in commercial and economic investigations into new projects, their operation and their exploitation.

Most planners and researchers in aviation are deeply convinced of the need for better-organised statistics, particularly in Europe, and the lack of these has often led to an instinctive temptation to jump to a conclusion which would not have been fully justified by the facts. Our economic and perhaps our political security may depend upon our ability to understand every aspect of our markets and to gauge the pattern of demand for products that we must, so to speak, develop outwards from the inner world of ideas. We must equally recognise the limitations of our resources and found our analysis upon a realism which they have often lacked in the past. The future prospects of aviation development in transport are truly fantastic, for we can be certain that throughout this century political forces will maintain a steadily developing technology. We must, however, cultivate assiduously the cool and independent commercial attitude in competitive aviation when the political and economic forces may tempt us to take short cuts to success.

BIBLIOGRAPHY

Research and Development: A Comparison between British and American Industry, National Institute Economic Review, May 1962

L. F. NICHOLSON, 'The Work of the Royal Aircraft Establishment', *Jnl. Roy. Aero. Soc.*, 1965

E. HEINEMANN, 'Aviation in Perspective', *Jnl. Roy. Aero. Soc.*, Feb. 1965

C. D. PERKINS, 'Man and Military Space', *Jnl. Roy. Aero. Soc.*, July 1963

R. R. JAMISON, 'Advanced Air-Breathing Engines', *Jnl. Roy. Aero. Soc.*, Nov. 1962

A. A. LOMBARD and J. G. KEENAN, *The Turbo-Rocket for High Speed Air-Breathing Vehicles*, Interavia, 1/1965

P. BONE, 'Pegasus: Beyond the Supersonic Airliner', *New Scientist*, 5 Nov. 1964

RT. HON. R. A. CALDECOTE, 'Economic Space Transportation', *Jnl. Roy Aero. Soc.*, June 1966

E. E. MARSHALL, 'The Role of Aircraft in Future Transport Systems', *Aircraft Engineering*, May 1969

J. E. STEINER, 'Aircraft Development and World Aviation Growth', *Jnl. Roy. Aero. Soc.*, June 1970

R. H. MILLER, 'Some Air Transportation Concepts for the Future', *Jnl. Roy. Aero. Soc.*, July 1971

A. J. EGGERS, R. H. PETERSEN and N. B. COHEN, 'Hypersonic

Aircraft Technology and Application', *Astronautics and Aeronautics*, June 1970

H. KAHN and A. WIERNER, *The Year 2000*, Macmillan, New York, 1967

A Miscellany of Papers. Looking Ahead in Aeronautics, Royal Aero. Soc., 1970

Index

Index